# Primavera®

## Contract Manager User's Guide

# Table of Contents

# Working with a Project

# Communicating Project Information

# Logging and Tracking Information

# Exchanging Contract Manager Module Data

# Preface

Primavera's Contract Manager module (formerly known as Expedition or Expedition Professional) is contract-control software designed to help you manage your projects more easily. From submittals to change orders, all the facts about your project are at your fingertips.

This manual shows you ways to plan and create a project in the Contract Manager module, and how to manage that project by logging and tracking project information, using meeting minutes, transmittals, contracts, purchase orders, requisitions, change orders, and so on. You will learn how to exchange data between the module and other programs, and identify the best methodology for tailoring the control process to your workflow.

Throughout this document, the phrase "the module" refers to the Contract Manager module unless otherwise specified.

# Contract Manager Module Documentation

- *Contract Manager Installation Guide* explains how to install the module for Microsoft SQL, Oracle, and Sybase, and explains how to convert data from previous versions for use in 10.0. The network or database administrator responsible for the initial installation of the module, ongoing maintenance of the system and database, and general troubleshooting should read this manual.

- *Contract Manager User's Guide* (this manual) shows how to manage and monitor documents from initial contracts through the last change order. All individuals who use the module should read this guide, even if they are already familiar with previous versions of the software.

See Help for the latest Contract Manager information. Use it as your primary source of information.

- *Contract Manager Help* is an integrated comprehensive help system that supplements the printed documentation. Help is available while you are working in the module for quick access to information about dialog boxes and fields. Help also includes step-by-step procedures for performing the module functions and answers to common questions. The Table of Contents provides a starting point for many major topics. You can also use Help's powerful Search and Index features to find topics related to any text you enter. Click How To for a list of all procedures contained in Help.

- *Online Documentation* can be accessed by inserting the Contract Manager CD-ROM in your computer's CD-ROM drive, then clicking View Documentation from the setup program menu. In addition to the *Contract Manager User's Guide* and *Installation Guide,* the following documentation is available online:

  - *Project Management Module Integration Field Mappings* contains the field mappings from the Contract Manager module to the Project Management module.

  - A *Getting Started* manual to help you use InfoMaker, the report writer included with the module software.

For a summary of some of these questions and their answers, see *Frequently Asked Questions* in Help.

  - *Technical Bulletins* on the Primavera Web site provide detailed, technical documents generated by Primavera Customer Support to answer questions asked by users.

 *Several areas of the Contract Manager module are customizable, such as the Project View, document names, log column headings, and document field labels. The examples throughout this manual and in the online help use the default settings shipped with the software.*

# About this Manual

Anyone who will be using the Contract Manager module to track projects should use this manual. This includes owners, construction managers, general contractors, subcontractors, architects, designers, engineers, administrators responsible for setting up the module, and persons who will enter data in. Whether you are an experienced user or are new to the program, the *User's Guide* contains the information you need to use the module to organize all your projects successfully.

| Part | Contents |
| --- | --- |
| Getting Started | Provides an introduction to the Contract Manager module, including workflow, the module workspace, sample projects, and the initial steps required to plan and add a project. Instructions are included for setting access rights, entering contacts, creating distribution lists, entering initial contract information, creating submittals, and linking with a Project Management module schedule. |
| Working with a Contract Manager Project | Explains how to work with, and customize, the module log and document windows, set up dictionaries and preferences, and print logs, forms, and reports. |
| Communicating Project Information | Describes how to send Contract Manager module documents to other users, prepare transmittals, track different types of communications, record meeting minutes, and manage safety-related documents. |
| Working with Contracts, Project Costs, and Changes | Describes how to set up the Cost Worksheet, manage contracts and purchase orders, use trends, prepare requisitions for payment, record invoices, use the module change management feature to customize the workflow for your company's needs, use procurement to track bidding, and create and track issues. |
| Logging and Tracking Information | Illustrates how the module logs and tracks important project information such as drawings, submittals, materials, daily reports, insurance certificates, and punch lists. |
| Exchanging Contract Manager Data | Describes how to link schedule data to the module, exchange module data with a Project Management module schedule, and export/import data to and from other applications. |

# Customer Support

If you have a question about using the Contract Manager module that you or your network administrator cannot answer using the printed or online documentation, call Customer Support at the times and locations listed below.

Please have your Contract Manager module serial number ready when you call; this number is printed on your serial number diskette. It can also be displayed when using the module by right-clicking on the Help icon in the header. Support staff log each call to help resolve your questions quickly.

| Office | Time Zone | Hours | Telephone | FAX | Internet Address* |
|--------|-----------|-------|-----------|-----|-------------------|
| Bala Cynwyd, PA, US | ET | 8:00-8:00 (Mon-Fri) | 1-610-949-6557 | 1-610-667-0652 | support@primavera.com |
| London, England, UK | GMT | 8:30-6:30 (Mon-Fri) | 44-20-8563-5555 | 44-20-8563-5533 | support@primavera.com |

*For 24-hour support, you can also visit Primavera's online Knowledgebase at http://customerportal.primavera.com/customer

*In the United States, Primavera periodically and randomly monitors Customer Support calls to ensure that you are receiving the highest quality support.*

All Primavera products are backed by comprehensive support and training. To request product literature, contact your local dealer, call Primavera at 610-667-8600, or send your request via e-mail to **info@primavera.com** in the United States. In the United Kingdom, call 44-208-563-5500 or e-mail your request to **intlinfo@primavera.com**.

*Sybase databases contain calculations called stored procedures. Although a Sybase database administrator has the ability to modify these procedures, Primavera does not recommend changing them. Modifying these procedures voids your Primavera Customer Support agreement.*

# Part 1

# Getting Started

**In this part**     **Overview**

**Planning and Adding a Contract
Manager Module Project**

*T*his part describes key concepts for using the Contract Manager module contract-control software. The Contract Manager module was formerly known as Expedition or Expedition Professional.

*Overview* explains how to start Contract Manager and how to use the sample projects provided with this release. It also discusses Contract Manager module terms and defines the different project roles that users perform.

*Planning and Adding a Contract Manager Module Project* describes how to set up your Contract Manager module database, including the company directory and distribution list, and how to assign access rights.

# Overview

This chapter introduces the key concepts for using the Contract Manager module as your contract-control software. It provides an overview of the module workspace, and includes an explanation of the sample projects. This chapter also suggests how you can start using the module, depending on your role in the project process.

In this document, the term "module" refers to the Contract Manager module, unless otherwise specified.

# Starting Contract Manager

Users open the Contract Manager module from a client Browser - there is no client software to install. The Contract Manager module administrator provides a Web address to users for accessing the module. To connect, open Microsoft Internet Explorer, and type the Web address of the Contract Manager module Web server provided to you.

The Contract Manager module administrator usually provides user IDs and passwords. Type your user ID and password, then click Log In.

For information about changing these defaults on a network, see *Adding Serial Numbers and Users* in *Maintaining a Contract Manager Module Database*, or *Contract Manager Administration Application* in Help.

 *The default Contract Manager user ID and password shipped with the module is EXP (for both fields).*

 *The minimum supported monitor resolution is 1024x768.*

# The Contract Manager Module Workspace

When you open the Contract Manager module, the Workspace appears; this is where all module tasks begin.

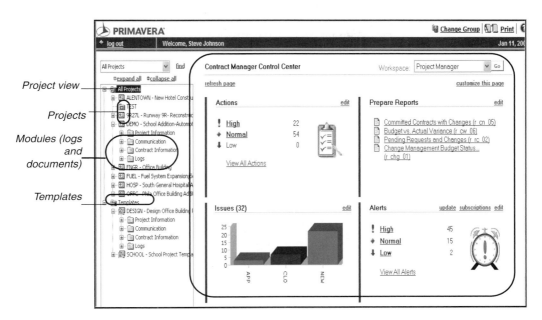

The Workspace is divided into two main areas: the Project View on the left and the Control Center (Workspace) on the right.

**Project View**   The Project View shows your project hierarchy, which includes the top-level folder called All Projects, followed by the folder for each project, the folders in each project, and the modules (logs and documents) inside these folders. It also contains a Templates folder which consists of any project templates you may have created, including the default templates, DESIGN and SCHOOL. The Project View functions the same way as Microsoft Windows Explorer. When a folder is collapsed, click its icon to display the names of the items in that folder. To collapse the folder, click the folder icon again.

For information about modifying Project View folders and log and document names, see *Customizing Log and Document Windows* or refer to Help.

To open a module log or document in an expanded project folder, click the log's name. You can also select a log by clicking on an expanded folder and then typing the first character of the item you want. For example, when the Communication folder is selected, type *c* to select Corr. Sent, type *c* again to select Corr. Received, and type *t* to select Transmittals.

You can right-click on the top-level folder or any project in the Project View to display a list of commands. If you right-click on the top-level project folder (All Projects), the available commands apply to all projects within that folder; if you right-click on a project, the available commands apply to that specific project.

**Control Center**   The Control Center contains information about either a selected project, a group of projects, or all projects. When no projects are open, the Control Center shows information relevant to all projects within the selected folder. When you select a project, the Control Center shows information specific to that project (some items allow you to choose whether to display information on all projects or just the selected project by clicking Edit from items offering this option).

For information on customizing the Control Center, see *Customizing the Control Center* in the *Planning and Adding a Contract Manager Module Project* chapter, or *Customize Workspace dialog box* in Help.

You can also right-click on the project and choose Project Settings to edit general information, key parties, and schedule information for the project.

For detailed information about the Control Center, see *Workspace* in Help.

You can customize the Control Center to display the information you want. For example, you can include items for reports, your Inbox, requests for information (RFIs), charts showing outstanding issues and requests, and any action and alerts. The Actions item contains the items in your court that need to be addressed. The Alerts item contains items that need to be addressed immediately. You can place up to 12 items in the Control Center, and you can save this arrangement as My Workspace. The next time you start the Contract Manager module, you can use this workspace or select one of the standard types delivered with the product. These include Administrative Assistant, General Contractor, Owner, Architect, and so on.

For more information on using actions and alerts, see *Actions* and *Alerts* in Help.

Viewing the information in the Control Center at the start of each workday reminds you of what you need to accomplish, who you need to contact, and when deadline items are due through actions and alerts. This information is generated by and/or directed to you, depending on your access permissions. An example of using items for viewing important information is shown on the next page.

You can quickly access documents in your court that require you to take an action, then print a report corresponding to these action items for the project. An example of an action is shown on the next page.

Click a section of the chart to display a list of Requests for Information documents.

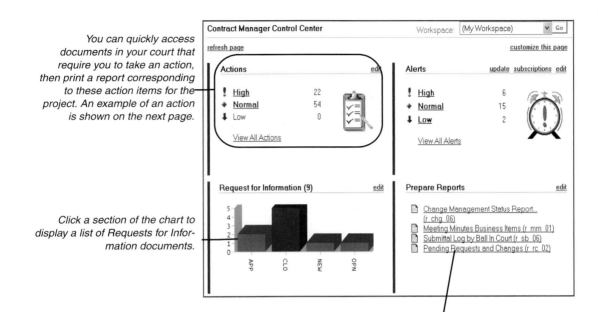

Click to display the selected report.

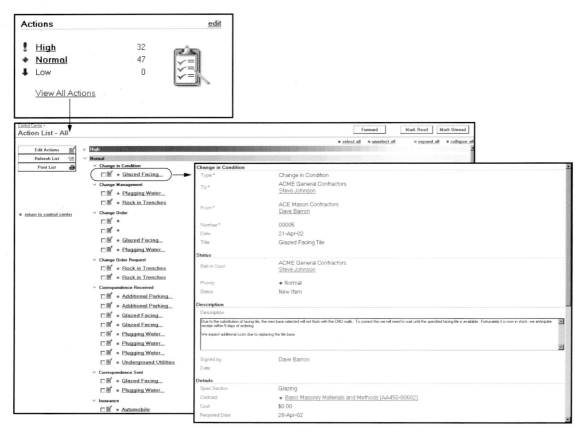

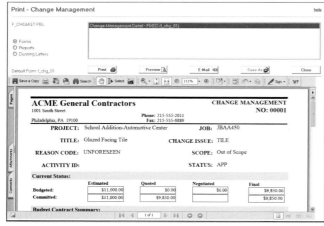

To display available forms and reports, from the document window, click Select an Action, Advanced Print, then click Go. Select the type of document, select the type of document, and then click Print or Preview.

The example at the left shows the Preview function. To print the document, click the printer icon next to Save a copy on the tool bar at the top of the document.

# Key Concepts

The Contract Manager module is a multiuser, multiproject application that provides a centralized way to store, organize, and track project information so you can keep your contracts on time and within budget.

**Record contracts and purchase orders**  Record the key information about contracts and purchase orders (POs) in the following documents.

Use *Contracts* and *Purchase Orders* to record the basic information.

Use the *Cost Worksheet* to track contract costs and categorize contract or purchase order amounts using cost codes for a detailed breakdown of the component costs for your project. You can distribute the value of any contract, purchase order, or change to any number of cost codes.

*Invoices/Requisitions* are generated from contracts/purchase orders (POs), then sent for payment approval. The amounts are posted to the Cost Worksheet to track actual costs.

Use *Materials Delivery* to record the date and quantity of materials received and noted against each contract or purchase order, and incorporate these and approved changes into requisitions for up-to-date payment amounts.

*Companies* contain physical and electronic addresses and communications numbers for all individuals with whom you interact. The module uses this information when you send any contract, purchase order, or other information to those individuals.

*Trends* are an expectation of future costs (estimated revisions). Use Trends in conjunction with the Cost Worksheet (where you can modify column headings to accommodate the way you handle costs) to track possible cost increases for the project.

**Track contract changes**  After participants accept a contract or purchase order and work begins, any changes resulting from changed specifications or changed conditions affect the initial contract.

*Change Management* enables you to manage project modifications due to changes. You specify which change documents are created, when they are created, and where they are calculated on the Cost Worksheet. By recording all necessary contract, contractor, and cost data early in the change process, you can evaluate the effect of the change on all contracts involved and see the current status of the change at a glance.

*Markup* provides a way to manage overhead and profit by adding markup values to change documents. The module can calculate overhead and profit automatically, and add additional costs to change orders and proposals. You can set default values for overhead, profit, and any other markup categories you create. Typically you will collect all proposals from committed parties, and then roll the costs and codes of each document to create a quote to the customer or owner of a project. With markup, you can add your overhead and profit prior to submitting the quote.

*Daily Reports* provide a record of daily activities and conditions. Use these reports to record conditions observed in the field, such as soil, rock, or underground utilities that were not moved correctly, as well as to track and communicate the potential effect of these recorded conditions in a timely manner. You can also include underway activities from Contract Manager module schedules that are linked to the project to see where the work is taking place on that report day.

*Telephone Records, Meeting Minutes, Correspondence, Requests for Information (RFIs),* and *Notices* enable you to record information that may affect both the submittal and change processes. For example, a change in condition may result in meetings, phone calls, notes, letters, and correspondence that lead to a formal contract change.

*Change Orders* result from changes in the scope of work, site conditions, or schedule delays. You can post costs associated with changes to the Cost Worksheet so you have a total financial picture of past events and projected future costs. With this view, you can measure the impact of each change order on any contract or purchase order.

**Track submittals**  Submittals include contract drawings, sample materials, and permits that need approval. Submittals help you ensure contract compliance by tracking who received what and when they received it.

*Daily Reports, Telephone Records, Meeting Minutes, Correspondence, RFIs,* and *Notices* also support the submittal process. For example, during a submittal cycle a reviewer may reject a submittal; as a result, the project team may have meetings and exchange phone calls, letters, and correspondence to clarify the requirements for resubmittal.

*Drawings* and *Drawing Sets* maintain a list of project drawings, facilitate the dissemination of these drawings to other parties, and provide information about the status of revisions. When you add distributions to drawing sets or create revisions, an entry is made in the Transmittal Creation Queue for each contact on the distribution list.

*Transmittals* accompany documents, such as submittals and drawings to create a permanent record of the actions taken. Submittal items and drawing revisions are automatically placed in the Transmittal Creation Queue; you can add any transmittals in this queue to the database and print them for recipients on your distribution list. The module can quickly generate transmittals, or you can customize your own.

*Dunning Letters* remind participants of overdue items such as submittals and drawings. Contract Manager can quickly generate dunning letters, or you can customize your own.

*Reports and Forms* provide quick and accurate project information in various formats. The flexible reporting feature produces reports that summarize when items such as submittals are due, who received what and when, what has been approved and what is pending, and how many days items are overdue.

**Use the cross-document tools**    The *Issues* feature cross-references and links documents from any Contract Manager module log to issues you define. You can link documents to issues directly as you add records to the documents, or you can link documents to issues automatically based on keywords such as *underground, electrical,* or some other item that may be related to a problem or other situation. The module then assembles the documents for review in a fully organized, indexed list so you can easily trace the sequence of actions taken, saving hours of work.

The *Inbox* stores items sent to you electronically by other participants. You can also use this feature to communicate quickly with other project team members by sending documents related to submittals and changes.

# Sample Projects

The Contract Manager module includes several sample projects, each set up from the perspective of a different team member in a construction project: general contractor, owner, subcontractor, and designer. DEMO is the sample general contractor project; HOSP and OFFC are from the owner and subcontractor perspectives, respectively. Another sample project, DESIGN, is provided to demonstrate how a designer tracks drawings during design review. These projects are included as templates on which you can base your own projects.

The sample projects relate to construction work that must be completed for Philadelphia County. Design Group is the architect/engineer; ACME General Contractors is the general contractor; A-1 Construction Management is the construction manager; and Stresson Industrials is the subcontractor to ACME for concrete work.

The information included in the sample projects is just an example of what is possible. Most projects contain more requisitions, change documents, transmittals, and submittal cycles than the examples shown.

**DEMO (School Addition – Automotive Center)**  contains project data from the general contractor's perspective, manages shop drawings and submittal items, tracks project issues, documents the change process, and records daily progress in the construction of a school addition. This addition is a masonry structure with brick siding that houses an automobile and light truck service center. The value of the contract between the owner and ACME General Contractors is $10 million.

**HOSP (South General Hospital Addition)**  contains project data from the owner's perspective regarding the construction of a new hospital wing for Philadelphia County. A-1 Construction Management is the construction management company awarded this job. The value of this contract is 9 million British pounds.

**OFFC (Phila Office Building Addition)**  contains project data from the subcontractor's perspective for concrete work required for renovations to City Hall. The subcontract is between ACME General Contractors and Stresson Industrials. The value of the subcontract with Stresson is $1.4 million.

**ENGR (Office Building)**  contains drawings and drawing sets for the Design Review phase of the drawing process. This project is used in the examples in the *Tracking Drawings* chapter to show how designers (or architects or engineers) track drawings.

# Roles

The roles of the construction manager, general contractor, owner, and the engineer/architect/designer are described in this section to help you understand how the Contract Manager module is implemented by various team members in a business workflow.

**Construction manager**   As the construction manager, you will use the module to manage changes and project costs, monitor progress, and communicate with other team members.

Because you represent the owner's interests throughout the design, construction, and post-construction phases of the project, you continually answer questions about costs, quality, and progress. How much funding is required to complete the project? What is the budget, given the changes to date? What are the pending changes and problem areas? Is the project progressing according to the schedule? Who is responsible for the overdue submittals? What are the areas of noncompliance?

The following list includes tasks that are usually the responsibility of the construction manager in the contract process. Included with each task is the corresponding chapter/part in this manual where you can find more information about those tasks.

- Managing submittals – *Managing Submittals* chapter

- Maintaining updated estimates of cost overruns or underruns – *Setting Up and Using the Cost Worksheet* chapter

- Tracking changes for each project issue and their effect on the cost at completion – *Part 4: Working with Contracts, Project Costs, and Changes*

- Quickly finding all the documents you need to resolve open issues – *Creating and Tracking Issues* chapter

- Monitoring progress through written and verbal communications – *Part 3: Communicating Project Information*

- Customizing Contract Manager to match your company's standards – *Customizing Log and Document Windows* and *Setting Up Dictionaries and Preferences* chapters

- Generating supporting reports – *Printing Logs, Forms, and Reports* chapter

**General contractor**  As the general contractor, you will use the module to manage shop drawings and submittal items, track project issues, document the change process, and record daily progress. When you want to compare progress to the schedule, you can retrieve your schedule.

The following list includes tasks that are usually the responsibility of the general contractor in the contract process. Included with each task is the corresponding chapter/part in this manual where you can find more information about those tasks.

- Using the Drawing and Submittals logs to track shop drawings and submittal items – *Tracking Drawings* and *Managing Submittals* chapters

- Coordinating submittal activities with the project schedule – *Managing Submittals* and *Exchanging Contract Manager Data with a Project Management Module Schedule* chapters

- Identifying issues that require resolution and creating change documents – *Creating and Tracking Issues* chapter and *Part 4: Working with Contracts, Project Costs, and Changes*

- Identifying areas with significant cost variance and analyzing the effects of pending changes on profit – *Setting Up and Using the Cost Worksheet* chapter, and *Part 4: Working with Contracts, Project Costs, and Changes*

- Tracking items that must be completed before final payment is made – *Part 4: Working with Contracts, Project Costs, and Changes*

- Reporting daily progress – *Using Daily Reports* chapter

- Generating supporting reports – *Printing Logs, Forms, and Reports chapter*

**Owner**  As the project owner, you will use the module to organize project data so you can stay on top of progress, coordinate activities with your operations people, and make sure that all of the project details are handled by the appropriate people. You will find the comprehensive records of documents, correspondence, and changes invaluable for claims avoidance.

The following list includes tasks that are usually the responsibility of the owner in the contract process. Included with each task is the corresponding chapter/part in this manual where you can find more information about those tasks.

- Analyzing the projected cost and identifying areas with significant cost variances – *Setting Up and Using the Cost Worksheet* chapter

- Approving requisitions – *Preparing Requisitions for Payment* chapter

- Identifying unfinished tasks for which final payment should be withheld – *Part 4: Working with Contracts, Project Costs, and Changes*

- Identifying issues that require resolution and issuing change orders – *Creating and Tracking Issues* chapter and *Part 4: Working with Contracts, Project Costs, and Changes*

- Managing submittals – *Managing Submittals* chapter

- Comparing daily progress to the schedule – *Using Daily Reports* chapter

- Generating supporting reports – *Printing Logs, Forms, and Reports chapter*

**Engineer/Architect/Designer**  As the project designer, you will use the module to track specifications and drawings, control the submittal review process, monitor progress by the design team, communicate with other team members, and coordinate the activities of outside consultants.

The following list includes tasks that are usually the responsibility of the designer in the contract process. Included with each task is the corresponding chapter/part in this manual where you can find more information about those tasks.

- Managing design and contract drawings – *Tracking Drawings* chapter

- Recording the design budget and expenses – *Setting Up and Using the Cost Worksheet* chapter

- Tracking changes in scope and their effect on the cost at completion – *Part 4: Working with Contracts, Project Costs, and Changes*

- Quickly finding all the documents you need to resolve open issues – *Creating and Tracking Issues* chapter

- Monitoring progress through written and verbal communications – *Part 3: Communicating Project Information*

- Generating supporting reports – *Printing Logs, Forms, and Reports chapter*

# Planning and Adding a Contract Manager Module Project

This chapter presents a general approach for structuring and entering project information in the Contract Manager module. Use these guidelines to set up the module in the most effective way for your business.

# First Steps

The module offers a wide range of features and functions. Depending on how you currently manage contracts—or how you *want* to manage them—you can use all the features or select only the ones you need to support your work process.

The following figure is a general plan for setting up and implementing Primavera. Step 1 is described in the *Installation Guide*. The remainder of this chapter describes steps 2 through 5.

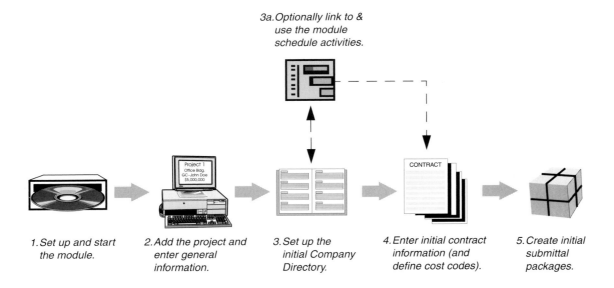

3a. Optionally link to & use the module schedule activities.

1. Set up and start the module.

2. Add the project and enter general information.

3. Set up the initial Company Directory.

4. Enter initial contract information (and define cost codes).

5. Create initial submittal packages.

The Contract Manager module flexibility enables you to realize its benefits even if you don't have all the details about your project at the beginning. As the project progresses, you can add and/or modify the information entered during the initial setup, such as new negotiated contracts, new or changed companies, and more clearly defined submittals and submittal packages.

For details on tailoring Contract Manager module functions to your company's requirements, see the *Customizing Log and Document Windows* chapter.

These are the basic steps to get started in the module; adapt them to your own work processes.

# Adding a Project and Entering General Information

For detailed information on adding a new project, in Help click How To, then click *Add a New Project*. From there, you can choose links to related topics.

**Add a new project**  You can add a new project in Contract Manager module at any time. Right-click on the top-level folder. You can choose from two ways to create a project.

■ Choose New Project to use the Add Project Wizard, which guides you from start to finish. This method is best when you have most of the information prepared for the project or are unfamiliar with creating a new project.

■ Choose Publish Project to create a project name and assign it to an administrator, who will then enter the project information. The module notifies the administrator that a project has been added that requires information.

 *The New Project option is not available if you do not have rights to create a new project.*

See Help for detailed information on using either of these options to create a new project.

*Type a unique abbreviation and title for the project. You must enter data in these fields to add a project.*

*Select any of these topics to move directly to that phase in the wizard.*

*Click Next to continue creating the project.*

**Add Project Wizard (first option)**

Select the administrator; the module notifies that person that a request has been made to create a new project.

**Administrator request (second option)**

For more information about setting access rights, see *Setting Access Rights (Project Access)* later in this chapter.

*When you add a new project, you become the project administrator. Project administrators have access to all documents in their projects. (Module administrators have access to all documents in all projects.) By default, all other users have no access rights to new projects. Assign users access to a project in the Project Access window (right-click on a project and choose Project Access).*

**Delete a project**  To delete an entire project, right-click on the project in the Project View, then choose Delete Project.

*When you delete a project, you permanently remove that project and all its associated documents.*

# Defining the Key Contact

For more information about defining default contacts per document type, see *Assigning Default Contacts* later in this chapter.

The contact you specify in the Your Company field (in the Key Parties section of the Add Project Wizard) is the key contact for the project. When you create documents, the module automatically enters the key contact in the To or From field, based on the type of document being created. For example, if the document being created is a contract or PO, the module automatically selects that company in the From field. To view or modify this assignment, right-click on the project and choose Project Settings. In the Key Parties section, click Select next to the Your Company field.

# Creating a Project Template

If you will be adding projects that use the same key parties, currency, and schedule information, you can create a project template that contains this information. Use this template as the basis for each new project you create.

**Add a new project template**  You can make an existing project a template. Right-click on the project and select Save As Template.

**Use the template as a basis for a new project**  When you want to create a new project that uses the information in the template, right-click on the top level folder and choose New Project. Enter a project name and title, then click Template on the left. Choose the first option, Use Template, and select the template from the drop-down list.

*Click Template to choose a template.*

*Select the template you want to use for this project.*

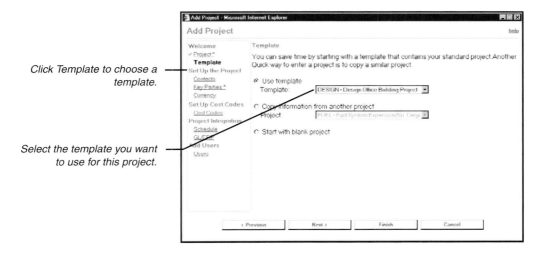

When you select a template, the module creates the new project based on the information contained in the template. You can edit this information in the new project.

# Setting Access Rights (Project Access)

For more information on security, see *Access* or *Security* in Help. Use the Search feature and type *access* or *security* for a list of related topics.

Contract Manager module has three user levels: Contract Manager administrator, project administrator, and restricted user.

Contract Manager administrators and project administrators can set access rights to a project for Contract Manager users. Access rights determine which modules and documents a user can view, add, edit, export, or delete. You can set a user's access rights for each Primavera module.

**Contract Manager administrator**  Contract Manager administrators have full access to all new and existing projects. They can

■ Change module and process-level security for all projects and users

■ Change the owner of any project and delete any project

■ Copy project access rights from any project and user to any project and user

 *A user name and password with Contract Manager administrator-level access rights is shipped with the module. When you start Contract Manager, type EXPADMIN in the User ID and Password fields to log on as an administrator.*

**Project administrator**  A project administrator is the user who created a particular project. Project administrators initially have full access to all projects they create. They can

■ Change module and process-level security in projects they create and change their own access rights

■ Change ownership of projects they create and delete projects they create

■ Copy project access rights from any project to projects they administer

 *Project administrator rules apply only if the user who created the project retains ownership. If ownership changes, the new owner gains full access to the project, and the original owner becomes a restricted user.*

**Restricted user**   By default, restricted users have no access to projects (including all modules and process-level security). A module administrator or project administrator can change a user's default access rights using the User Project Access window and the module Administration Application. To change a user's project access rights, right-click on a project and choose Project Access. Click the document icon next to the user to open the User Project Access dialog box.

To change a user's general module access rights, open the module Administration Application and click User Accounts. Click the document icon next to the user.

**Set a user's access rights**   Right-click on the project in the Project View and choose Project Access. Click the document icon next to the user for which you want to set access rights. Set the user's rights by module.

■   Mark View to enable a user to only view data in a module.

■   Mark Add to enable the user to add data in a module.

■   Mark Edit to enable the user to edit data in a module.

 *In order for users to add items to documents, users must have Add and Edit rights to the module. If users have Add rights, but not Edit rights, they will not be able to add items to a document.*

■   Mark Export to enable the user to export data from the module.

■   Mark Delete to enable the user to delete data from a module.

To prevent a user from opening a module, clear the checkboxes for all access types. If a user has no access rights to a particular module, that module will not appear in the Project View.

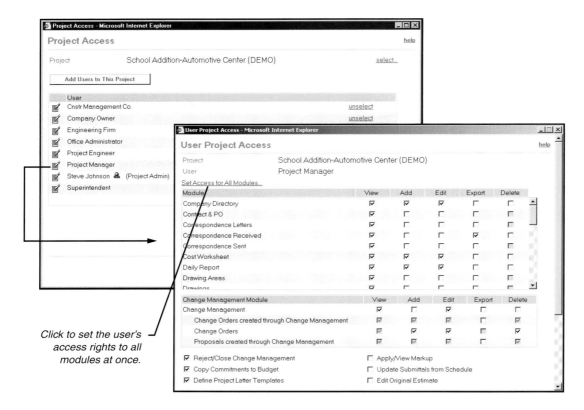

Click to set the user's
access rights to all
modules at once.

To restrict a user's access to documents that have a certain To or From Contact, and to submittals in which that same contact is listed as a Received, Sent, Returned, or Forwarded reviewer, click Select next to the Access by Company field (at the bottom of the dialog box). Click Select next to the company you want to assign.

 *You cannot change Access rights for administrators. They always have full access to all projects.*

**Set access rights for a group of users across projects**  To save time, the project administrator can copy the access rights for users in one project to another project. Right-click on the project to which you want to copy access rights, then choose Copy User Access.

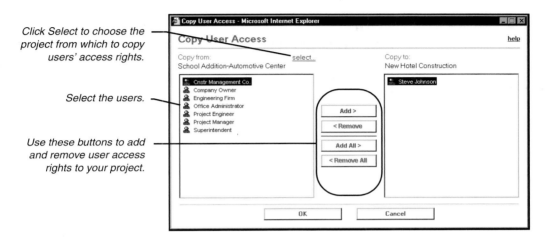

*Click Select to choose the project from which to copy users' access rights.*

*Select the users.*

*Use these buttons to add and remove user access rights to your project.*

# Setting Up the Company Directory

The Company Directory enables you to store information about everyone involved in your project. You can include names, phone numbers, and addresses of subcontractors, managers, suppliers, your own staff, and any other companies or individuals involved in the project.

Nearly all module documents use the information included in the Company Directory. Entering this information at the beginning of the project ensures that your unique abbreviations are consistent, avoiding confusion and mistakes. Even if you have only part of the company's information, enter at least the company abbreviation, name, office address, and a key contact; you can add missing details later.

For more information on adding companies and contacts, see *Add Companies and Contacts* in Help.

**Add a company and contact**  Click Companies in the Project Information folder, then click Add Company.

Click Add to create a contact for the company. The first contact you add becomes the key contact.

Type important details about the company in the Remarks section.

In the Details section, mark to indicate if the company is a Disadvantaged- (DBE), Minority- (MBE), or Woman-owned (WBE) business enterprise.

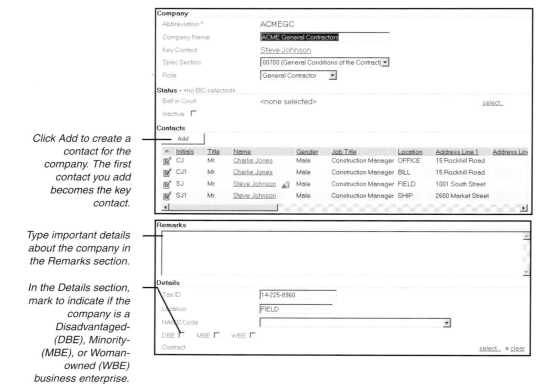

*Contract Manage module requires that you enter the key contact's initials.*

In the Company section, enter an abbreviation for the company and the company name. The key contact is the person to whom most documents will be addressed. This field is filled once the first contact is entered in the Contacts section.

Select a specification section code. Specification section codes are a part of a standard coding system developed by the Construction Specification Institute (CSI). You can select these codes from any Specification Section data field, or you can create your own codes (right-click on the top-level folder, then choose Dictionaries, Specification Sections).

For information on creating your own roles and specification section codes, *see Setting Up Dictionaries and Preferences*, or *Create Contact Roles* in Help.

Select the company's role. You can select an existing role, or you can create a new role and add it to the list (right-click on the top-level folder, then choose Dictionaries, Company Roles).

**Add contacts for the company**  To add contacts for the company, expand the Contacts section in the Company document window and click Add. You can add as many contacts as needed for each company.

**Add remarks to a contact**  Expand the Remarks section in the Company document window and type any important details, such as directions or office hours.

*To define standard paper sizes, right-click on the top-level folder and choose Dictionaries, Drawings, Paper Sizes.*

**Add an address, paper size, and number of copies for drawing distribution to a contact**  Expand the Contacts section in the Company document window and click the document icon next to the contact you want to update. Enter information for all applicable addresses, such as office, shipping, or billing; phone numbers; and e-mail information. Select the paper size, and type the number of copies you will be using to send drawings for design review or distribution for this contact. This information is used in the Drawings and Drawing Sets logs. Click Save & Close when finished.

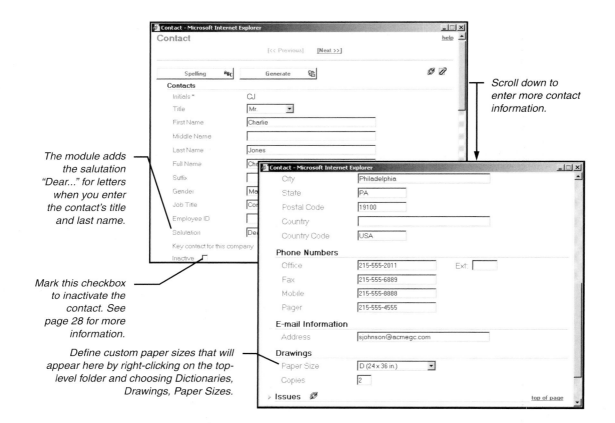

The module adds the salutation "Dear..." for letters when you enter the contact's title and last name.

Mark this checkbox to inactivate the contact. See page 28 for more information.

Define custom paper sizes that will appear here by right-clicking on the top-level folder and choosing Dictionaries, Drawings, Paper Sizes.

Scroll down to enter more contact information.

 The module *does not apply changes you make in this window to any documents where the original address already appears (such as contracts). This practice protects the validity of the original document information.*

**Copy the Company Directory**  To set up a new project more quickly, you can copy the Company Directory from a similar project in the same database or from the group Company Directory. Right-click on the project and choose Copy Companies.

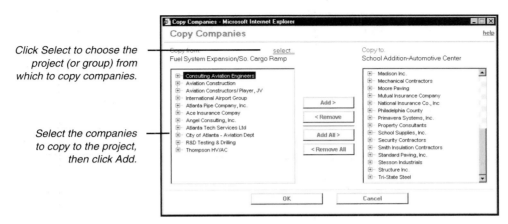

*Click Select to choose the project (or group) from which to copy companies.*

*Select the companies to copy to the project, then click Add.*

You can also copy companies and contacts from a project to the group level. Right-click on the top-level folder and choose Copy Companies.

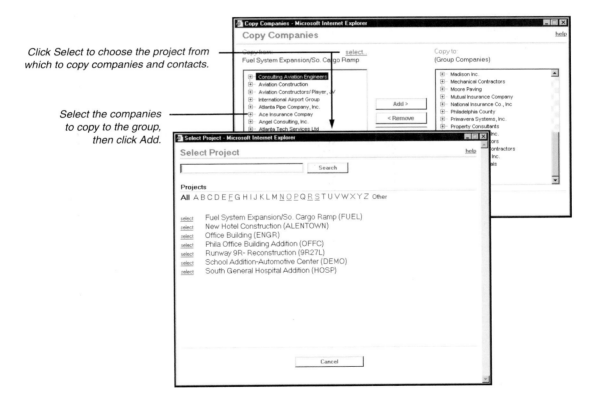

*Click Select to choose the project from which to copy companies and contacts.*

*Select the companies to copy to the group, then click Add.*

For more information, see *Company document window* and *Contact dialog box* in Help.

### Inactivate a company or contact

You can label a company that you are no longer dealing with as inactive. Inactivating a company or contact disables the company or contact without deleting it. When a company is made inactive, all of its contacts also become inactive; the company and contacts do not appear in dialog boxes that contain lists of companies and/ or contacts. The company and its contacts remain in the database, but do not appear in the lists.

Expand the Status and Contacts sections in the Company document window to inactivate companies and contacts.

*Mark this checkbox to remove inactive contacts from the Contacts list. Clearing the checkbox returns them to the list.*

*Mark this checkbox to inactivate (disable) this company without deleting it. To activate the company so that it appears in lists of Primavera companies, clear the Inactive checkbox.*

*Click the contact's icon to open the Contact dialog box, in which you can inactivate the individual contact, as shown on page page 26.*

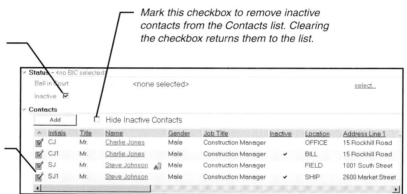

### Delete a contact or address

Expand the Contacts section in the Company document and click Delete for the contact you want to remove. When prompted to confirm whether you want to delete the item, click Yes.

## Saving Companies and Contacts in the Project/Group List

Each project contains its own directory of project companies. The module also maintains a directory of database companies that all projects in the same database can share.

*For more information on how to set contact preferences, see Setting Project Preferences in the Setting Up Dictionaries and Preferences chapter.*

When you add a new project, the module uses the Project Company Directory by default. To use the same companies for all of your projects, switch to the Group (database) Company Directory. Right-click on a project and choose Project Settings. In the Companies section, click Switch. "Project" will change to "Group" to indicate that the Group directory is in use.

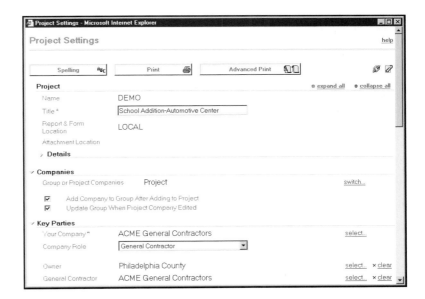

You can save new companies in the Group Company Directory while using the Project Company Directory. In Project Settings, mark the Add Company to Group After Adding to Project checkbox.

If you change an existing company in a project, the module also updates the Group Company Directory, even if the active directory is Project, as long as you marked the Update Group When Project Company Edited checkbox in the Project Settings dialog box.

## Adding Companies and Contacts from Other Documents

When you add a document, you may need to enter information for a company that is not in the Company Directory. Rather than interrupt your current task, you can add companies and contacts from most documents without going back to the "Companies" dialog box.

For more information, see *Select Contact dialog box* in Help.

When you click Select for a company or contact field, the Select Company or Select Contact dialog box opens. To add a new company or contact, choose whether to organize by company or contact, then click Add Contact or Add Company, depending on which you want to add.

Type the company name and abbreviation (if adding a new company), the contact's full name and initials, and other information, if available, then click Save. Primavera adds the company and contact information to the Company Directory. You can edit the information later if necessary.

# Company Directory Reports and Forms

Primavera provides several standard reports you can use to print company information. From the Company Directory

log window, click Select an Action, then Advanced Print. Click Go. Select a report, then click Print.

| ACME General Contractors | | | | | | | | School Addition-Automotive Center | |
|---|---|---|---|---|---|---|---|---|---|
| **Primary Contact List** | | | | | | | | | |
| Job No: JBAA450 | | | | | | | | Date: 4/10/00 | |
| Project No: PRJAA450 | | | | | | | | Page: 1 of 1 | |

| Company | Contact ID | Role | Contact | City | State | Phone | Fax | EMail |
|---|---|---|---|---|---|---|---|---|
| A & S Supply | SUPPLY | SUP | Sue Johnson | Upper Darby | PA | 610-555-0222 | 610-555-0224 | |
| ACE Mason Contractors | MASON | SUB | Dave Barron | Cherry Hill | NJ | 609-555-2222 | 609-555-2220 | david.barron@mason.com |
| ACME General Contractors | ACMEGC | GC | Steve Johnson | Philadelphia | PA | 215-555-2011 | 215-555-6889 | sjohnson@acmegc.com |
| Adams Masonry | ADAMS | SUB | Greg Fox | Ardmore | PA | 610-555-8463 | 610-555-8459 | |
| Baines Steel | BAINES | SUB | Helen Prugh | Westtown | PA | 610-555-7250 | 610-555-7201 | helen.prugh@baines.com |
| Brink Contractors | BRINK | SUB | Lou Jackson | Philadelphia | PA | 215-555-1111 | 215-555-1113 | |
| Button Paint & Paper | BUTTON | SUB | Jan Shady | Wynnewood | PA | 610-555-9999 | 610-555-9997 | |
| Concrete Pipe Company | CPIPE | SUP | Chuck Statsen | New Britain | PA | 610-555-9829 | 610-555-9899 | |
| CPM Consultants | CPM | SUB | Don Newman | Wayne | PA | 610-555-0000 | 610-555-0001 | |
| Design Group | DESIGN | ARC | Chris Atkinson | Philadelphia | PA | 215-555-0444 | 215-555-0446 | chris.atkinson@design.cor |
| Electrical Contractors | ELECTR | SUP | Eric Thompson | Philadelphia | PA | 215-555-0333 | 215-555-0334 | |
| Finish Ceilings, Inc. | FINISH | SUB | George Lafferty | Upper Darby | PA | 610-555-1277 | 610-555-1450 | |
| Gelco Space | GELCO | SUP | Karen Andrews | Bala Cynwyd | PA | 610-555-0555 | 510-555-0550 | |
| Internat'l Insurance Company | INSURE | OTH | Jane G. Babrielle | | | | | |
| JP Johnson Paving | JOHNSON | SUB | Michael | Paoli | PA | 610-555-4888 | | |
| Madison Inc. | MADISON | SUB | Wes Thompson | Broomal | PA | | | |

# Customizing the Control Center

For detailed information on using the Control Center, see *Workspace* or *Customize Workspace dialog box* in Help.

For information on items, type the item topic (such as *alerts* or *actions*) in Help's Index or Search tab.

The Control Center is a customizable window that enables you to quickly view and access your information.

- You can use the Control Center as a starting point for all the tasks you need to perform in Primavera.

- You can view information across all projects, multiple projects, or one project at a time.

- You can add items to the Control Center that enable you to view issues, requests for information (RFIs), actions, alerts, and reports. Other items allow you to integrate with a Project Management module schedule, view your Inbox, and prepare documents.

- You can click a section of a graph to display the details.

*Click Customize this Page to change the appearance of the currently selected Control Center window.*

*Click Refresh Page to update the Control Center information.*

*You can include up to 12 items in the Control Center.*

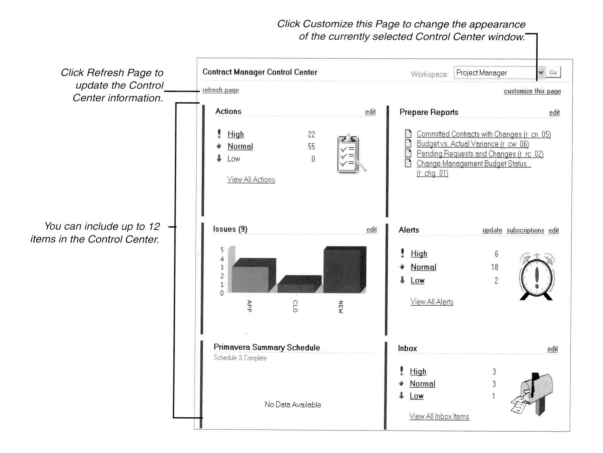

**Customize the Control Center** Click Customize this Page to select which items appear in the Control Center and where they are placed.

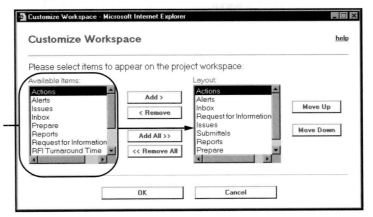

*Select the items to include in the Control Center, then click Add to move the items to the Layout area.*

For detailed information on customizing your desktop, see *Customize Workspace dialog box* in Help.

Items can be included more than once in the Control Center. For example, if you want issues to appear as a graph, a bar chart, and a pie chart, move three Issue items to the Layout area, then edit each item's appearance by clicking the Edit link above it in the Control Center.

# Setting Up Distribution Lists

After you set up your company directory, you can create distribution lists for project participants involved in the transmittal, submittal, or drawing processes. Primavera displays the defined distribution group names in the distribution selection lists in these documents. You can use the same lists in any project in the same database, add or delete names, and combine them as necessary.

Setting up distribution lists saves time by enabling you to quickly select a group of participants to whom you want to send a document instead of selecting each one individually.

You can establish different distribution lists depending on the document and person to whom you want it sent. For example, if you're the general contractor, you may want to set up a distribution list that contains your subcontractors so you can send them the transmittals resulting from their submittals. All of the contacts in the list will receive a copy of the document. At the beginning of a project, you may need to communicate with different team players to determine who requires a copy. As contract work progresses, you can refine the lists and copy them to other projects. If you assign contacts to a group (switch to Group in the Companies section of Project Settings), they apply to all projects in that group.

**Add a distribution list**  In the Company Directory log window, click Define Distribution Lists. Click Add, then type a distribution list abbreviation and title.

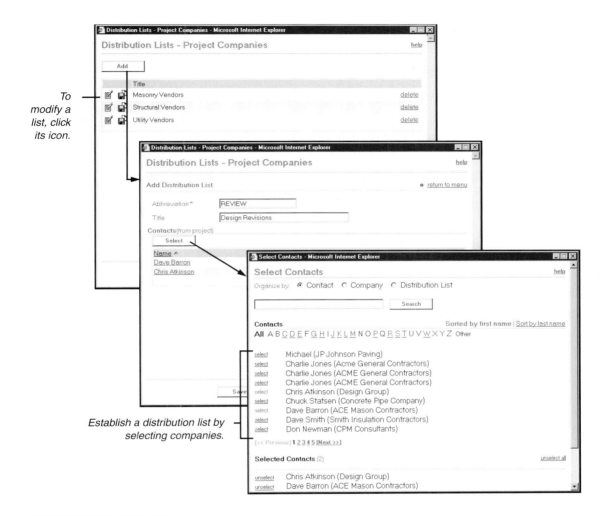

To modify a list, click its icon.

Establish a distribution list by selecting companies.

Any changes you make to your company directory are also reflected for the corresponding company in distribution lists.

Click Select in the Contacts section to open the Select Contacts dialog box. To easily find the contacts you need, you can organize by contact, company, or distribution list. All companies in the current project appear if the Project Setting is set to Project; all group companies appear if the Project Setting is set to Group. Companies assigned to the Group level apply to all projects in that group. Click Select next to each contact you want to add, then click Save.

To remove items from a distribution list, click Unselect next to the name of the contact you want to remove. Click Save and Return to Menu when you finish defining the list. To delete the distribution list, click Delete next to the list you want to remove.

**Edit a distribution list**  You can also edit an existing distribution list name and/or title. In the Company Directory log window, click Define Distribution Lists, then click the document icon next to the list you want to modify. Make the changes. Click Save and Return to Menu when you finish modifying the current list. Primavera reflects any changes in future uses of the list; the original version of the list (before editing) remains unchanged where it is already used in Primavera.

Click Close from the Distribution Lists dialog box when you finish defining distribution lists.

**Copy a distribution list to a new list**  To save time, you can create a new distribution list based on an existing one. In the Company Directory log window, click Define Distribution Lists, then click the Save Distribution List As icon next to the list you want to copy. A new distribution list is created containing the names from the copied list.

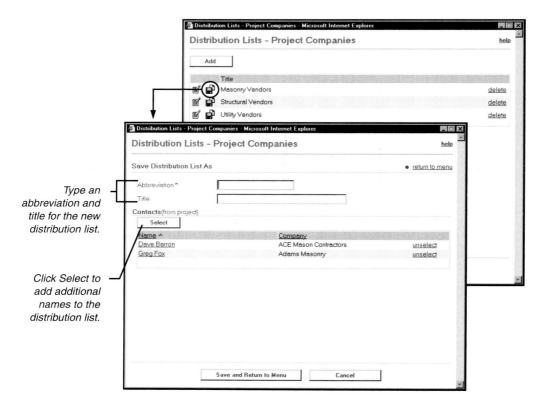

*Type an abbreviation and title for the new distribution list.*

*Click Select to add additional names to the distribution list.*

# Assigning Default Contacts

To specify which contacts the module automatically displays in the To and From fields of a particular document, right-click on the project and choose Default Field Values.

The Set Default Field Values window displays the default contact assignments for the currently open project.

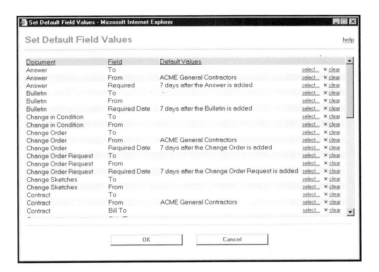

**Customize contact assignments**  To customize this information, click Select next to the field to which you want to assign a default contact. In the Select Company dialog box, click Select next to the company you want to assign as the default, then click OK.

 *You can edit or delete default contacts at any time. Changing the default contact affects new documents only. Contact names for existing documents remain unchanged.*

# Entering Initial Contract Information

For details on setting up the Contract log, see the *Managing Contracts and Purchase Orders* chapter.

If you plan to use the module to track costs in change documents or invoices, set up the Contracts log next. Entering this information enables you to connect all subsequent change documents, requisitions, or invoices with the appropriate contracts, and it simplifies creation of reports and related correspondence. In the Contract Information folder, click either Contracts - Budgeted or Contracts - Committed (depending on the type of contract) to open the Contracts log. Click the document icon in the log to open the contract document window in Edit mode. (Clicking the document's title opens it in View mode.)

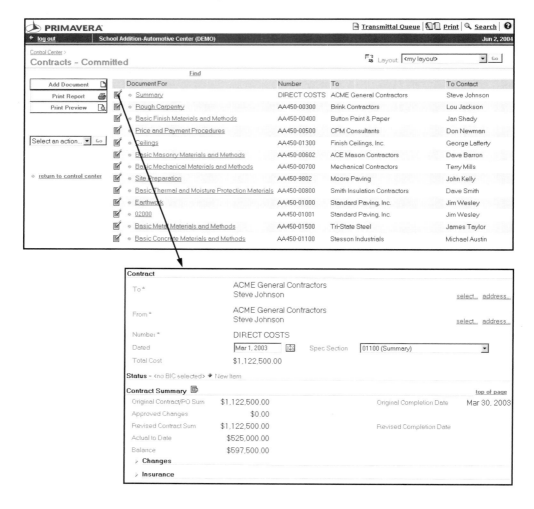

## Setting Up Cost Codes and Modifying Cost Worksheet Headings

For details about using cost codes, see the *Setting Up and Using the Cost Worksheet* chapter.

If you plan to track project costs in the module, you need to set up cost codes to classify different types of work associated with the project. As the project progresses, you can then compare budgeted, committed, and actual costs for each cost code. Developing one set of codes across all projects at the start ensures that your account structure is complete and consistent. To set up the Cost Worksheet more quickly, you can copy the cost codes and titles from a similar project in the same database. Right-click on a project and choose Copy Cost Codes.

For details about customizing column names, see *Customizing Text in the Contract Manager Module* in the *Customizing Log and Document Windows* chapter.

You can also modify Cost Worksheet column names (as well as other module column names) to match terms you use in your business. For example, you may use *Revenue* rather than *Budget*. It is recommended that you make column name changes at the start of the project, since these changes affect all projects within the same database or project group. To change the column titles, right-click on the top-level folder and choose Customize Text.

# Creating Submittal Packages and Submittals

For details on creating submittals, see the *Managing Submittals* chapter.

You can easily track submittal review cycles with the module. No matter how many revisions a submittal goes through, you will always know who received it and when they received it; which submittals were approved and which are pending; which are overdue and by what amount of time; and, perhaps most important, who is currently responsible. The module also provides distribution copies, transmittals, and dunning letters.

For more information on submittal packages, see *Adding a Submittal Package* in the *Managing Submittals* chapter.

You can group related submittals into packages to help organize them. For example, you can assemble a submittal package for all items pertaining to a specific supplier, floor of a building, or area of work. Set up packages at the beginning of the project so you already have an organized structure when you are ready to enter individual items.

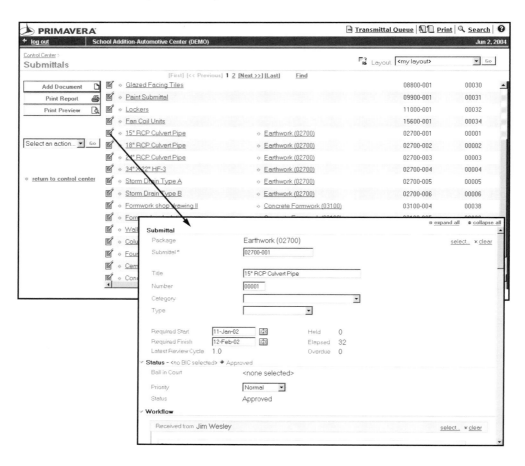

# Linking with a Project Management Module Schedule

For details on linking the Contract Manager module with a Project Management module schedule, see the *Exchanging Contract Manager Module Data with a Project Management Module Schedule* chapter.

You can link projects scheduled in the Project Management module to Contract Manager module projects. Once this link is established, you can use activities in Project Management module projects to build and update the Contract Manager module project data. You can create a connection from the Contract Manager module to any Project Management module project. You can then specify the path and project name in Contract Manager module using the Schedule section in Project Settings.

The link enables you to review dates from a Project Management module schedule from within the Contract Manager module to see how schedule delays or other factors affect a project. Once you specify the project schedule to link to the Contract Manager module project, you can use early and actual activity dates from the schedule to update start and finish dates in the Contract Manager module.

# Working with a Project

In this part

*T*his part explains how to set up log and document windows, dictionaries, and other options in the Contract Manager module to your preferences. It also describes how to change and save the module databases.

*Working with Log and Document Windows* explains how to use the log and document windows as well as the common features for those windows.

*Customizing Log and Document Windows* discusses how to modify the workspace and settings to fit your needs.

*Setting Up Dictionaries and Preferences* explains the project, dictionary, user, and letters preferences you can set.

*Maintaining a Contract Manager Module Database* discusses how to add Microsoft SQL, Oracle, and Sybase databases, and back up and restore your Contract Manager module databases.

*Printing Logs, Forms, and Reports* describes how to print the content of any log or document window and the predefined reports delivered with the module.

# Working with Log and Document Windows

This chapter describes common features of the Contract Manager module, and explains how to use them. These features include adding and deleting documents; using the spelling checker to proof work; filtering, sorting, and grouping documents; and attaching and viewing files. In this section, the phrase "the module" refers to the Contract Manager Module.

# Using Log and Document Windows

Most functions within the Contract Manager Module consist of a log and a document window. The log window lists the existing documents for that function. The document window, accessed from the log window, contains detailed information about an item grouped in sections related to the item and also features an Edit mode in which you can add, edit, and delete items.

**Use log windows**  The following example is a typical log window from which you can view a summary of existing documents, or add a new document.

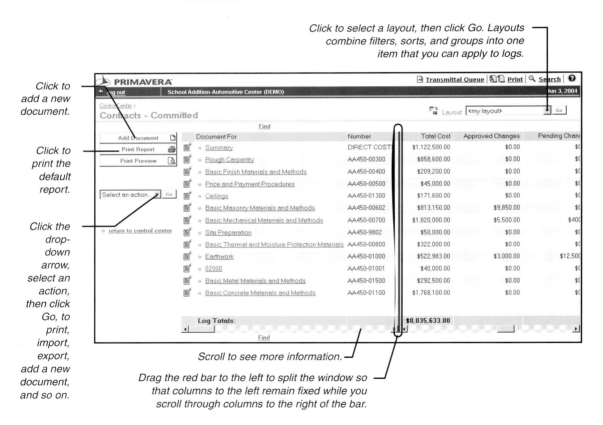

Click to select a layout, then click Go. Layouts combine filters, sorts, and groups into one item that you can apply to logs.

Click to add a new document.

Click to print the default report.

Click the drop-down arrow, select an action, then click Go, to print, import, export, add a new document, and so on.

Scroll to see more information.

Drag the red bar to the left to split the window so that columns to the left remain fixed while you scroll through columns to the right of the bar.

**Open a document from a log window**  To open a document window in View mode, click the linked (underlined) description/document title listed in the first column of the log window. Click the document icon to the left of the title to open the document window in Edit mode.

# Adding, Editing, and Deleting Documents

You can add documents from most log windows and document windows by using a variety of techniques. Choose the method you are most comfortable with or that is easiest for the function you are performing.

**Add a new document or document item**   Use any of the following methods to add a new document:

- Click Add Document while working in any log window.

- Click Select an Action, select Add Document, then click Go while working in any log window and most document windows (in View mode).

- You can also add a document by copying all or part of an existing one, by clicking Select an Action, Generate Document.

*The module prompts you to save your changes when you exit the document window.*

**Edit a document**   Use one of the following methods to edit a document:

- Open the document in Edit mode by clicking its document icon in the log window.

- Open the document by clicking its linked (underlined) title in the log window. Click Edit Document, or Select an Action, Edit Document, then Go.

- From a log window, scroll to the last column and click Select an Action, Edit Document, then Go.

**Delete a document**   To delete a document, open the document window, click Select an Action, Delete Document, then click Go. Some document windows contain lists of items, such as the line items in a daily report. You can delete these items by scrolling to the last column and clicking Remove.

 *When you delete a document from a log window, the module removes its associated document window and any links to issues and attachments.*

# Using the Spelling Checker

The module provides a spelling checker so you can detect misspelled words in documents.

The spelling checker looks for misspelled words using the main dictionary provided and the customizable dictionaries you create. The main dictionary is comprehensive, but it does not contain proper names or many specialized words; you can add these words to your user dictionary so that the module can recognize them.

In addition to misspellings, the spelling checker looks for repeated words, such as "that that." The spelling checker does not check single-character words (such as a) or text that does not contain letters (such as 75% or 23). The spelling checker also does not allow you to change information in noneditable fields.

**Use the spelling checker**  Open the document for which you want to check spelling in Edit mode. Click Spelling. If the module does not find any mistakes, the spelling checker displays the following message: The Spell check is complete. If it finds a word it does not recognize, it will provide several options.

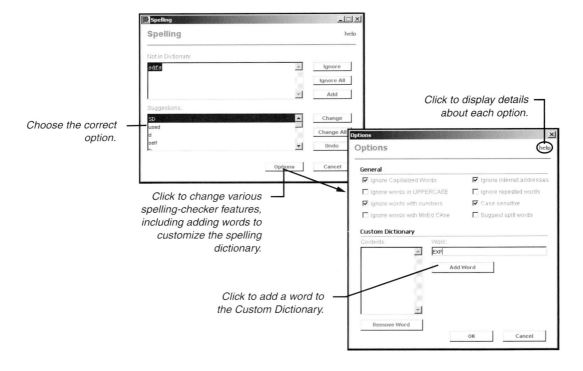

Choose the correct option.

Click to display details about each option.

Click to change various spelling-checker features, including adding words to customize the spelling dictionary.

Click to add a word to the Custom Dictionary.

For each word the module does not recognize, select one of the following options:

■   To keep the spelling, click Ignore. Click Ignore All to ignore all instances of the highlighted word.

■   To keep the spelling and add the word to your user dictionary so that the module recognizes the word the next time, click Add.

■   To change the spelling, type a different spelling or choose a suggestion and then click Change (click Change All to replace all occurrences of the misspelled word in the current document).

■   To undo a change you made within one field, click Undo.

# Creating, Editing, and Assigning Layouts

You can define filter, sort, and group specifications to customize a layout and apply it to a log window. For example, if you use a certain combination of a sort, filter, and/or group repeatedly, you could create a layout using them and apply that layout to a log window.

Once you create a layout, you can save it and use it again in other projects. A layout will appear in the same log window for all projects within a database. If you create a layout called Layout1 for the Contracts log in project DEMO, Layout1 will appear in the Contracts log in every project in that database

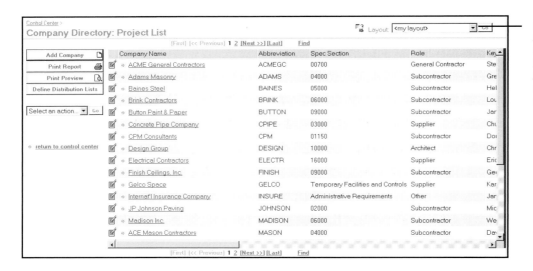

Click to select an existing layout to apply to the log window.

For detailed information on adding layouts, start with the topic *Layouts Overview* in Help.

**Add a new layout**  To create a layout from a log window:

1  Select Customize Layouts from the Layout drop-down list, and click Go.

2  Click Add to define the layout.

### Assigning a layout to a log window

1  In a log window, and click the Layout drop-down list.

2  Select the layout you want to use.

3  Click Go. Any filter, sort, or group settings specified for the selected layout will apply to the log window.

### Edit a layout

1  Select Customize Layouts from the Layout drop-down list, and click Go.

2  Click the document icon next to the layout you want to edit. You can specify the filter, sort, or grouping to use for the selected layout.

3  Select the document-related columns you want to show in the log window.

4  In the Set Column Properties window, you can adjust the width of the columns you choose to display in the log window, select which columns to display totals, and select the position of the Select an Action drop-down list. Click Set Column Properties to adjust these settings.

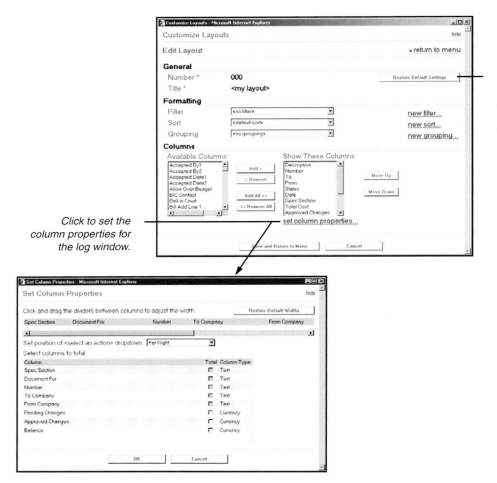

Click to restore the layout to the default settings.

Click to set the column properties for the log window.

# Selecting Layouts

**Set your favorite layouts**   You can have the Contract Manager module list your favorite two layouts at the top of the Layout drop-down list.

1   In a log window, select Layout, Customize Layouts.

2   Click Set Favorite Layouts, and select a First Layout and Second Layout. The selected layouts will appear above all existing layouts in the list.

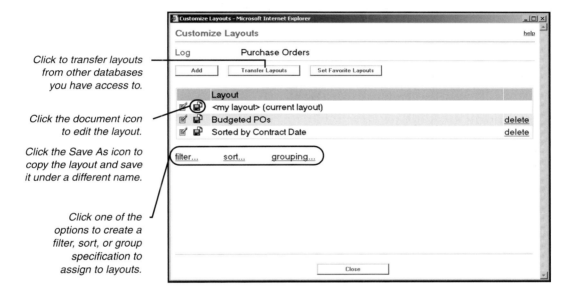

*Click to transfer layouts from other databases you have access to.*

*Click the document icon to edit the layout.*

*Click the Save As icon to copy the layout and save it under a different name.*

*Click one of the options to create a filter, sort, or group specification to assign to layouts.*

# Filtering Data in Layouts

You can select and rearrange the displayed sequence of a list of documents in a log using the Contract Manager module filter features for a layout.

A filter shows some documents in a log while hiding others, depending on the options selected. For example, you can assign a filtered layout for the Contracts log so you see only contracts for which ACMEGC is the From Company. The following table defines the valid operators you can use to define a filter, along with each operator's meaning.

| Condition | Description |
| --- | --- |
| = | Is equal to |
| <> | Not equal to |
| > | Is greater than |
| >= | Is greater than or equal to |
| < | Is less than |
| <= | Is less than or equal to |
| Is Null | Date field does not contain a value |
| Is Not Null | Date field contains a value |
| OR | When one expression or another is true, the row is selected |
| AND | When one expression and another expression is true, the row is selected |
| NOT | Inverse logic; when an expression is false, the row is selected |
| Is Blank | The field is blank |
| Is Not Blank | The field is not blank |

### Apply an existing filter to a layout

1  Open the log window you want to filter, select Customize Layouts from the Layout drop-down list, and click Go.

2  Click the document icon for the layout you want to edit, or click Add to define a new layout. In the Formatting section, select the filter you want to use.

3  Click Save and Return to Menu, and click Close. The module displays documents in the list based on the selected filter.

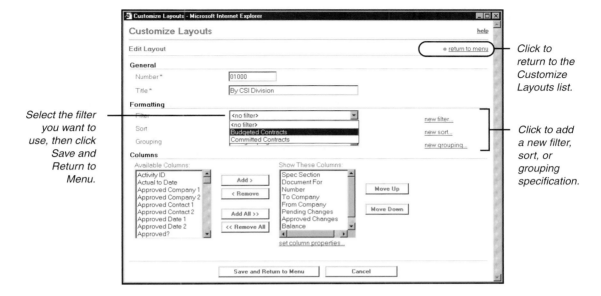

*Select the filter you want to use, then click Save and Return to Menu.*

*Click to return to the Customize Layouts list.*

*Click to add a new filter, sort, or grouping specification.*

**Add a standard (simple) filter** If no predefined filter matches your needs, you can create your own.

1 Open the log window you want to filter. Choose Layout, Customize Layouts, and click Go.

2 Click Filter.

3 Click Add and specify information about the documents you want to filter. You can also edit simple filters.

The following example shows only contracts where the To Company is equal to A & S Supply or Electrical Contractors. Click Organize Rows to rearrange the filter statements. Click Verify to check whether the filter is valid. Click Advanced Filter to build more sophisticated filters. Edit or add a new layout in the Customize Layouts window to assign the filter to a layout.

 *Once you edit a filter in Advanced mode, the filter cannot be changed back to the standard format.*

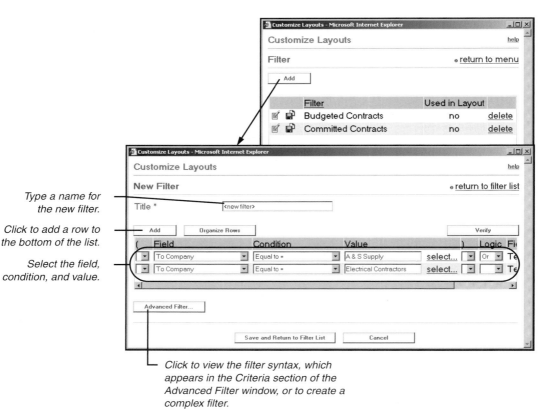

Type a name for
the new filter.

Click to add a row to
the bottom of the list.

Select the field,
condition, and value.

Click to view the filter syntax, which
appears in the Criteria section of the
Advanced Filter window, or to create a
complex filter.

**Add a complex filter**  If you require more powerful filters, you can
create advanced SQL statements by using the Advanced Filter feature; to
create a complex filter, click Advanced Filter.

 You should **only** use this feature if you are familiar with SQL
statements.

The following two examples, using Sybase SQL syntax, list all contacts
that have a contract value greater than $100,000:

Filter syntax for the IN operator:

    vendor_abbrev IN (Select from_vendor from cnmt WHERE total_cost > 100000.00)

Filter syntax for the EXISTS operator:

    EXISTS (Select * from cnmt WHERE cnmt.from_vendor = vnmt.vendor_abbrev AND
    total_cost > 100000.00)

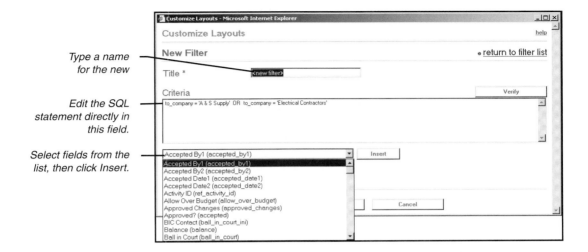

*Type a name for the new*

*Edit the SQL statement directly in this field.*

*Select fields from the list, then click Insert.*

## Filtering Schedule Data

If the Contract Manager module is linked to a Project Management module schedule, and you want to filter activities in the Schedule log (click Schedule in the Project Information folder), remember that Project Management module data is stored in a different format than the Contract Manager module data, and the syntax of activity criteria based on dates differs slightly. Examine the syntax for the sample filters in the Criteria field before you create a new filter for the Schedule log based on dates.

## Filtering Tips

A filter applies only to the log to which you add it. For example, if you create a filter in a contracts log, that filter does not apply to transmittals.

If the Contract Manager module does not list certain documents, remove the filter, if any, and re-examine the log or document.

# Sorting Data in Layouts

A sort specification changes the order in which documents are displayed. For example, you can sort the Contracts log so the module lists contracts in order of accepted date, starting with the latest date at the top.

**Apply an existing sort specification to a layout**  The Contract Manager module includes several predefined sort specifications.

1   Open the log you want to sort, then select Customize Layouts from the Layout drop-down list.

2   Click Go.

3   Click the document icon to edit the selected layout, or click Add to define a new layout.

4   In the Formatting section, select the sort specification you want to use.

5   Click Save and Return to Menu, then click Close. The module rearranges documents in the list based on the selected sort specification.

**Add a new sort specification**  If no predefined sort specification matches your needs, you can create your own.

1   In the Project View, open the log you want to sort, then select Customize Layouts

2   from the Layout drop-down list.

3   Click Go. Click Sort.

4   Click Add in the Sort window and specify which fields you want to sort and the order in which you want to sort them. You can sort by as many fields as you want.

5   Edit or add a new layout in the Customize Layouts window to assign the sort to a layout.

In the following specification example, the module sorts the log entries by balance, in ascending order.

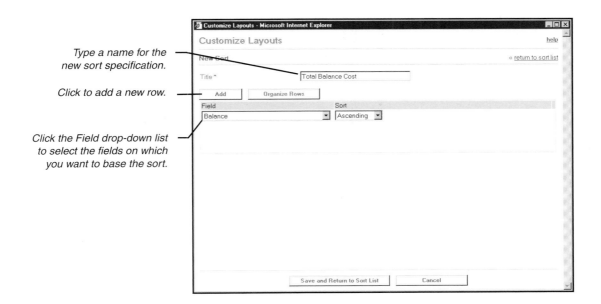

*Type a name for the new sort specification.*

*Click to add a new row.*

*Click the Field drop-down list to select the fields on which you want to base the sort.*

## Sorting Tips

A sort applies only to the log to which you add it. For example, if you create a sort in a contracts log, that sort does not apply to transmittals.

# Grouping Data in Layouts

Grouping enables you to group and display log documents by criteria that you specify. For example, you can group and display documents by ball-in-court, activity ID, package number, or any other available field. You can also apply different background and text colors to header rows to differentiate sections, and you can create multiple groups.

### Apply an existing group to a layout

1  Open the log to which you want to apply a group, and select Customize Layouts from the Layout drop-down list.

2  Click Go.

3  Click the document icon to edit the selected layout, or click Add to define a new layout.

4  In the Formatting section, select the group specification you want to use.

5  Click Save and Return to Menu, then click Close. The module rearranges documents in the list based on the group you select.

*Select the grouping you want to use, then click Save and Return to Menu.*

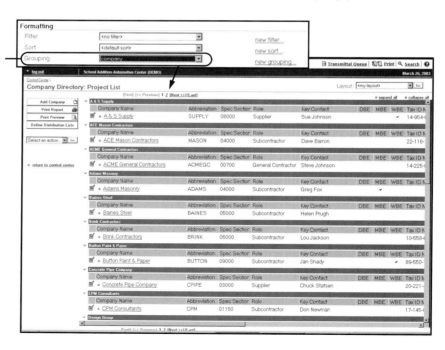

**Add a new group**  If no predefined group matches your needs, you can edit an existing one or create your own.

1   Open the log for which you want to group its documents. Select Customize Layouts from the Layout drop-down list, and click Go.

1   Click Grouping.

2   Click Add in the Grouping window, and type a title for the new grouping specification.

3   Select the field by which you want to group documents, along with the colors for the group. You can create multiple groups in a log, with the top group taking precedence and each subsequent group taking precedence over any below it.

4   Click Organize Rows to rearrange the grouping rows.

5   To save the specification, click Save and Return to Grouping List. Click Cancel to return to the grouping list without saving any changes.

Edit or add a new layout in the Customize Layouts window to assign the grouping to a layout.

*Type a name for the new group.*

*Select the field, background color, sort order, and whether to total the group.*

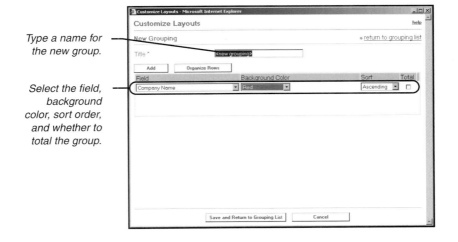

## Grouping Tips

A group applies only to the log to which you add it. For example, if you create a group from the Contracts log, that group does not apply to transmittals.

# Attaching Files and URLs to Documents

You can attach files such as word processor documents, graphics, or spreadsheets to any module document. You can then start the application in which the attached document was created directly from the module to view or modify the attachment.

 *Attachments cannot be larger than 750 MB. The system displays an error message if the attachment is larger than the limit.*

You can also attach URLs (Internet addresses) to a module document. You (or a user to whom you sent the document and attachment) can then click the URL to open the Web page in your Internet browser.

*When creating a new transmittal from an existing one, you can also copy the attachments from the existing transmittal to the new transmittal.*

**Attach a file or URL to a Contract Manager document**  Open a document from a log window. In the Attachments section, click Attach File to attach a file to the document; click Attach URL to attach a Web address. You can also launch an attached document or URL in its native application or delete an attachment.

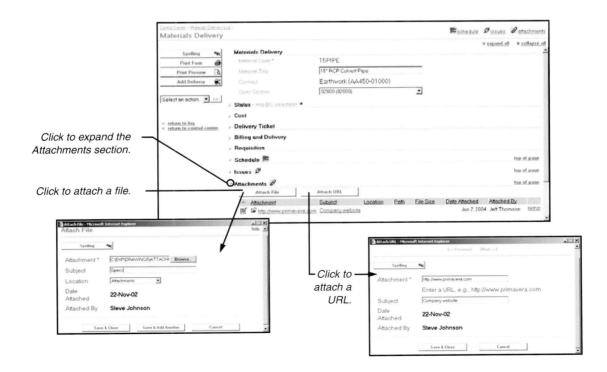

Click to expand the Attachments section.

Click to attach a file.

Click to attach a URL.

**View the attachment**  To view an attachment, go to the Attachments section of the document window and click the attachment's underlined title. To edit the attachment properties, click the its document icon.

**Delete an Attachment**  To delete an attachment, go to the Attachments section of the document window and click Remove for the attachment you want to delete. When prompted to detach the file, click Yes.

# Customizing Log and Document Windows

This chapter explains how to customize the Contract Manager module to meet the special needs of your company. You can modify titles in the Project View, as well as log column headings and field labels; customize acronyms and titles on documents; create custom fields; and add fields to any document using custom fields. In this section, the phrase "the module" refers to the Contract Manager module.

# Customizing the Project View

To accommodate your work environment, you can change the names that the Contract Manager module uses to identify folders and documents, and the order of the folders in the Project View. For example, you can change the name of the Contract Information folder to Accounts Payable and include only Purchase Orders, Trends, and Payment Requisitions. You can then move the Cost Worksheet, Contracts, and the other modules to the Communication, Logs, or Project Information folder.

Project View changes are not project-specific; any name changes affect the entire database and all projects in it. You can edit folder names and the document order within each folder, change the order of the entire Project View, and move documents between folders. You cannot add new items to a folder or remove a folder or log from a project.

To change the Project View folder names and sort orders, right-click on the top-level folder and choose Folders when no project is open.

*Click to add a new folder to the Project View.*

*Click to change the name of the selected folder or log.*

*Click to move the document to another folder in the Project View or change the order of a document.*

*Click to restore Project View items to the defaults distributed with the software.*

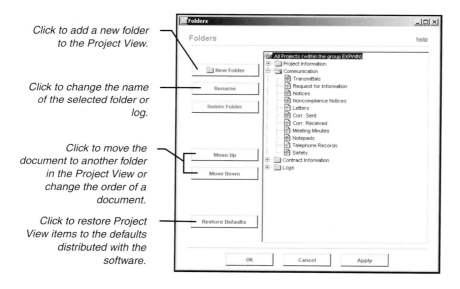

# Customizing Text in the Contract Manager Module

You can change the names of logs, and customize the text for headings in log windows and field labels in document windows to match your company's terminology. For example, in the Cost Worksheet, you may want the column name *Original Budget* to display as *Revenue*.

**Customize the text**   To customize the text, do the following:

1   Right-click on the top-level folder in the Project View, and choose Customize Text to edit the text for headings and field labels.

2   Type text in the Search field or click a letter to jump to the fields you would like to edit. Any change made to headings and labels affects all projects in the current group. If more than one user changes the same heading, the module uses the last change made.

   *Since these changes apply to the entire database, no other users can be working in the database when you customize the text. Right-click on the top-level folder and choose Current Users to ensure that no one else is using the database.*

Adjust the width of the column as necessary to accommodate heading changes.

Change the text label and click OK.

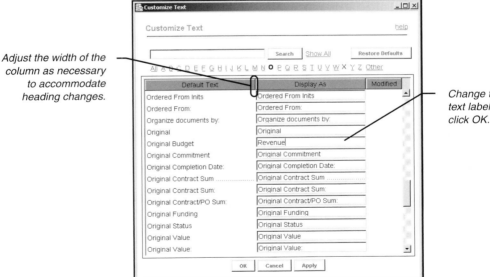

**3** Click Restore Defaults to return to the default text supplied with the module. The Print Preview and printed versions of the logs reflect customized column names. However, if you print a standard report or form from either the module or InfoMaker, the default column headings are used.

# Choosing Acronyms and Descriptions

You can change the names and acronyms of documents to match your company's terminology. Right-click on the All Projects top-level folder and choose Document Setup when no project is open.

For example, to change the name of the document window called Company to another name, type a new description (such as Vendor), which will then appear at the top of the document window. If you change the description, the new description will appear in document type drop-down lists.

Click to create documents that will appear in logs.

Click any item to view and edit the document details.

Type the new name for the document.

Edit the default report and form libraries and print files associated with the document.

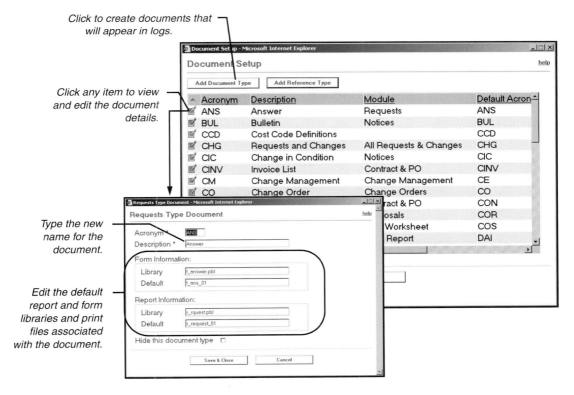

If you want to restore the default names later, refer to the Default Acronym and Default Description columns.

# Creating User-Defined Document Types

To add your own document types and reference types in the Contract Manager module, right-click on the All Projects top-level folder and choose Document Setup, when no project is open. Then do one of the following:

- Click Add Document Type to create new types of change orders, notices, noncompliance notices, proposals, or requests.

- Click Add Reference Type to create documents you can reference in correspondence sent and correspondence received.

For example, if you want to include a fax as part of a correspondence document, define a reference type called FAX, then reference it in the Type field in the Source Document section of the correspondence document window.

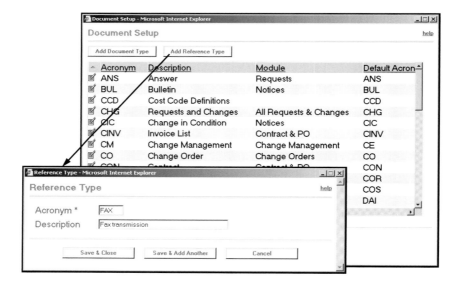

# Creating and Using Custom Fields

A custom field is a field that you can add to the Contract Manager module database to contain any information you want. You can create and use a custom field to track certain information, perhaps at a client's request, that is not part of a standard Contract Manager module document.

For example, you may be managing a project that consists of three phases. To print reports and sort information by phase, you can create a custom field called PHASE, add it to the document in which you need to track the phase, and then assign a value to the custom field that distinguishes each phase, such as First, Second, or Third.

For more detailed information about custom fields, see *Custom Fields Overview* in Help.

**Add a custom field**  Make sure no one else is working in the current group (right-click on the top-level folder in the Project View and choose Current Users to display the current users). You cannot add a custom field to a group if any other users are connected to that group. To add the custom field, do the following:

1  Right-click on the top-level folder in the Project View and choose Custom Fields.

2  Scroll down and click the module for which you want to view or add custom fields.

3  Expand the module to which you want to add a custom field. Click Add.

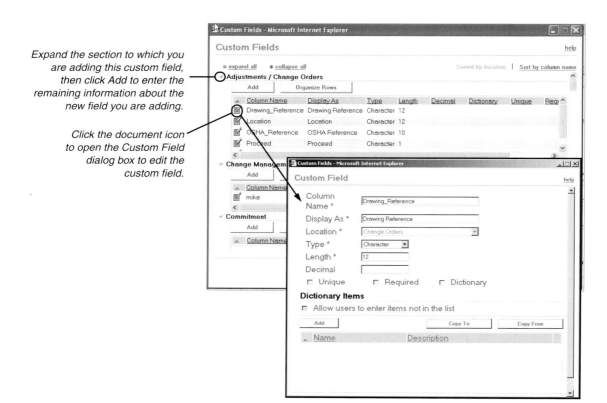

*Expand the section to which you are adding this custom field, then click Add to enter the remaining information about the new field you are adding.*

*Click the document icon to open the Custom Field dialog box to edit the custom field.*

**4**  Click Organize Rows to arrange the order in which you want the custom fields to appear in documents.

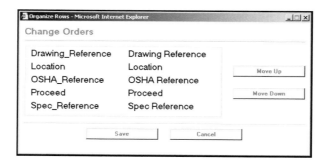

*When you add a custom field, you add a new field to the Contract Manager module database. Custom fields are a database-level feature; a custom field is available to every project in that database.*

*For custom fields to appear in log windows, you must use layouts. Click Layout, then select Customize Layouts and click Go. Click the document icon for the layout you want to edit. Choose the custom fields from the Available Columns list and add them to the Show These Columns list. After saving the changes, apply the layout to the log.*

**Create a dictionary of terms for a custom field** You can create a dictionary of terms for custom fields and select the module to which the custom field applies. When you add dictionary definitions to custom fields, the entries appear when you click Select next to the custom field in the document window. You can then choose these definitions to apply to the corresponding document. To add dictionary terms, mark the dictionary checkbox in the Custom Field dialog box, then click Add in the Dictionary Items section to open the Dictionary Item dialog box.

Mark the Allow Users to Enter Items Not in the List checkbox to allow users to type definitions directly in the custom fields. Definitions entered directly are not added to the Custom Field Dictionary.

*Click Add to type the definition for the custom field that appears in the drop-down list.*

**Use a custom field with a document**   To use the custom field with a document, do the following:

1   Open a document, and click Custom Fields to display the custom fields available for the document.

2   Type a value or click Select to choose the custom field definition you want to associate with the open document.

*Open the document you want to associate with a custom field.*

*Assign values for the custom fields you have associated with this document type.*

For details about creating, modifying, and printing reports, see *Printing Logs, Forms, and Reports* in *Part 2*, or refer to Help.

**Include custom fields in reports**   You can include custom fields in reports. For example, using the custom field above, you can create or modify a report so that it shows only the contracts associated with the First Phase of the project.

# Setting Up Dictionaries and Preferences

This chapter describes how to set configuration options that enable you to tailor the Contract Manager module to fit your specific needs. You can:

- Specify the names used on documents and the codes used to identify work categories, roles, and status; set transmittal queue options.

- Choose whether to use a group or project-specific company directory.

- Set requisition preferences and retainage calculations.

- Define a schedule link.

- Establish a change management workflow.

- Assign default contacts for specific documents.

# Defining Dictionaries

You can edit or add codes and categories to existing dictionaries in the Contract Manager module. The defined categories and codes of the dictionaries appear throughout the projects in drop-down lists. Right-click on the top-level folder and choose Dictionaries, to choose from a list of database-specific dictionaries that enable you to change or add the following:

■   Reason codes that identify the source of a particular change

■   Company roles

■   Equipment types, length of suitable conditions, precipitation, sky, temperature, wind, and weather impact associated with daily reports

■   Bid packages associated with drawings

■   Drawing disciplines used to categorize drawings

■   Phase codes specific to drawing revisions

■   File numbers associated with drawings

■   CSI divisions and purchase types for procurement

■   NAICS codes, accident causes, and dispositions related to safety

■   Specifications codes used to classify work

■   Status codes

■   Submittal categories and types

■   Work impact

■   Various other codes

Setting Up Dictionaries and Preferences 77

*Right-click the top-level folder in the Project View to access database-specific dictionaries.*

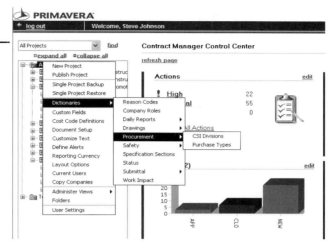

**Edit or add reason codes for change management** Right-click on the top-level folder in the Project View and choose Dictionaries, Reason Codes. During a project, different participants and factors inevitably introduce changes that affect project contracts. In change management, these codes enable you to identify the reason for a change.

■ Create a new reason code by clicking Add and typing a reason code and title.

■ Click Delete to remove a reason code from the Contract Manager module database.

*Codes defined here appear in all projects in the database.*

*Click to sort columns in ascending or descending order.*

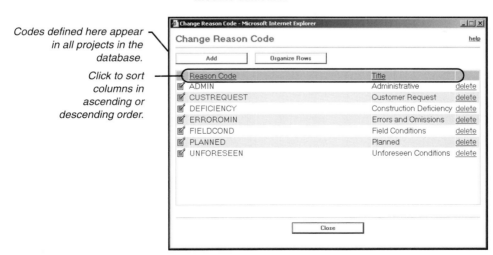

### Change the names of company roles and define new roles

Right-click on the top-level folder in the Project View and choose Dictionaries, Company Roles. Click Add.

You can change role acronyms and descriptions to any values you prefer, but you must select a type from the list in the Type Name field. The module uses types to categorize the role names you create. These types include owner, supplier, general contractor, and so on.

*Click to set the order in which codes appear in specification drop-down lists.*

*Click to delete a company role.*

### Add or edit weather conditions and types of equipment used for daily reports

Right-click on the top-level folder in the Project View and choose Dictionaries, Daily Reports, then choose the type of weather condition or equipment type you want to define to add to the appropriate drop-down list in the Daily Report document window in the module.

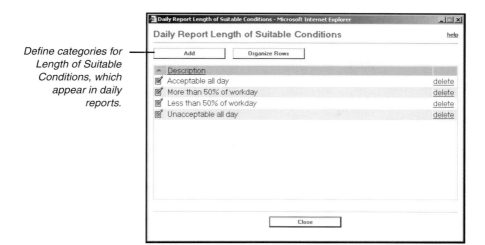

*Define categories for Length of Suitable Conditions, which appear in daily reports.*

**Define the bid packages for drawings**  Right-click on the top-level folder in the Project View and choose Dictionaries, Drawings, Bid Packages. Once the design cycle is finished for architectural drawings on a project, drawings are sent to different contractors to bid on work.

You can keep track of drawings and their revisions by defining a bid package for each contractor, then logging the drawings by bid package in the Drawings log. You can modify this list if you send additional contractors drawings for bid. You can also filter drawings by bid package.

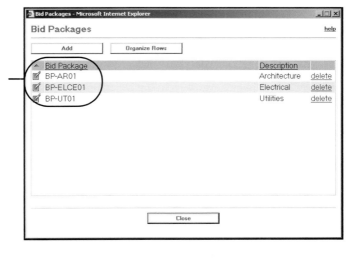

*Enter up to 15 characters for the bid package abbreviation.*

**Define disciplines for drawings**  Right-click on the top-level folder in the Project View and choose Dictionaries, Drawings, Disciplines. You can categorize drawings in the Drawings and Drawing Sets logs by discipline, such as ELECT, MECH, ARCH, and CIVIL. When you define disciplines, keep in mind how your company tracks drawings throughout a project. These categories can be used to sort, filter, and report drawing information.

*Use disciplines to classify drawings.*

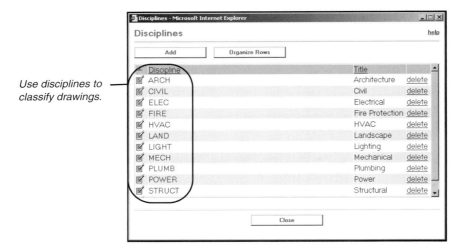

**Define phase codes for drawing revisions**  Right-click on the top-level folder in the Project View and choose Dictionaries, Drawings, Drawing Phases. Drawings are sent out for different purposes during different phases of the distribution cycle.

For example, Issued for Bid (IFB) or Issued for Construction (IFC) identify the purpose of a drawing sent to project participants. In the Design cycle, drawings in the Design Development (DESIGN) phase require revision cycles similar to submittal review cycles. Predefined codes are included for drawing phases, but you can add additional codes to meet your requirements.

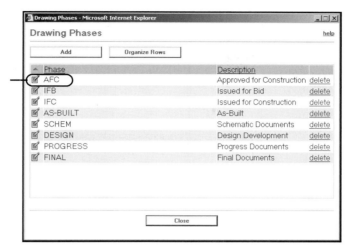

You can enter up to eight characters for the Phase code.

For more information about the Drawings and Drawing Sets logs and how disciplines are used, see the *Tracking Drawings* chapter.

**Define drawing file numbers**  Right-click on the top-level folder in the Project View and choose Dictionaries, Drawings, File Numbers. If you set up a filing system specifically for drawings, you can add your file numbers to this dictionary, then select the appropriate number when you log drawings.

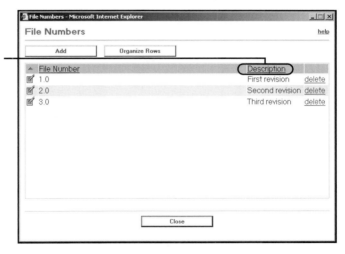

Enter up to 23 characters for the file number description.

**Define paper sizes for drawings**  Right-click on the top-level folder in the Project View and choose Dictionaries, Drawings, Paper Sizes. Specify a size code and corresponding measurements for the individual paper sizes you use for drawings.

Click to set the order in
which codes appear in
drop-down lists.

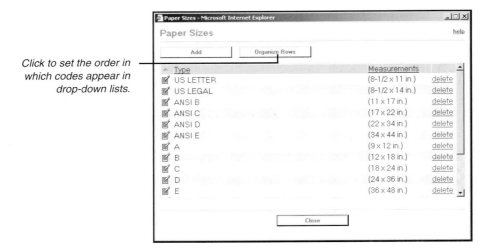

**Define codes used for procurement**  If you use procurement, you can create new CSI division codes and purchase types. Right-click on the top-level folder in the Project View and choose Dictionaries, Procurement, then click the appropriate item for which to create codes.

Click to open the
Purchase Types Detail
dialog box in which you
can define new
purchase types to apply
to procurement.

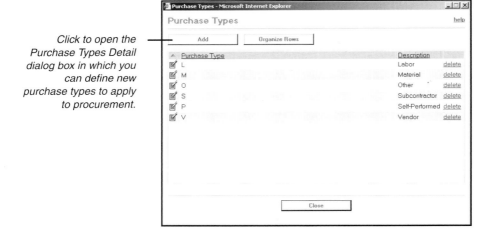

## Define codes used to specify safety concerns and violations

Recording safety violations, concerns, and injuries on the job site is critical for conforming to OSHA regulations and keeping records. The Safety module enables you to track safety violations and accidents. Right-click on the top-level folder in the Project View and choose Dictionaries, Safety, then click the appropriate safety code to define. You can define categories and codes for accident sources, safety dispositions, violations, and NAICS codes.

*Define accident sources to track accidents.*

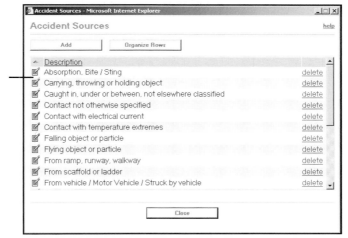

## Add or edit the specification codes used to classify work

For a list of CSI section titles and numbers, see *Masterformat/CSI Codes* in Help.

Right-click on the top-level folder in the Project View and choose Dictionaries, Specifications Sections. The codes in the Specification Sections Dictionary classify construction work using the Masterformat coding system developed by the Construction Specification Institute (CSI). A Specification Code field is available in most document windows.

Click Organize Rows to set the order in which the codes appear in drop-down lists, or create a new specification section by clicking Add and typing a value and description. Click Save and Close.

Click Delete to remove a code from the list.

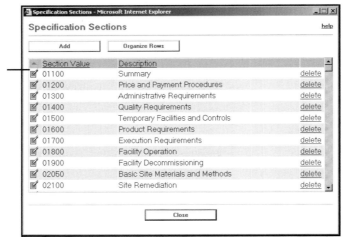

*These codes are used in reports and forms, and are available for sorting and filtering data.*

**Add or edit status codes**   The module displays status description values in the Status field in various windows. You can change these codes and descriptions to match your company standards, and you can add new codes to the list. Use status codes in documents (such as submittals and change documents) to identify their status in various stages of the project.

**1**  Right-click on the top-level folder in the Project View and choose Dictionaries, Status.

**2**  Click Add.

**3**  For each code you add, select a type from the drop-down list in the Type Name field, then select a color to represent the status.

**4**  Click Save and Close.

The module uses these standard types to categorize the code names you create.

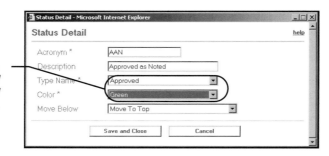

*When adding a new code, you must select the type and color from the predefined values and colors available.*

*You can delete codes from this list, but you must keep at least one Approved, Open, Closed, Rejected, and New Item type. Only the Description, Color, and Move Below fields are editable for the New Item status.*

**Add or edit submittal categories and types**  Right-click on the top-level folder in the Project View and choose Dictionaries, Submittal, then select Categories or Types.

To organize submittals, you can define different categories and types. The submittal categories and types you define are available in the Category and Type drop-down lists in the Submittal document window.

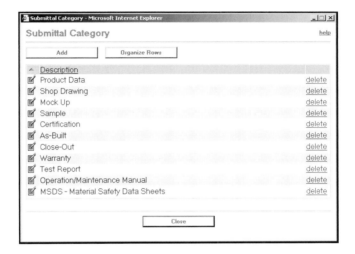

# Defining Project Dictionaries

When a project is open, you can add or change drawing areas, punch list elevations, and punch list rooms. The items defined in the Drawing Areas and Punch Lists dictionaries appear only in the opened project.

*Right-click on a project to access the project's dictionaries.*

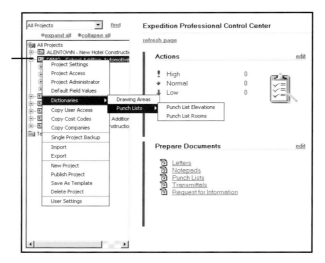

**Assign the areas associated with drawings**  Right-click on a project in the Project View and choose Dictionaries, Drawing Areas. Drawings typically correspond to specific areas of construction work, such as the reception area in an office building. Areas are useful for a general association of which particular drawing or set of drawings is referenced in construction or design work. These areas help to further categorize drawings so you can more easily determine outstanding requirements in revisions.

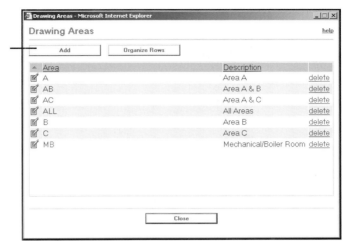

Click to define a drawing area.

**Define elevations and rooms for punch lists**  Right-click on a project in the Project View and click Dictionaries, Punch Lists, then click Punch List Elevations or Punch List Rooms. You can define elevations and rooms that are applied to individual punch list items in the Elevation and Room fields in the Location section of the Punch List Item dialog box (accessed from a punch list document). Elevations and rooms are project-specific.

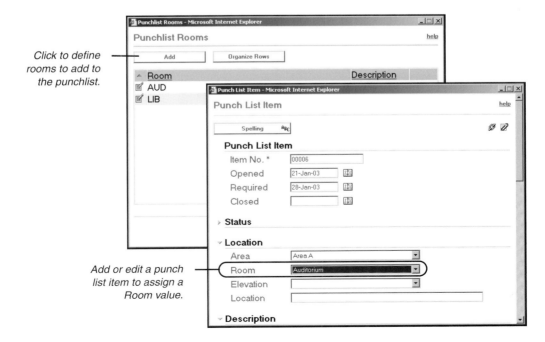

Click to define rooms to add to the punchlist.

Add or edit a punch list item to assign a Room value.

# Specifying Project Settings

To specify preferences about key participants, contacts, transmittals, contracts/purchase orders, schedules, requisitions, change management, procurement, currency, markup, and attachments, you must have a project open. Right-click on a project name in the Project View and choose Project Settings. Settings made here form the basis for how these areas work as you use them throughout the Contract Manager module. You can set Project Settings for the current project only; the module displays its name and title at the top of the dialog box.

*Click to expand and view project details, such as ID, job number, project number, location, value, and status.*

 *The examples shown in this section show the default settings for a new project.*

**Set Companies**  In the Companies section, you can indicate whether you want to use contacts from the project or from the group contact list, which is a global contact list shared by all projects. To do so, click Switch to choose either Group (database) or Project.

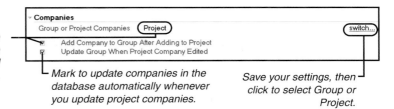

*If you select Project, mark to add new companies to the database when you add them to the project.*

*Mark to update companies in the database automatically whenever you update project companies.*

*Save your settings, then click to select Group or Project.*

**Specify key parties**  In project settings, you can specify a key contact for the project. The module automatically defaults to this company when creating documents.

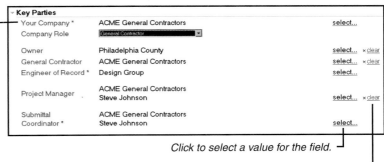

*Click Select to choose the key party for this project.*

*Click to select a value for the field.*

*Click to clear the value for the field*

For details on using the Transmittal Queue for distribution lists, see *Compiling a Submittal Distribution List* in the *Managing Submittals* chapter.

**Communication settings**  Communication settings determine whether and how transmittals are placed in the transmittal queue. If more than one transmittal exists for any contact in the transmittal queue, you can combine the information from all of them into one transmittal. You can also update the queue for every contact on your submittal or drawing sets distribution list.

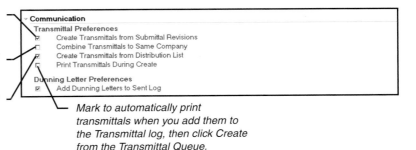

*Mark to update the Transmittal Queue every time you update a submittal.*

*If more than one transmittal exists per contact, mark to combine them.*

*Mark to generate a transmittal for each contact on a submittal distribution list.*

*Mark to automatically print transmittals when you add them to the Transmittal log, then click Create from the Transmittal Queue.*

The Transmittal Queue link at the top of the module displays the number of transmittals in the Transmittal Queue, if there is at least one. If you update sent dates or distribution information for drawings, the number is updated. After you close the Submittal log you can print (or send) transmittals after they are added to the Transmittal log. To set up a distribution list to send transmittals to specific contacts, click Define Distribution Lists from the Company log window.

You can also specify whether to automatically add a dunning letter to the Correspondence Sent log; mark the Add Dunning Letters to Sent Log checkbox. Clear this checkbox if you'd rather add letters manually, or if you don't want to track dunning letters sent in the Correspondence Sent logs.

For details on linking to a Project Management module schedule, *see Linking to a Project Management Module Schedule* in the *Exchanging Contract Manager Module Data with a Project Management Module Schedule* chapter, or refer to Help.

**Schedule settings**   Schedule preferences enable you to specify the Project Management module project you want to link to the project so you can access schedule data in most document windows. The module can extract early and actual start and finish dates from the Project Management module project and use them to update dates. You can also simply reference the related activity in the specific document window.

*Select a schedule to access the fields below.*

*Mark to filter underway activities in daily reports by the Responsibility code.*

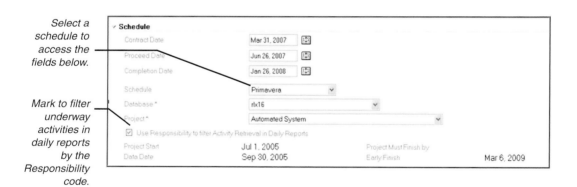

For detailed information on using multicurrency formats, refer to Help.

**Currency settings**  The Currency section enables you to set the format used in all currency fields throughout your project. For example, if you want to use the British pound as the currency, select British pound as the currency format for the project. The currency setting applies only to the current project.

*Select the currency to use in the project.*

*Select the conversion direction.*

*Select the conversion rate.*

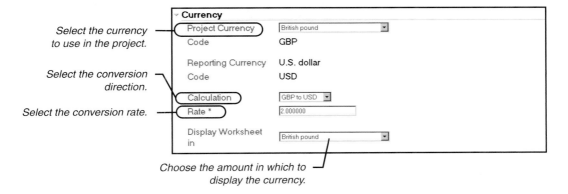

*Choose the amount in which to display the currency.*

 *To set the currency used in cost worksheet reports, right-click on the top-level folder in the Project View and click Reporting Currency when no project is selected. See* Reporting Currency dialog box *in Help for more information.*

**Contract and purchase order settings**    Contract and purchase order options establish whether the module assigns unique contract and/or purchase order (PO) numbers to each contract in a project. For example, if unique numbers are used, every contract/PO defaults to a different number. This preference is only used to default the contract/PO number, and will not override any changes to the contract/PO number.

*Mark to assign unique contract/PO numbers to each new contract. Clear to use the To and From contacts to determine the next available number.*

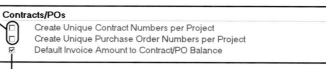

Contracts/POs

Create Unique Contract Numbers per Project
Create Unique Purchase Order Numbers per Project
Default Invoice Amount to Contract/PO Balance

*Mark to automatically set the Amount column of the invoice using the contract/PO balance and to distribute the amount of the invoice to the Cost Worksheet using cost codes from the associated contract/PO.*

**Costing settings**    Specify which documents must be fully costed. Mark these checkboxes to force users to distribute costs for change orders, contracts, invoices, proposals, purchase orders, requisitions, and/or trends in their respective Line Items sections. Users must distribute the full amount to cost codes for the documents checked. There cannot be a Not Costed amount.

Costing

Document must be fully costed:

☐  Change Orders
☐  Contracts
☐  Invoices
☐  Proposals
☐  Purchase Orders
☐  Requisitions
☐  Trends

**Requisition preferences**  The options in this section determine schedule of value preferences and retainage calculations for all requisitions that have not been generated from a contract or PO. Set requisition preferences in this section for new contracts and purchase orders. To change requisition preferences on an existing contract or purchase order:

1  Select the project, and select Contract Information.

2  Navigate to the location of the contract or purchase order, and click the name.

3  Choose Requisition Options from the Select an Action drop-down list.

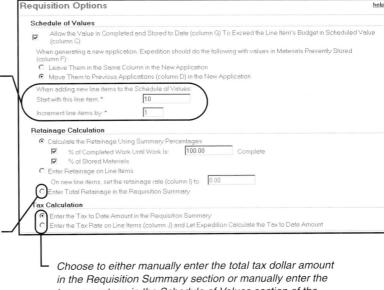

*Using leading zeros, specify the first line item number and the increment number to use when the Schedule of Values is created.*

*Choose this option to manually enter the total retainage in the requisition summary.*

*Choose to either manually enter the total tax dollar amount in the Requisition Summary section or manually enter the tax percentage in the Schedule of Values section of the requisition for the module to calculate the total tax dollar amount based on the percentages you enter.*

You can also specify that values can exceed the budget (scheduled value) by marking the Allow the Value in Completed and Stored to Date (column G) to Exceed the Line Item's Budget in Scheduled Value (column C) checkbox. Mark this checkbox if you want to collect delivery documents for the requisition schedule of values, since delivery values often cause the sum of the This Period column (Column E) and the Previous Applications column (Column D) to exceed the value in the Scheduled Value column (Column C).

When you generate a new application, to retain costs for materials stored in the Materials Presently Stored, Not in D or E column (Column F) in the Schedule of Values, choose the option to Leave Them in the Same Column in the New Application. If you want to move cost data for materials stored to Previous Applications (Column D) in the Schedule of Values, when generating a new application, choose Move Them to Previous Applications (Column D) in the New Application.

For Retainage Calculation, you can choose Calculate the Retainage Using Summary Percentages. If you prefer to enter summary percentages for completed work and stored materials in the Summary section for the requisition, mark the % of Completed Work Until Work is Complete and % of Stored Materials checkboxes.

You can also specify a maximum contract percent complete value in the Complete field. You must use this option in conjunction with the "% of Completed Work Until Work is" option for the module to use the calculation. For example, to stop calculating retainage once the contract is 50 percent complete, enter 50 in the Complete field and mark the "% of Completed Work Until Work is" checkbox. You cannot edit the Total Retainage field in the Requisition Summary section of the Requisition document window if you apply this "ceiling" calculation.

If you prefer to use retainage amounts or percentages for each line item in column I in the Schedule of Values section, choose Enter Retainage on Line Items. To use the same percentage to calculate retainage for most line items, type the percentage in the On New Line items, Set the Retainage Rate (Column I) to field. The module automatically enters this percentage in the Retain % column (Column I) in the Schedule of Values section for the requisition. For example, if you enter 10 percent, the module enters 10 percent in Column I for every line item. You can then edit the items that use a different percentage.

**Change management preferences**   The Change Management section enables you to define the relationship, if any, of committed values to revenue values, and to set up the Change Management process for your work process.

You can select change order and proposal documents for these fields.

Mark to automatically add a transmittal entry for each row added for the estimated phase when you click Add in the Commitments section of the Change Management document window.

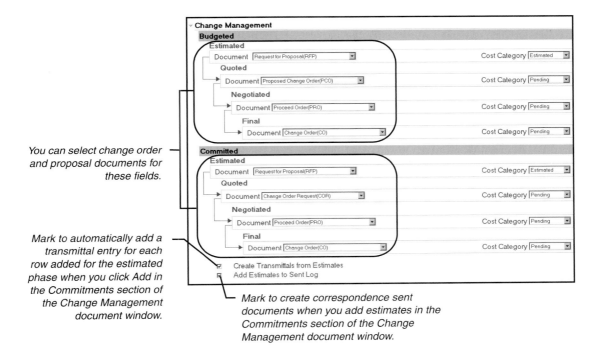

Mark to create correspondence sent documents when you add estimates in the Commitments section of the Change Management document window.

For more information about change management, see the *Using Change Management* chapter, or refer to Help.

Each Estimated, Quoted, Negotiated, and Final Budgeted value and each Estimated, Quoted, Negotiated, and Final Committed value creates a document that is posted to a user-defined column of the Cost Worksheet. Use this section to supply the document type you want to create and the corresponding cost category column on the Cost Worksheet where you want to distribute change amounts.

For detailed information on markup, see *Applying Markup* in the *Using Change Management* chapter. In Help, see *Project Settings dialog box*, or type *markup* using the Search or Index features for a list of topics.

**Markup preferences**  The Markup section allows you to set the markup percentage or amount to apply to change documents. You can create as many markup categories and values as you need.

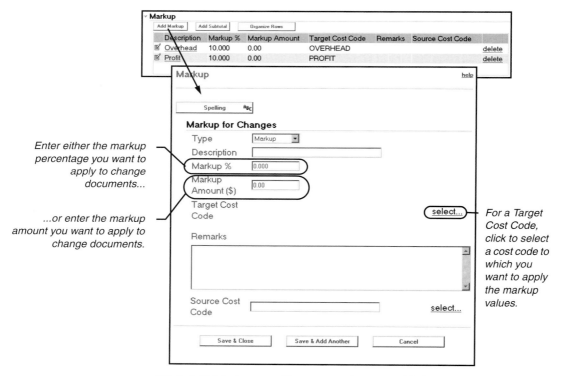

*Enter either the markup percentage you want to apply to change documents...*

*...or enter the markup amount you want to apply to change documents.*

*For a Target Cost Code, click to select a cost code to which you want to apply the markup values.*

Click Add Markup to add a new markup row. Click Add Subtotal to add a subtotal to the change document. The module subtotals the markup values above this row in the change document and places them here.

In the Markup section, you can also select a Source Cost Code, which allows you to break costs into individual components. Instead of basing markup on one lump sum (such as overall cost), you can divide the cost into labor, materials, and bond, and you can apply markup categories to each of those.

When applying markup, the module calculates the amount to mark up in the Markup for Changes section of a change order or proposal document as follows:

■   If a source cost code is used, the applied cost for that row is used as the amount to apply markup against.

■   If there is no source code, the previous Subtotal amount will be marked up.

■   If there is no previous Subtotal row, the Document Start row's Total Cost column will be marked up.

You can use wildcards in the Source Cost Code field. Use a question mark (?) to replace one letter or an asterisk (*) to replace multiple letters. For example, if you created cost codes A1B and A2B, and you enter A?B, both cost codes will be used. Similarly, if you use A*, all cost codes that begin with A will be selected.

# Specifying User Settings

You can set personal settings for how you want certain functions performed. Right-click on the top-level folder or a project in the Project View and choose User Settings. Settings selected here are user-specific per the Contract Manager module server. The module saves the changes for your user ID and uses them for any workstation which you use to log into the Contract Manager module.

Mark to automatically log your mail.

Choose whether to show or hide the Select an Action menu on logs and documents.

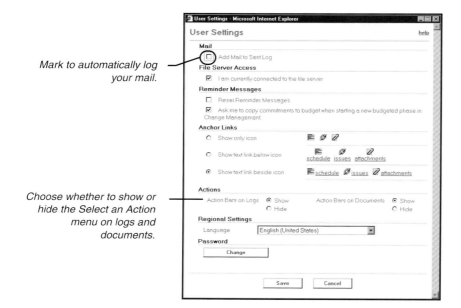

If you have a direct connection (access) to the location on the server where attachments are stored, mark the I am currently connected to the file server checkbox under File Server Access. Check with your Contract Manager module administrator before changing this setting.

You can choose how to display anchor links within the module. You can also change the password you use to log into the module.

# Setting Layout Options

Use the Layout Options window to choose how layout titles appear in the Layout drop-down list in log windows: number and title, title and number, or title only. Right-click on the top-level folder in the Project View to set layout options.

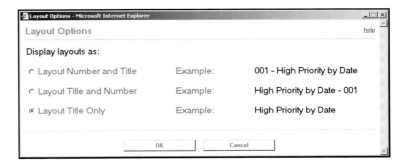

# Maintaining a Contract Manager Module Database

## In this chapter

**Adding Contract Manager Module Databases**

**Backing Up a Sybase Server Database**

This chapter describes the types of information in Contract Manager module databases. It tells where to find the information for adding, updating, and migrating Contract Manager module databases, which can contain data common to several projects. It also explains how to back up a Sybase database and multiple databases at a scheduled time.

In this chapter, the phrase "the module" refers to the Contract Manager module.

# Adding Contract Manager Module Databases

A Contract Manager module database is a file that contains one or more projects. Contract Manager includes two project databases: CMDEMO.DB and CMPROJ.DB. The default database installed is based on your installation selection. CMDEMO contains the sample projects for this version, but you can add projects to it. CMPROJ.DB is an empty database containing only the information necessary to start using Contract manager.

For details on the sample projects, see the *Overview* chapter.

 A database is sometimes referred to as a "Group" (as in the Change Group dialog box).

Projects in a database share the following information:

- *Companies and contacts.* Details about all of the contacts involved in your projects. For details about adding company information, see *Setting Up the Company Directory* in the *Planning and Adding a Contract Manager Module Project* chapter.

- *Custom fields.* Fields you can add to the module database for tracking information that is unique to your company and projects. For details about adding and using custom fields, see *Creating and Using Custom Fields* in the *Customizing Log and Document Windows* chapter.

- *Cost code definitions.* Descriptions of your cost code structure, for reporting purposes, if you are using the Cost Worksheet. For details about cost code definitions, see the *Setting Up and Using the Cost Worksheet* chapter.

- *Specification sections, company roles, status, document settings, group-level distribution lists, reason codes, bid packages, disciplines, file numbers, paper sizes, phases, equipment types, length of suitable conditions, sky, precipitation, temperature, wind, weather impact, CSI divisions, purchase types, accident sources, NAICS codes, dispositions, safety violations, submittal categories, submittal types, work impact, alerts, reporting currency, Project View names, and reference types.* For details about adding and using these items, see the *Setting Up Dictionaries and Preferences* chapter.

Since much of this information is probably the same for your company across all databases, Primavera recommends that you install the CMPROJ.DB file.

For detailed, step-by-step information for adding, updating, and migrating databases, see the *Primavera Contract Manager Installation Guide.*

# Backing Up a Sybase Server Database

This section describes how to back up a Contract Manager module server database and its associated logs in a network environment using DBBACKUP. DBBACKUP.EXE is a program that is installed with Adaptive Server Anywhere 7. It is located in the \PROGRAM FILES\SYBASE\SQL ANYWHERE 7\WIN32 folder. ASA7 must be successfully installed for DBBACKUP.EXE to work properly.

The module's database server keeps database files open when the server is running, which prevents network backup utilities from copying the files. However, DBBACKUP copies the database files to another location where your scheduled network backup can access them to perform a successful backup. This option enables you to keep the database server running at all times. You must run the online backup utility manually for each database.

**Create a network database backup**  Creating a backup of your Contract Manager module databases involves the following steps:

1  Run the online backup utility, DBBACKUP, from the database server to create a set of online backup files of your Contract Manager module databases that your scheduled network backup can access.

2  Run your scheduled network backup.

 A database consists of two files, a database file and its associated transaction log file. The database file has a .DB extension, such as CMPROJ.DB; the transaction log file has a .LOG extension, such as CMPROJ.LOG. To create a reliable backup, include both of these files in your scheduled network backup.

To run the online backup utility from the database server, click Start, then choose Run and type the following command in the Run dialog box:

DBBACKUP -Y -r -C "DSN=*CMSRVR.CMPROJ*" c:\*BACKUP*

*For instructions on creating the DSN manually on the server, refer to the Tech Tip #200228153445.*

Replace *cmsrvr.cmprom* with the ODBC DSN of your Contract Manager module server database. The DSN can be created manually on the server. *CMPROJ* is the name of the database you want to back up. Replace *f:\backups* with the name of the destination folder for the backup files; this should be a folder on a different drive, not the one that contains your database files.

The -y option replaces any older files in the destination folder with the same name without a confirmation. The -c option signals that the database connection parameters are being supplied. The -r option renames and restarts the log file.

 *If you use online backups, Primavera recommends that you perform them when all users are logged out of the Contract Manager module. Although you can perform online backups while users are logged on to the Contract Manager module, such backups require more time.*

DBBACKUP copies the group's database and transaction log files to the destination folder and confirms that the files were backed up successfully. If DBBACKUP displays the message "Database backup completed," the process was successful and you can use your network backup procedures to back up the copies of the database and log files.

*The first set of numbers represents the database file; the second set represents the transaction log file. A page is 4096 bytes.*

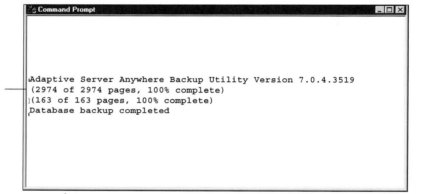

```
Adaptive Server Anywhere Backup Utility Version 7.0.4.3519
(2974 of 2974 pages, 100% complete)
(163 of 163 pages, 100% complete)
Database backup completed
```

If the confirmation message flashes too quickly to view, you can write the output messages from DBBACKUP to a file. Use the backup utility option -o in the command, and specify the output file.If DBBACKUP displays any error messages, contact Primavera Customer Support for assistance.

For a complete list of option switches for DBBACKUP, refer to the Adaptive Server Anywhere 7.0 documentation.

 *You must run DBBACKUP for each database (group) you need to back up.*

# Printing Logs, Forms, and Reports

The Contract Manager module provides many flexible ways to print project data. You can print any log, the contents of a document using a predefined form, or a predefined report or dunning letter. You can also modify predefined forms, reports, or dunning letters or create your own using the InfoMaker report writer included with the software. In this chapter, the phrase "the module" refers to the Contract Manager Module.

This chapter explains the basics of printing logs, forms, reports, and dunning letters.

# Printing Overview

In the Contract Manager module, you can print a copy of any log, print the contents of a document using a predefined form, or print a predefined report or dunning letter. Several multiproject reports are also available to print data from all projects in your database for the document type.

Depending on your printer designation, you can also print multiple copies of logs, forms, reports, or dunning letters. This is helpful if you need to send a copy to several people.

# Printing a Log

The logs contain all documents for that module, and columns showing general information about each document.

**Print a log**  Open the log window you want to print, and then click Print Report to print the default report for the log.

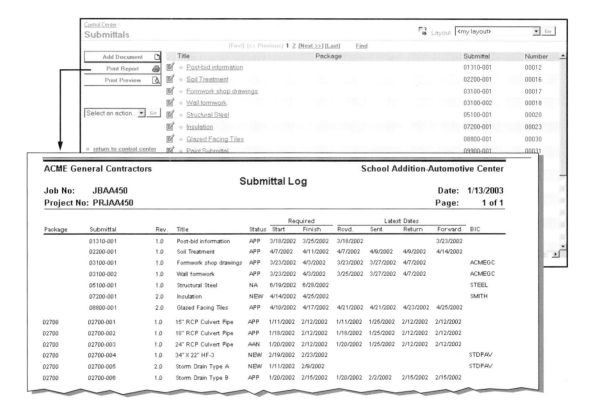

Preview and print logs as-is (including selected layouts) by sending the log to Microsoft Excel, keeping the formatting of the current log layout. Any layouts (grouping, filtering, or sorting) will preview and print as-is.

1  Open a log, and choose Select an Action, Send to Excel, and then click Go.

2  When the log opens in Excel, you can use Excel's functionality to print the log.

Refer to the Microsoft Excel Help for more information on using Excel.

# Printing Forms

Use forms to print detailed information from a document, such as a transmittal. You can:

- Choose a standard form from those included with the module.

- Use InfoMaker to customize an existing form or create a new form.

**Print a specific form**

1  Open the document window for which you want to print a form.

2  Choose Select an Action, Advanced Print, and then click Go.

3  Choose Forms.

4  Select the form you want to print, and then click Print.

The form displays in an Adobe Acrobat pane at the bottom of the window, as shown in the example on the following page. An Adobe Acrobat query displays asking you to confirm that you want to print the document. Click Yes.

**Print the default form**    To print the default form from the document window:

1  Click Print Form or click Select an Action, Print Form.

2  Click Go.

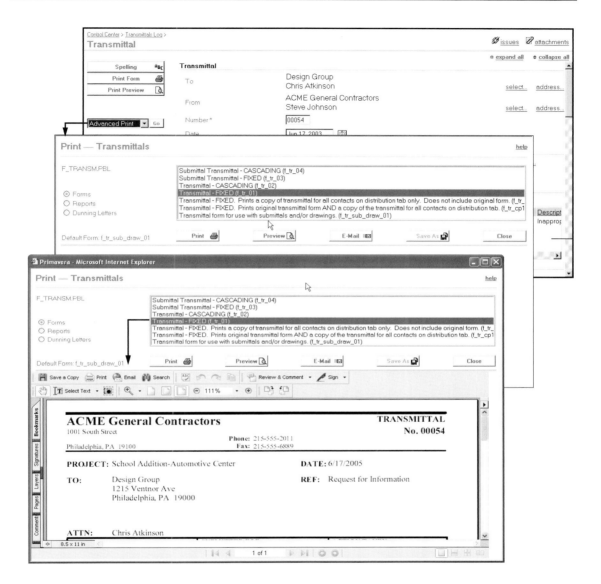

# Printing Reports

Reports usually include information that the module collects from multiple documents, such as a list of submittals. You can choose a standard report from those included with the module, or you can use InfoMaker to customize an existing report.

**Print a report**  From any log or document window:

1   Choose Select an Action, Advanced Print, and then click Go.

2   Choose Reports, select the report to print, and then click Print.

3   Click Print again after the report displays in Adobe PDF format.

To print the default report from the log window, click Print Report.

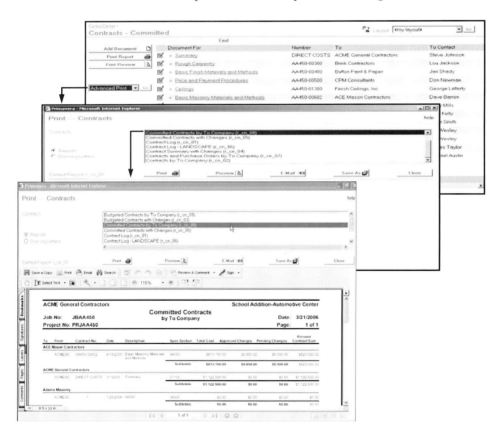

# Printing Multi-Project Reports

You can print certain reports that contain data from all projects in a folder for a particular document type. For example, you can list items required within seven days for all projects, print the Contract log grouped by project with totals, or print submittals by ball-in-court (BIC) for all projects. Multi-project reporting provides a convenient way for you to gather all the data you need to assess status, requirements, and outstanding issues for all projects. Multi-project reports are denoted by an m_ prefix; single project reports are identified with an r_ prefix.

**Print a multi-project report**  In the Project View:

1  Click the top-level folder so that no project is selected.

2  Click the Print icon located on the right side of the header.

3  From the drop-down list, choose the log for which you want to print a report, and click Show.

4  Select the report from the list on the right side, and then click Print or Preview.

5  Click Print again after the report displays in Adobe PDF format to print the report.

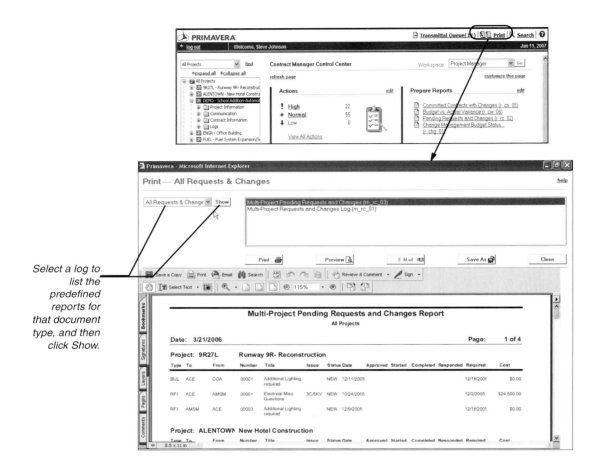

*Select a log to list the predefined reports for that document type, and then click Show.*

# Printing Dunning Letters

A dunning letter is a specific type of report used to remind project participants to deliver certain items or perform certain tasks. You can use the sample dunning letters included with the module, or you can create your own using InfoMaker. For example, you can generate a dunning letter from a punch list to remind a contact of overdue items.

**Print dunning letters**  From the log or document window:

1  Choose Select an Action, Advanced Print, and then click Go.

2  Choose Dunning Letters, select the appropriate dunning letter, and then click Print.

3  Click Print again after the letter displays in Adobe PDF format to print it.

  *Not all logs and documents contain dunning letters.*

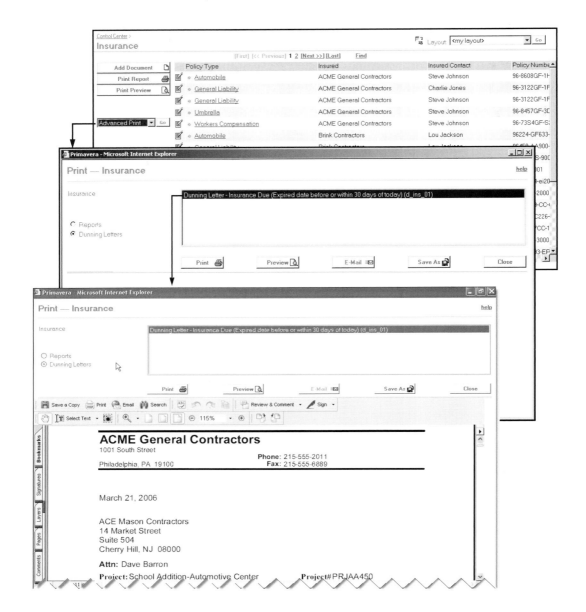

# Using Print Preview

The Print Preview function enables you to view a document as it will appear when printed. The document displays in Adobe PDF format.

You can preview a document by clicking the Print Preview button from the top level of a function (in this case, it will be the default document for the function), or by using the Advanced Print function.

**Previewing a document from the top level**  If you click the Print Preview button from the top level of a function without selecting a document, the default document for the function (Notice Log in the following example) displays.

**Previewing a document through the Advanced Print function**
From the log or document window:

1  Choose Select an Action, select Advanced Print, and then click Go.

**2** Click the button next to the type of document to preview (Forms, Reports, or Dunning Letters).

**3** Choose the document, and click the Preview button.

# Part 3

# Communicating Project Information

In this part    **Sending Contract Manager Module
Documents to Other Users**

**Preparing Transmittals**

**Recording and Tracking
Communications**

**Recording Meeting Minutes**

*C*ompleting a project successfully requires the cooperation of all the participants. This requires the clear and continual exchange of information, and the ability to track communications to avoid costly misunderstandings. This part describes Contract Manager's extensive logging and tracking system for every type of project communication.

*Sending Contract Manager Module Documents to Other Users* explains how to manage the Inbox, which enables you to send and receive Contract Manager Module information from other users. *Preparing Transmittals* discusses how to prepare transmittal letters.

*Recording and Tracking Communications* describes how to use the Correspondence logs, Letters, Phone log, Notepads, and Notices log in Contract Manager to store information about all other correspondence. *Recording Meeting Minutes*, explains how to record meeting proceedings.

# Sending Contract Manager Module Documents to Other Users

The Contract Manager module enables you to transfer documents electronically between users to speed and simplify exchanges between project participants.

Users can use the Inbox feature to exchange documents with other team members using the same projects and databases.

This chapter also describes how to enter the e-mail addresses of your contacts so that you can use the request notification feature to notify your contacts with regards to RFIs. The e-mail addresses you enter can also be used in conjunction with the Publish Project and Send PDF feature.

In this Chapter, the phrase "the module" refers to the Contract Manager module.

# Inbox Overview

The Contract Manager module Inbox and related Send to Inbox feature provide a convenient method for transferring documents electronically between users. Use the Inbox to retrieve documents other users have sent you.

You can open documents from other projects while in the Inbox without closing the project you are currently in; while previewing the document, you can forward it to another user.

The Inbox stores documents sent to you by other users. the module automatically records documents here that are sent by choosing Send to Inbox from the Select an Action drop-down. The Inbox displays the linked name of the document, the date and time sent, the name of the contact who sent the document, its project, and a comment icon, if applicable.

**Notes:**

- To open a document, click the document icon (Edit mode) or the document's title (View mode).

- To forward a document, mark the document's checkbox and click Forward.

- To mark a document as read or unread, mark the document's checkbox and click Mark Read or Mark Unread.

- To delete a document, mark the document's checkbox and click Delete.

- You cannot manually add a document to the Inbox from the Inbox.

- You cannot send a document to another user's Inbox if the user does not have access to the document.

- When the item is deleted from the Inbox, the Inbox record and its comments are deleted from the database. The actual document (such as a submittal) is not deleted.

**Send documents to users**  When you send a document to a user, it is equivalent to handing someone a document and asking them to review it. For example, you may want Steve Johnson, the project manager, to review the daily report you just entered for the day. To do this, send the document to Steve's Inbox. The difference between sending it this way and sending it to users through e-mail is that you are not creating an attachment. You are providing a link to the actual document in the contact's Inbox. When the contact opens the document from their Inbox, they are opening the actual document.

*You can also send documents from the log window.*

To send documents to users, open the document window for the document you want to send. Choose Select an Action, Send to Inbox, and then click Go. The Send to Inbox dialog box opens. Select the recipient of the document in the Send To field. Enter any comments you want attached to the document in the Comment field. Click Send.

*Select the recipient from a list of users.*

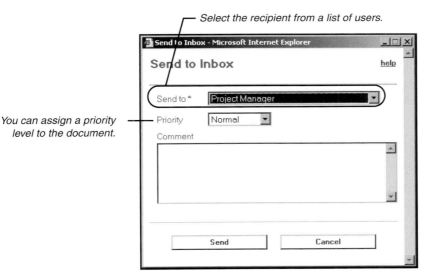

*You can assign a priority level to the document.*

*Any comments you send appear as a sticky note icon in the user's Inbox.*

# Setting Up the Inbox

Follow these basic steps to set up your Inbox.

**To change how items appear in your Inbox**   From the Inbox object in the Workspace, click Edit.

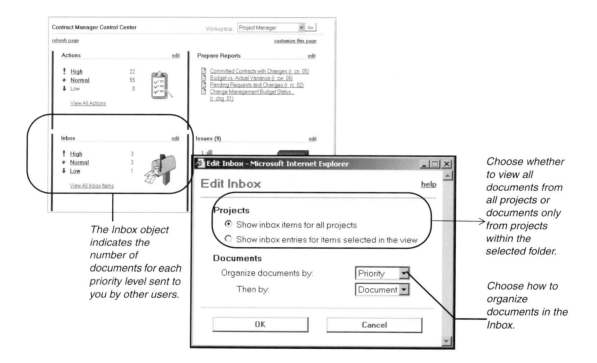

The Inbox object indicates the number of documents for each priority level sent to you by other users.

Choose whether to view all documents from all projects or documents only from projects within the selected folder.

Choose how to organize documents in the Inbox.

# Entering E-Mail Addresses for Contacts

You must enter e-mail addresses to use the request notification feature. This feature automatically sends an e-mail to the RFI's Ball in Court when you first enter the RFI. It sends a notification to the Ball in Court when the answer is provided. Your contacts can provide you with their correct e-mail addresses. This feature can also send one response to other contacts via the Answer Distribution section.

*Any e-mail address entered here can also be used with the Publish Project and Send PDF feature.*

**Enter an e-mail address for a contact**  In the Project Information folder, click Companies. Click a company name or its document icon to open the document window. Scroll down to the Contacts section and click the contact's name to open the Contact dialog box. In the E-Mail Information section, enter the contact's e-mail address. Click Save & Close.

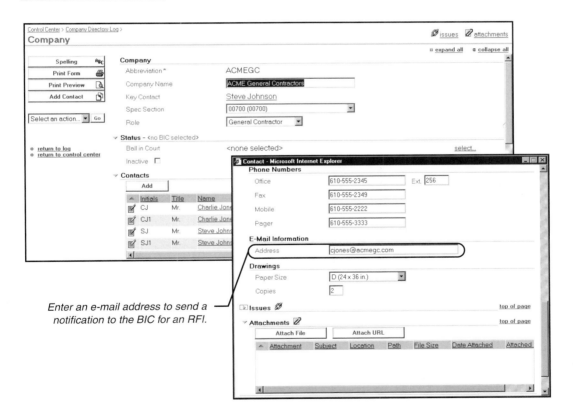

*Enter an e-mail address to send a notification to the BIC for an RFI.*

# Preparing Transmittals

Transmittals are memos or cover letters that accompany submittals, drawings, and material samples sent during a project.

This chapter describes how you can automatically generate transmittals from most Contract Manager module document types, including submittals, various change documents, drawings, contracts and purchase orders (POs), and requisitions.

The module uses names and addresses from predefined distribution lists you set up in the Company Directory so you can prepare transmittals quickly. You can also attach files to generated transmittals, such as drawings, that were attached to the original document.

The module also enables you to quickly indicate the reason you are sending the transmittal and the status of the attached items.

In this chapter, the phrase "the module" refers to the Contract Manager module.

# Preparing a New Transmittal

Use the Transmittal document window to record information about the items that will accompany a transmittal.

*Click to add a new transmittal.*

*Click to modify a transmittal.*

*Click to view a transmittal.*

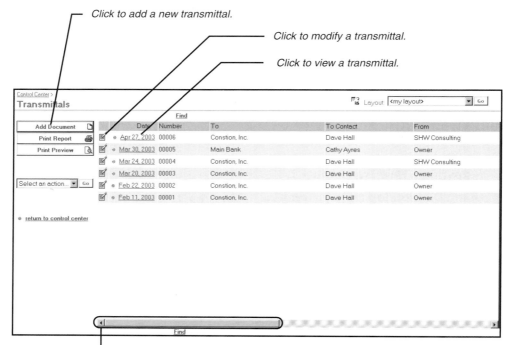

*Scroll to see additional columns, such as contract and priority level.*

**Prepare a transmittal**   In the Communication folder, click Transmittals to open the Transmittals log, and then click Add Document. The module supplies the current date and the next available sequential number, along with your company's abbreviation and default contact. You can edit these values. Enter the remaining information about your transmittal in the appropriate sections.

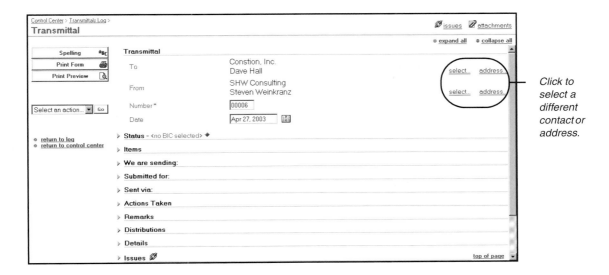

**Viewing or changing Transmittal details** Click the triangle beside each section to expand or collapse its details. Click Expand All or Collapse All at the top of the window to open or close all sections at once.

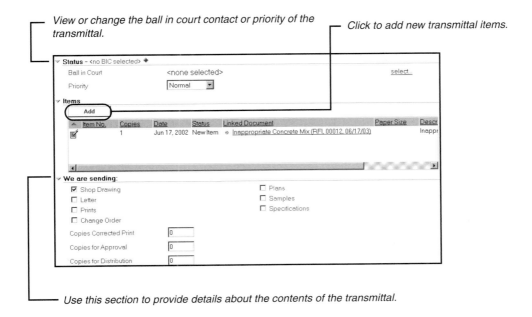

Use this section to provide details about the contents of the transmittal.

Use this section to communicate why the transmittal is being sent.

Specify how the transmittal contents will be sent. If you choose Separate Cover Via, type the method in the corresponding field.

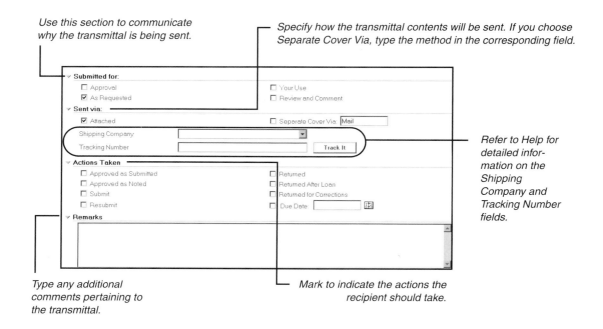

Refer to Help for detailed information on the Shipping Company and Tracking Number fields.

Type any additional comments pertaining to the transmittal.

Mark to indicate the actions the recipient should take.

Click to distribute the transmittal to other contacts. See the next section for more details.

Record additional information associated with the transmittal.

Attach related issues or attachments to any transmittal.

**Delete a transmittal**   Open the transmittal document you want to delete. Click Select an action, Delete Document. Click Go. Click Yes to confirm. When you delete a transmittal from the Transmittals log, The module removes its attachments and any links to issues.

# Using Distribution Lists in Transmittals

Use distribution lists to record the distribution of a transmittal to the appropriate people. Scroll down to the Distributions section and click Add. From the Select Contacts window, click Distribution List in the Organize by field. Click Select beside any section to choose a specific list of names. Click Save to add the distribution list to the transmittal.

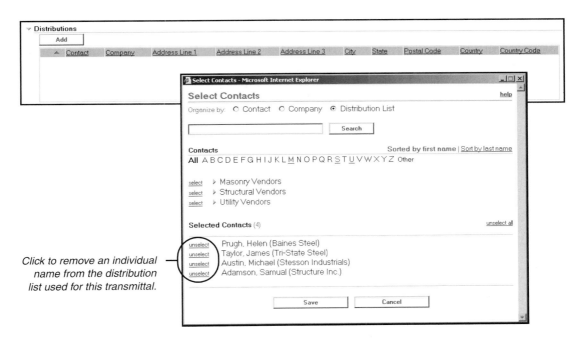

*Click to remove an individual name from the distribution list used for this transmittal.*

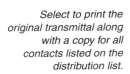

When you print transmittals, you can select the option to print a copy for all contacts listed on the Distribution list. Choose Select an Action, Advanced Print, and then click Go.

*Select to print the original transmittal along with a copy for all contacts listed on the distribution list.*

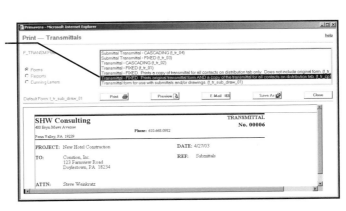

# Copying a Transmittal

You can quickly create a new transmittal from an existing one if both transmittals will contain similar information. For example, you may want to send information from an existing transmittal to a different contact, but only the recipient's address is different. Instead of typing the information again, you can generate a copy of the existing transmittal and then modify it.

**Generate a transmittal copy**  In the Transmittals log window:

1  Select the transmittal you want to copy.

2  In the Select an Action list, click Generate Transmittal, and then click Go.

3  Choose whether to copy the same issues and attachments to the new transmittal, and then click Finish. The next available number and the current date are assigned to the new transmittal.

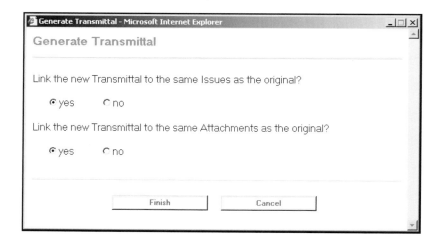

# Generating Transmittals from Other Documents

For instructions on generating a transmittal from a submittal, see *Producing Transmittals from Submittals* in the *Managing Submittals* chapter.

You can generate a transmittal from various change documents, contracts and POs, daily reports, meeting minutes, and requisitions. Any attachments to the original document can also be attached to the generated transmittal. Issues associated with the source document are transferred to the generated transmittal.

**Generate a transmittal from another document**  From the Project View, open the log and then the document from which you want to generate a transmittal. Click Select an Action, Generate Transmittal.

For documents that do not have a To and From contact, On the Generate Transmittal Wizard dialog box, supply the To and From company and contact information.

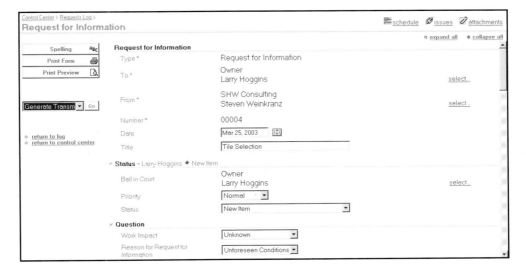

For documents that have a To and From contact, the module automatically generates the transmittal and places it in the Transmittals log. The Reference field identifies the document type from which the transmittal was generated.

# Delivering Transmittals

*To e-mail a transmittal to someone, open the transmittal you want to send, and then click Select an Action, E-mail form.*

When you generate transmittals from submittals, drawings, or revisions, they are placed automatically in the Transmittal Queue. From the queue, you can print the transmittal. Once the transmittal is created, you can also print, fax, or e-mail it to one or more participants directly from its document window. If you send a transmittal via e-mail, you can mark the Include Attachments checkbox to include any attachments if they are detected by your mail program.

### Display the Transmittal Queue and specify a delivery method

From a project, select any log, and then click Transmittal Queue at the top of the window.

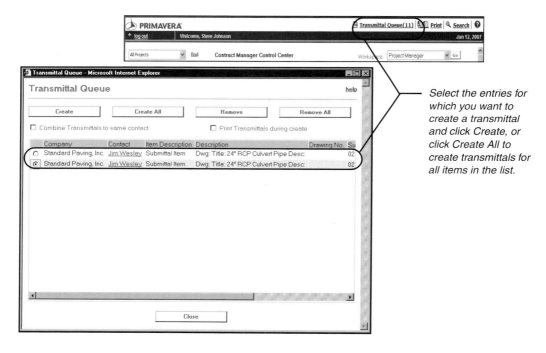

*Select the entries for which you want to create a transmittal and click Create, or click Create All to create transmittals for all items in the list.*

In either case, the transmittals are added to the Transmittals log.

### Print, fax, or e-mail a transmittal directly from its document window

1 Open the transmittal that you want to print, fax, or e-mail from the Transmittals log.

2 From the transmittal's document window, click Select an Action, Advanced Print, and then Go.

3 Choose Forms, Reports, or Dunning Letters.

4 Choose a form, report, or letter from the list, and then preview, print, or e-mail the document. You can also choose Save As to save the document in CSV or Excel format.

5 Click Close when you are finished.

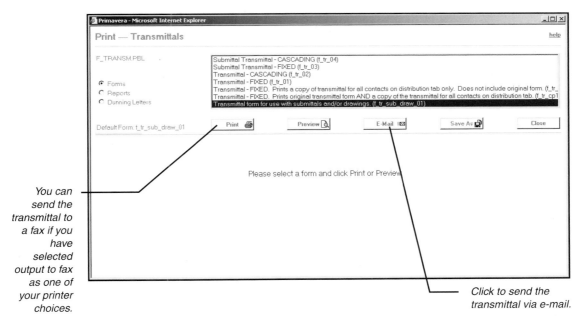

You can send the transmittal to a fax if you have selected output to fax as one of your printer choices.

Click to send the transmittal via e-mail.

# Transmittal Reports and Forms

Standard reports and forms are provided for you to use to print information about transmittals.

From the Transmittal document window, click Select an Action, and then Advanced Print. Click Go. Select the report or form, and then click Print.

**ACME General Contractors**                                                    **School Addition-Automotive Center**

**Transmittal Log**

Job No:    JBAA450                                                              Date:    4/10/00
Project No: PRJAA450                                                           Page:    1 of 2

| Date | Number | Re: | To | Attention | From | Signed |
|------|--------|-----|-----|-----------|------|--------|
| 12/17/99 | 00035 | Drawing Distribution Rev | Baines Steel | Helen Prugh | ACME General Contractors | Steve Johnson |
| 12/17/99 | 00036 | Drawing Distribution Rev | Tri-State Steel | James Taylor | ACME General Contractors | Steve Johnson |
| 12/17/99 | 00037 | Drawing Distribution Rev | Stesson Industrials | Michael Austin | ACME General Contractors | Steve Johnson |
| 12/17/99 | 00038 | Drawing Distribution Rev | Structure Inc. | Samual Adamson | ACME General Contractors | Steve Johnson |
| 12/17/99 | 00039 | Drawing Distribution Rev | Adams Masonry | Greg Fox | ACME General Contractors | Steve Johnson |
| 12/17/99 | 00040 | Drawing Distribution Rev | ACE Mason Contractors | Dave Barron | ACME General Contractors | Steve Johnson |
| 12/17/99 | 00041 | Drawing Distribution Rev | Moore Paving | John Kelly | ACME General Contractors | Steve Johnson |
| 12/17/99 | 00042 | Drawing Distribution Rev | Standard Paving, Inc. | Jim Wesley | ACME General Contractors | Steve Johnson |
| 12/31/99 | 00047 | Drawing Sketches | Baines Steel | Helen Prugh | ACME General Contractors | Steve Johnson |
| 12/31/99 | 00048 | Drawing Sketches | Tri-State Steel | James Taylor | ACME General Contractors | Steve Johnson |
| 12/31/99 | 00049 | Drawing Sketches | Stesson Industrials | Michael Austin | ACME General Contractors | Steve Johnson |
| 12/31/99 | 00050 | Drawing Sketches | Structure Inc. | Samual Adamson | ACME General Contractors | Steve Johnson |
| 3/1/00 | 00054 | Request for Information | Design Group | Chris Atkinson | ACME General Contractors | Steve Johnson |
| 3/6/00 | 00001 | Submittals | Design Group | Chris Atkinson | ACME General Contractors | Steve Johnson |
| 3/15/00 | 00031 | Submittals | Tri-State Steel | James Taylor | ACME General Contractors | Steve Johnson |
| 3/23/00 | 00002 | Submittals | Electrical Contractors | Eric Thompson | ACME General Contractors | Steve Johnson |
| 3/23/00 | 00003 | Submittals | Philadelphia County | Michael Stull | ACME General Contractors | Steve Johnson |
| 3/23/00 | 00004 | Submittals | Security Contractors | Paul Jefferies | ACME General Contractors | Steve Johnson |

# Recording and Tracking Communications

This chapter describes how to use the Contract Manager module communication logs to track items sent and received during a project, record telephone calls, save notes, and manage safety-related documents.

You can record incoming and outgoing documents in the Correspondence logs, and create letters in the Letters log in various fonts and formats.

You can gather and send information using requests for information (RFIs), notices, and noncompliance notices, as well as keep track of important details such as insurance information, work lists, and reminders using the Notepads log.

Use the Safety feature to document safety violation notices, record injuries on the job site, and conform to federal safety regulations.

In this chapter, the phrase "the module" refers to the Contract Manager module.

# Sending Documents to a Correspondence Log

The Contract Manager module Correspondence Received and Correspondence Sent logs enable you to track all items you receive and send during a project. Use the Correspondence Sent log to record outgoing documents and prepare form letters. Use the Correspondence Received log to record incoming documents, especially those that require follow-up. These logs consolidate incoming and outgoing documents and provide a historical reference when you need supporting information, such as in a contract dispute.

Use the Send To command to automatically send an open document to a Correspondence log, or you can manually create Correspondence documents and enter the information directly in each section.

**Send a document**  Open the document you want to record in the Correspondence log and choose Select an Action, Send to Corr Sent (or Send to Corr Rcvd), and then click Go.

*Click to send information about the selected document to the Correspondence Sent or Received log.*

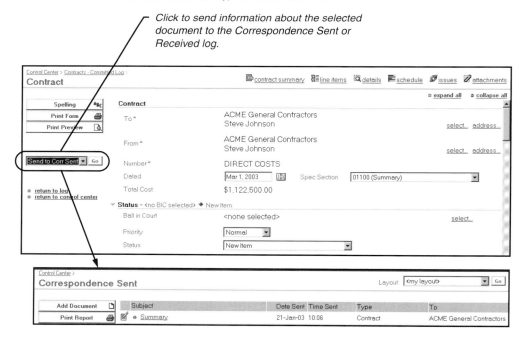

 *If you can select an item in a document window, you can log it as a correspondence document (except from the Cost Worksheet).*

The module numbers the item sequentially and enters the name of the person currently logged into the Contract Manager module. Expand the Status and Log Information sections to view the ball-in-court, priority, status, and who entered the document in the Correspondence log.

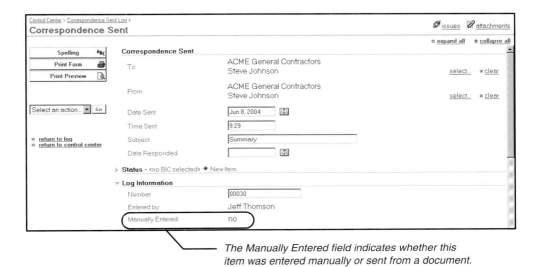

The Manually Entered field indicates whether this item was entered manually or sent from a document.

Any dunning letters you print are automatically recorded in the Correspondence Sent log. A separate record, or row in the log, is created for each contact included on the letter. If you don't want to automatically record dunning letters, turn off this default preference by clearing the Add Dunning Letters to Sent Log checkbox in the Communication section of the Project Settings dialog box.

**View correspondence document items**   While in View mode, you can view the details of a Sent item by expanding the Source Document section and clicking the link to open the original source document (except for dunning letters). If you are in Edit Mode, the link is not available.

*Click the link to view the source document (available in View mode).*

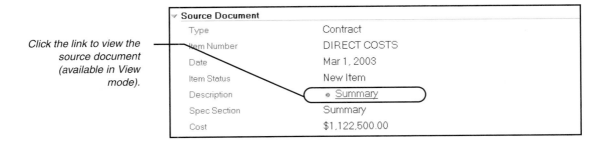

Use the remaining sections of the Correspondence document to append additional details such as remarks, details, issues, or attachments to the correspondence record.

*Enter any remarks associated with the correspondence.*

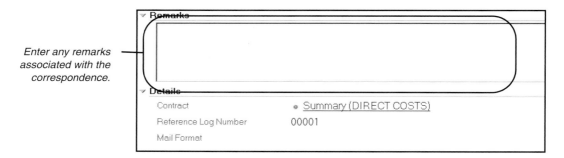

# Adding Correspondence Documents Manually

You can manually add documents that are not included in other logs to the Correspondence logs.

**Add a correspondence document manually** From the Communication folder of the Project View, click Corr. Sent (or Corr. Received), and then click Add Document. The module enters the current date and time, Entered By, Manually Entered (set to Yes), and your company name in the From (or To) field.

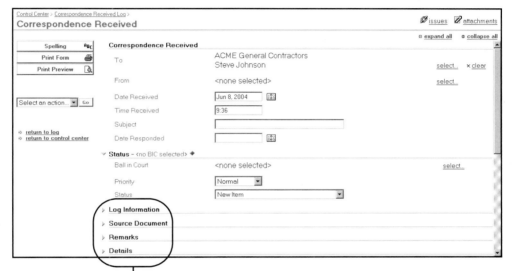

Enter the remaining information for the record,
including information about the source document.

# Correspondence Reports and Forms

Standard reports and forms are provided for you to use to print correspondence records.

From the Correspondence log or document window, click Select an Action, and then Advanced Print. Click Go. Select the report or form, and then click Print.

| ACME General Contractors | | | | | | | School Addition-Automotive Center | | |
|---|---|---|---|---|---|---|---|---|---|
| | | | | **Correspondence Received Log** | | | | | |
| Job No:    JBAA450 | | | | **by Month Received** | | | | Date:    4/11/00 | |
| Project No: PRJAA450 | | | | | | | | Page:    1 of 1 | |

| Month | From | Date | Item | Number | Status | Description | Spec Section | Log No. | Logged By |
|---|---|---|---|---|---|---|---|---|---|
| March | | | | | | | | | |
| | MASON | 3/30/00 | RFI | 00001 | NEW | Glazed Facing Tile | 08800 | 00006 | INI |
| | PRIMAV | 3/30/00 | INV | PRMV-001-052 | APP | Expedition / P3 / SureTrak | 01150 | 00004 | SJ |
| April | | | | | | | | | |
| | MASON | 4/21/00 | CIC | 00001 | NEW | Glazed Facing Tile | 08800 | 00007 | INI |
| | PHILASCH | 4/28/00 | CO | 00001 | APP | Underground Utilities | | 00009 | INI |
| | STDPAV | 4/22/00 | COR | 00001 | CLO | Underground Utilities | | 00008 | INI |
| May | | | | | | | | | |
| | PHILASCH | 5/22/00 | RFI | 00001 | NEW | Additional Parking Required | | 00013 | INI |
| June | | | | | | | | | |
| | MECH | 6/2/00 | CIC | 00001 | CLO | Plugging Water line | | 00010 | INI |
| | MECH | 6/9/00 | COR | 00001 | CLO | Plugging Water line | | 00011 | INI |
| | PHILASCH | 6/12/00 | CO | 00004 | APP | Plugging Water line | | 00012 | INI |
| | STDPAV | 6/11/00 | COR | 00003 | CLO | Additional Parking Required | | 00014 | INI |

# Recording Letters

During a project, participants often exchange important information through letters that you may want to record. For example, letters that outline contractual obligations or clarify a delay can later function as supporting evidence in a claim. If you have Microsoft Word installed on your computer, you can use the Letters feature to compose letters to record information on any topic, such as when you expect a response from the recipient.

 *If the temp directory exists on a network drive, the Contract Manager module must be run as a user account and not a system account.*

*You can use mixed versions of Microsoft Word with the module, including versions 2000, 2002, and 2003.*

**Add a letter**  From the Communication folder of the Project View, click Letters, and then Add Document.

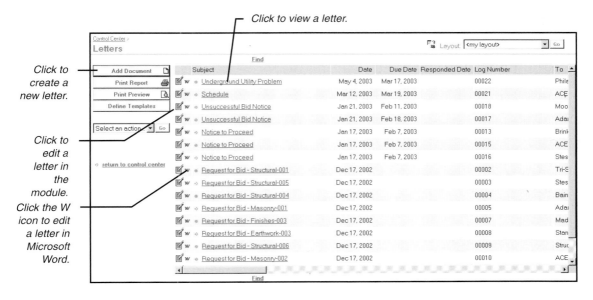

*Click to view a letter.*

*Click to create a new letter.*

*Click to edit a letter in the module.*

*Click the W icon to edit a letter in Microsoft Word.*

The module enters the current date, time, log number, and due date (two weeks from the current date). Click Add to select the To contact for the letter. Click Select to choose the From contact.

Type a subject and enter the body of the letter. Continue to fill in the remaining fields in each section of the window as necessary, and then click Save and Create Letter.

*The remaining sections of the window provide additional details including any related issues or attachments.*

 *The Issues and Attachments sections do not appear until the letter has been created in Microsoft Word.*

*Click to edit this document.*

*Click to open the letter in Microsoft Word.*

For more details on creating letter templates, see *Create Templates for Letters* in Help.

**Create a letter template**  If you did not set up your own template for letters, the default template displays in the letter portion of the window. You can select a different template by clicking the drop-down list in the Template field when you first create a letter.

To create your own letter template, click Define Templates in the Letters log window.

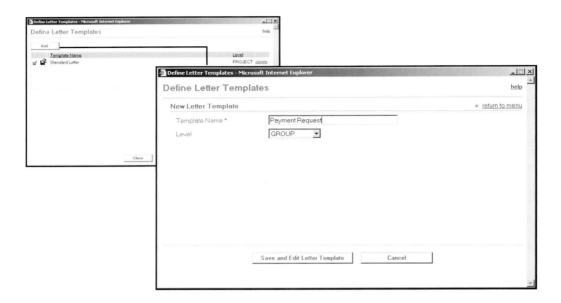

**Generate a new letter from an existing letter**  If you need to send a letter similar or identical to an existing one, you can choose Select an Action, Generate Letter, and click Go from the existing letter. Complete the entries in the window, and then click Finish.

*A separate letter is generated for each recipient you add.*

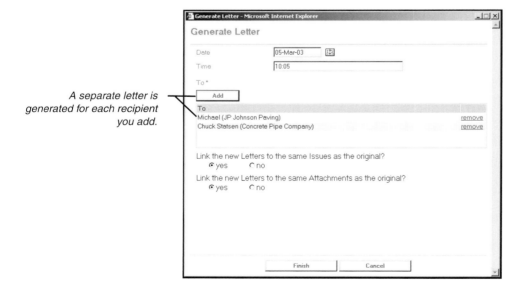

Each generated letter is assigned the next available number, in consecutive order, in the Letters log.

**Save a letter as a separate file**  Click Modify Document in the Letter document window. The letter is opened in Microsoft Word. Choose File, Save As and then select the drive and folder in which to save the file, and type a name.

# Letters Reports and Forms

The module provides a report showing all letter records created to date and a form letter duplicating the contents of the selected letter from the log or document window. From the Letter document window, click Select an Action, and then Advanced Print. Click Go. Select the report or form, and then click Print.

| ACME General Contractors | | | | | School Addition-Automotive Center | |
|---|---|---|---|---|---|---|
| | | | Letters | | | |
| **Job No:** JBAA450 | | | | | **Date:** | **4/11/00** |
| **Project No: PRJAA450** | | | | | **Page:** | **1 of 1** |

| Date | To | | Subject | From | | Responded |
|---|---|---|---|---|---|---|
| 12/1/99 | PHILASCH | MS | Pre-Construction Meeting Letter | ACMEGC | CJ | |
| 12/17/99 | ADAMS | GF | Request for Bid - Masonry-001 | ACMEGC | CJ | |
| 12/17/99 | BAINES | HP | Request for Bid - Structural-004 | ACMEGC | CJ | |
| 12/17/99 | MADISON | WT | Request for Bid - Finishes-003 | ACMEGC | CJ | |
| 12/17/99 | MASON | DB | Request for Bid - Masonry-002 | ACMEGC | CJ | |
| 12/17/99 | MOORE | JK | Request for Bid - Earthwork-001 | ACMEGC | CJ | |
| 12/17/99 | STDPAV | JW | Request for Bid - Earthwork-003 | ACMEGC | CJ | |
| 12/17/99 | STEEL | JT | Request for Bid - Structural-001 | ACMEGC | CJ | |
| 12/17/99 | STRESS | MA | Request for Bid - Structural-005 | BRINK | LJ | |
| 12/17/99 | STRUCT | SA | Request for Bid - Structural-006 | ACMEGC | CJ | |
| 1/17/00 | BRINK | LJ | Notice to Proceed | ACMEGC | CJ | |
| 1/17/00 | MASON | DB | Notice to Proceed | ACMEGC | CJ | |
| 1/17/00 | STRESS | MA | Notice to Proceed | ACMEGC | CJ | |
| 1/21/00 | ADAMS | GF | Unsuccessful Bid Notice | ACMEGC | CJ | |
| 1/21/00 | MOORE | JK | Unsuccessful Bid Notice | ACMEGC | CJ | |
| 3/12/00 | MASON | DB | Schedule | JOHNSON | MK | |
| 5/4/00 | PHILASCH | MS | Underground Utility Problem | ACMEGC | SJ | |

# Using Requests for Information

Use requests for information (RFIs) to enter request and answer documents. These requests and the answers they solicit provide additional information or clarify some aspect of the project, such as procedures, equipment, and materials.

**Add a request for information document**  From the Communication folder of the Project View, click Request for Information, and then, and then Add Document. Enter basic information about the new RFI (the type, who it is to and from, its title, number, and date).

*Select the document type.*

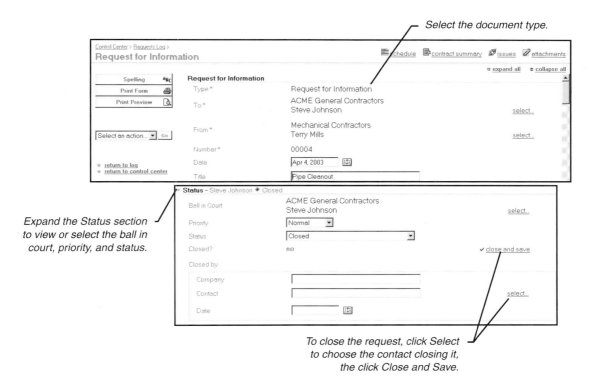

*Expand the Status section to view or select the ball in court, priority, and status.*

*To close the request, click Select to choose the contact closing it, the click Close and Save.*

For details on question and answer access rights, see *Request for Information/ Answer document window* in Help.

**Enter a question and answer**  Use the Question and Answer sections to enter questions, proposed solutions, and answers. You can also create distribution lists for the questions and answers.

*Type the question, and then enter other details about the question, if necessary.*

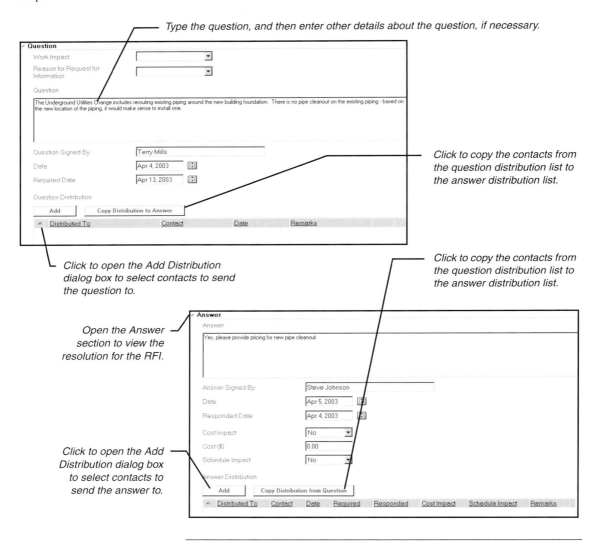

*Click to copy the contacts from the question distribution list to the answer distribution list.*

*Click to open the Add Distribution dialog box to select contacts to send the question to.*

*Click to copy the contacts from the question distribution list to the answer distribution list.*

*Open the Answer section to view the resolution for the RFI.*

*Click to open the Add Distribution dialog box to select contacts to send the answer to.*

 *When you initiate change management from an RFI that has a question and answer, (choose Select and Action, Initiate CM, and then click Go), The question and answer to the Remarks section are copied in the Change Management document window.*

### Add details, drawings, and schedule information to the RFI

Use the Details section to select items associated with the request, such as a specification item, reference document, contract, architect number, subcontractor, and so on.

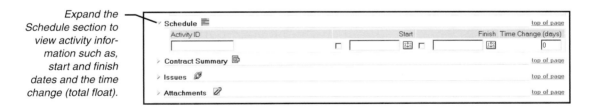

*If the RFI was generated from change management, the number appears here.*

*Click to append drawing documents to the RFI.*

Open the Schedule section to see how the resolution to this request for information might impact the project schedule.

*Expand the Schedule section to view activity information such as, start and finish dates and the time change (total float).*

# Sending Notices

Use notices to inform project participants of the latest project developments including changes in condition, bulletins, or change sketches.

**Add a notice**  From the Communication folder of the Project View, click Notices, and then Add Document. Enter basic information about the new notice. In the Type field, specify whether the notice is a change in condition, bulletin, or change sketch. Enter other details such as the title, who it is to and from, its number, its related contract, and the cost.

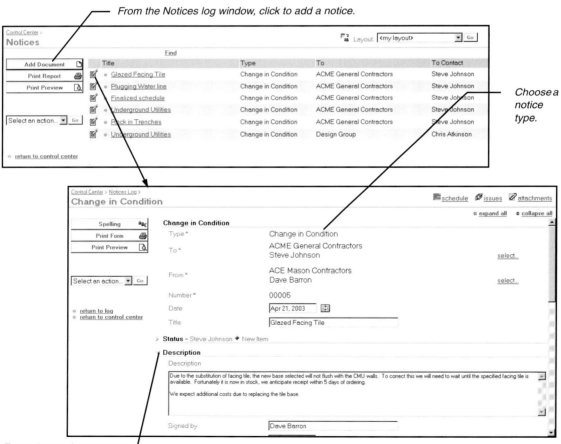

*From the Notices log window, click to add a notice.*

*Choose a notice type.*

*Expand a section to enter more information, such as a detailed description.*

# Sending Noncompliance Notices

Use noncompliance notices to inform project participants of deviations from the contract specifications. For example, the owner might send a noncompliance notice to the general contractor (GC) because of a contract safety and health requirement violation. The GC will then generate a noncompliance notice to the appropriate subcontractor. In most cases, the recipient will need to respond with brief details of corrective actions required/taken.

**Add a noncompliance notice**   From the Communication folder of the Project View, click Noncompliance Notices, then Add Document. Enter basic information about the new notice (its type, title, who it is to and from, its number, title, if it is related to a change issue, and the cost).

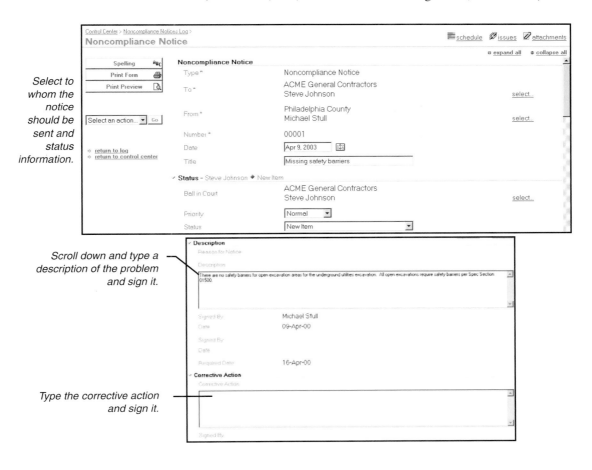

*Select to whom the notice should be sent and status information.*

*Scroll down and type a description of the problem and sign it.*

*Type the corrective action and sign it.*

# Generating a New Document from an Existing One

Although you can add documents manually, using the Generate feature saves time. In addition to reducing data entry by copying data from an existing document to a new one, generating ensures that the information in related documents is

consistent. You can generate documents from RFIs, notices, noncompliance notices, and trends. For example, to generate a change in condition from an existing RFI, open the RFI document window and choose Select an Action, Generate Document, and then click

*Select the type of document you want to create.*

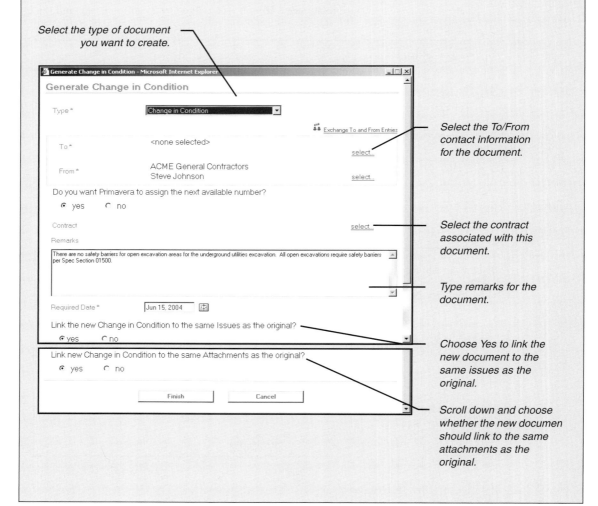

*Select the To/From contact information for the document.*

*Select the contract associated with this document.*

*Type remarks for the document.*

*Choose Yes to link the new document to the same issues as the original.*

*Scroll down and choose whether the new documen should link to the same attachments as the original.*

# Writing Notes with Notepads

Contract Manager module notepads make it easy to track important details, such as comments, work lists, and reminders. Create a different notepad for each category of information you need.

Writing notes is a two-step process: first add a notepad that refers to a specific subject, and then add as many items as you want to that notepad.

**Add a notepad**   From the Communication folder of the Project View, click Notepads, and then Add Document. Type a name for the notepad and a brief description of its subject matter.

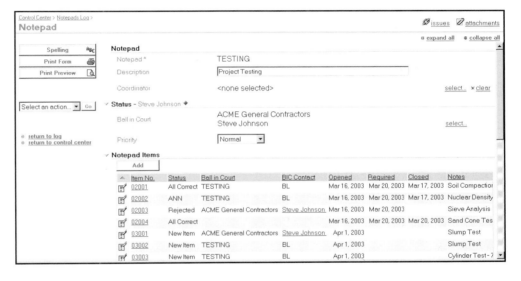

**Add an item to a notepad**   In the Notepad Items section, click Add. The current date is entered and assigned the notepad item the next available number. When you are finished, click Save & Close or Save & Add Another.

**Delete notepad information**  You can delete an item from a notepad, or delete an entire notepad from the log.

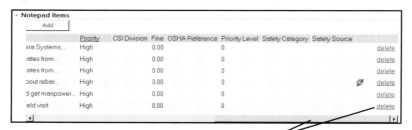

*To delete a notepad item, scroll to the right
and click Delete. Click Yes to confirm.*

To delete a notepad document, open the document, and then choose Select an Action, Delete Document, and then click Go. Click Yes when prompted to confirm the deletion. Any links to issues are also deleted.

# Notepad Reports, Forms, and Dunning Letters

Standard reports, forms, and dunning letters are provided for you to use to print notepad records.

From the Notepad document window, click Select an Action, and then Advanced Print. Click Go. Select the report, form, or dunning letter, and then click Print.

**ACME General Contractors**

| 1001 South Street | **Phone:** 215-555-2011 |
|---|---|
| Philadelphia, PA 19100 | **Fax:** 215-555-6889 |

April 11, 2000

Standard Paving, Inc.
7 West Oak Lane
2nd Floor
Camden, NJ 08000

**Attn:** Jim Wesley

**Project:** School Addition-Automotive Center    Project# PRJAA450

**Re:** Note Pad Items Due    Job# JBAA450

Please note that the following items are past due. These items were discussed during our progress meeting and we have determined that they are your responsibility.

**Note Pad    Item No. Opened  Notes                                    Status Required**

# Documenting Telephone Calls

Project participants often communicate important project information via telephone conversations, such as follow-up calls that clarify work included in bid estimates. A Telephone Records log is provided to enable you to document the date, content, and names of persons involved in each call.

**Documenting a telephone call**   From the Communication folder of the Project View, click Telephone Records, and then Add Document. The module enters the current date and time, the next available consecutive number, and your name. You can edit these entries. Type a brief subject and description of the call, the participating parties, and the status of the call.

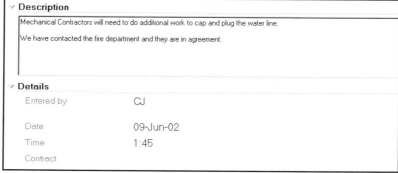

# Telephone Record Reports and Forms

Standard reports and forms are provided for you to use to print telephone records.

From the Telephone Record log or document window, click Select an Action, and then Advanced Print. Click Go. Select the report or form, and then click Print.

| ACME General Contractors | | | | | School Addition-Automotive Center | |
|---|---|---|---|---|---|---|

**Telephone Record Log**

| Job No: | JBAA450 | | | | Date: | 4/11/00 |
|---|---|---|---|---|---|---|
| Project No: PRJAA450 | | | | | Page: | 1 of 1 |

| Date | Time | From | | To | | Subject | Ball In Court |
|---|---|---|---|---|---|---|---|
| 12/31/99 | 9:04 | ACMEGC | Charlie Jones | PHILASCH | Timothy Stapleton | First Pre-construction meeting | |
| 3/1/00 | 9:00 | ACMEGC | Steve Johnson | DESIGN | Chris Atkinson | Brick | |
| 4/10/00 | 4:32 | ACMEGC | Steve Johnson | DESIGN | Chris Atkinson | Underground Utilities | |
| 4/11/00 | 9:08 | ACMEGC | Steve Johnson | PHILASCH | Timothy Stapleton | Steel Placement | |
| 5/1/00 | 6:56 | ACMEGC | Steve Johnson | DESIGN | Chris Atkinson | Underground Utilities | |
| 6/2/00 | 9:16 | ACMEGC | Steve Johnson | MECH | Terry Mills | Water line | |
| 6/8/00 | 1:30 | MECH | Terry Mills | ACMEGC | Steve Johnson | Water line | |
| 6/9/00 | 1:45 | ACMEGC | Charlie Jones | PHILASCH | Timothy Stapleton | Water line | |

# E-mailing Forms

You can e-mail document windows as forms in PDF files, as well as a link back to the actual Contract Manager module document using the E-mail dialog box. From a document window, choose Select an Action, E-Mail Form (E-Mail Letter from the Letter document window), and then click Go.

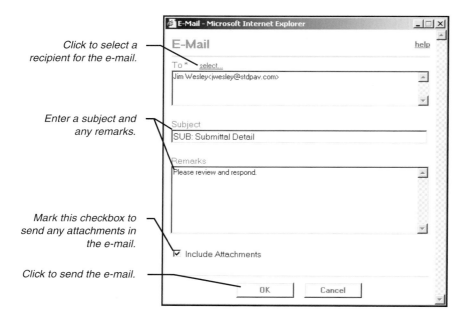

*Click to select a recipient for the e-mail.*

*Enter a subject and any remarks.*

*Mark this checkbox to send any attachments in the e-mail.*

*Click to send the e-mail.*

When the recipients receive the e-mail, they can either open the PDF to display the form (or DOC file if it is a letter), or click the link to open the document window.

```
You can view this document in Expedition Professional by clicking the following link (you will
need an Expedition Professional User Name and Password):
http://SATELLITE:80/exponline/documentrequestforward.do?redirect.rd=true&masterkey=DEMO++++PRIM
INI+REARwM9407&basesysitemtype=SUB&projectname=DEMO&groupname=EXPWIN
```

exp_1088097842375.pdf

*Click to open the Contract Management module document window in*
*Contract Manager module.*

# Managing Safety Notices and Reports

Use the Safety Notices and Reports feature to record information about safety violations, injuries, illnesses, and to keep records for federal regulations such as Occupational Safety & Health Administration (OSHA).

The Safety notices and reports address the following areas:

**Injury or illness reports** Fill out these reports each time there is an accident, injury or illness at a site. You can also record "near miss" items, and use them for training to help prevent future mishaps. Also, once an injury or illness report is recorded, you can send e-mail to a distribution list to inform contacts what is documented.

**Safety violation notices** You can create and print out a safety notice to inform a vendor of a potential hazard, and e-mail it to contacts in a distribution list.

**Federal reporting requirements** The safety notices and reports satisfy OSHA's 300, 300a, and 301 federal reporting requirements. Individual states may have additional requirements. It is up to you to be aware of these regulations. You can print the forms required by OSHA. Any company with more than 10 employees is required to track information for OSHA.

Form 301 is one of the first forms a company must fill out when an injury or illness has occurred. This form, along with forms 300 and 300a (300 Summary), helps the employer and OSHA develop a picture of the extent and severity of work-related incidents. According to public law 910596, form 301 must be kept on file for five years following an incident.

Form 300 is the log of work related injuries and illnesses. Companies must complete form 300 for every work-related illness or injury. One form is required for each person involved.

Form 300a is required to be posted at the workplace from February 1 to April 30 of the year following the one covered on the form. All employees and former employees are entitled to review Form 300 entries in their entirety upon request as part of OSHA's record keeping rules.

**Create a safety notice**  In the Communication folder, click Safety, and then Add Document. In the Safety Violation document window, the new safety notice is assigned the next available number and the current date is entered.

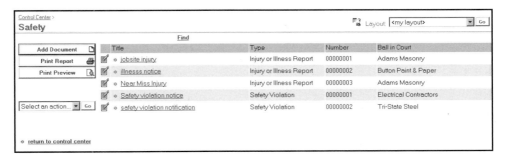

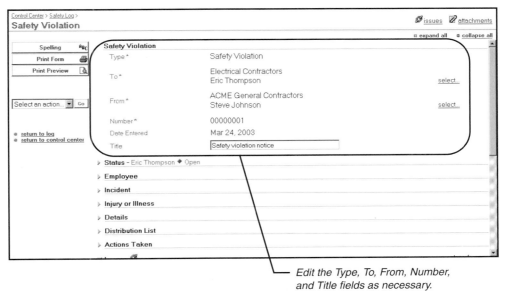

*Edit the Type, To, From, Number, and Title fields as necessary.*

**Viewing or changing safety notice details**  Expand the Status section to view or change the ball in court contact, priority, status, and so on of the safety document. Use the Employee section to enter information about the employee.

Enter a description of the incident.          Record details of any injury or illness that occurred.

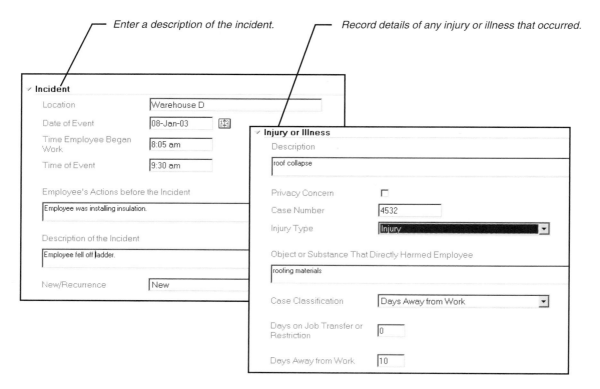

Use the Details section to view the project manager to whom the safety violation pertains to, and any associated fine levied against the company. Use the Distribution List section to record the names of contacts who should receive a copy of the safety violation notice.

The Actions Taken section keeps historical records of changes made to the safety notice. Any changes made to fields in this notice corresponding to the columns in this section will add a new row to this section. This section is not editable. You can view the row by clicking Select and Action, View, and then Go.

Attach related issues or attachments to any safety document.

If you make any changes to the Safety Notice, click Save at the bottom of the document window.

 *If an Injury or Illness Report is being generated, the Case Number is incremented automatically.*

**Generate a safety notice based on an existing one**  Safety notices often contain similar information. To reduce data entry time, use the Generate Document feature to create a copy of a safety notice, and then edit the copy to reflect any differences.

From the safety notice you want to copy, choose Select an Action, Generate Document, and then click Go.

Choose which sections to copy to the new safety notice, and then click Finish to create the new safety notice.

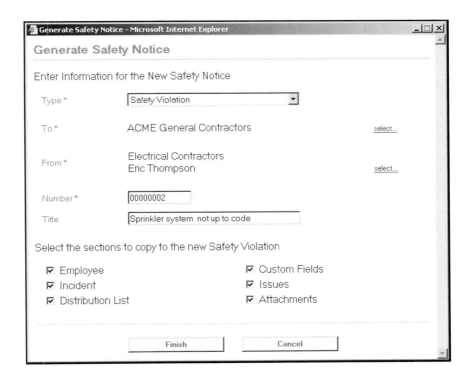

# Safety Reports and Forms

Standard reports and forms are provided for you to use to print safety reports and documents.

From the Safety document window, click Select an Action, and then Advanced Print. Click Go. Select the report or form, and then click Print.

---

OSHA's Form 301

### *Injury and Illness Incident Report*

Attention:    This form contains information relating to employee health and must be used in a manner that protects the confidentiality of employees to the extent possible while the information is being used for occupational safety and health purposes.

**U.S. Department of Labor**
Occupational Safety and Health Administration

Form approved OMB no. 1218-0176

This Injury and Illness Incident Report is one of the first forms you must fill out when a recordable work-related injury or illness has occurred. Together with the Log of Work-Related Injuries and Illness and the accompanying Summary, these forms help the employer and OSHA develop a picture of the extent and severity of work-related incidents.

Within 7 calendar days after you receive information that a recordable work-related injury or illness has occurred, you must fill out this form or an equivalent. Some states worker's compensation, insurance, or other reports may be acceptable substitutes. To be considered an equivalent form, any substitute must contain all the information asked for on this form.

According to Public Law 91-596 and 29 CFR

**Information about the employee**

1) Full name

2) Street

City            State            ZIP

3) Date of birth

4) Date hired

5) ☐ Male
   ☐ Female

**Information about the physician or other health care professional**

6) Name of physician or other health care professional

**Information about the case**

10) Case number from the Log    00000001    (Transfer the case number from the Log after you record the case.)

11) Date of injury or illness

12) Time employee began work            AM / PM

13) Time of event            AM / PM    ☑ Check if the time cannot be determined

14) **What was the employee doing just before the incident occurred?**    Describe the activity, as well as tools, equipment, or material the employee was using. Be Specific.

15) **What happened?**    Tell us how the injury occurred.

# Recording Meeting Minutes

Every project includes a number of meetings to discuss progress and delays and to clarify specifications or designs. This chapter shows you how to use the Contract Manager module to record the details of every meeting—the attendees, discussion items, decisions, and persons responsible for action items.

Once you record meeting minutes, you can easily locate any detail about a meeting and create an agenda for the next meeting by generating unresolved items forward.

# Adding a Meeting

Use the Meeting Minutes module to record all pertinent information about a meeting, such as attendees and business items.

**Add a meeting**  In the Communication folder, click Meeting Minutes to open the Meeting Minutes log window.

*Click to create a new Meeting Minutes document.*

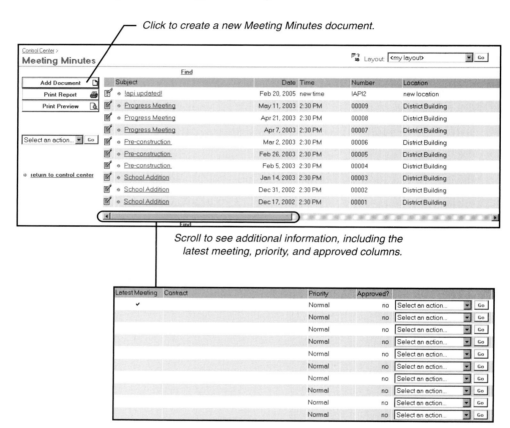

*Scroll to see additional information, including the latest meeting, priority, and approved columns.*

*Type the subject, time, and location of the meeting in their respective fields. Click Save.*

*When you click the Return to Log link, the module marks the Latest Meeting checkbox in the log, indicating that this is the most recent meeting.*

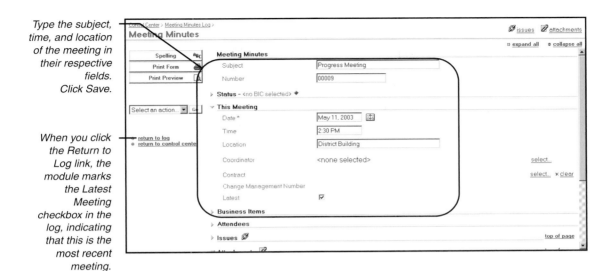

Click the Edit Document button within any Meeting Minute document to view or change details about the meeting.

In the Status section, click Select in the Ball in Court field to select the contact responsible for acting on this meeting. Select the priority level for this meeting, which will appear in the coordinator's Action List.

**Approving Minutes** Meeting Minutes are generally approved after sending the document to the attendees and getting their comments. To approve minutes, select a contact in the Approved by field and then click Approve and Save. The Approved field displays Yes indicating that the meeting minutes are approved.

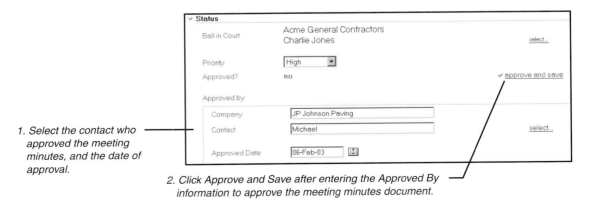

*1. Select the contact who approved the meeting minutes, and the date of approval.*

*2. Click Approve and Save after entering the Approved By information to approve the meeting minutes document.*

**Add a business item**  Scroll to the Business Items section of the Meeting Minutes document window, then click Add. The item is assigned the next available number. Type a description of the item, and then select a status in the Status field. Click Select adjacent to the Ball In Court field to select a company abbreviation from a list.

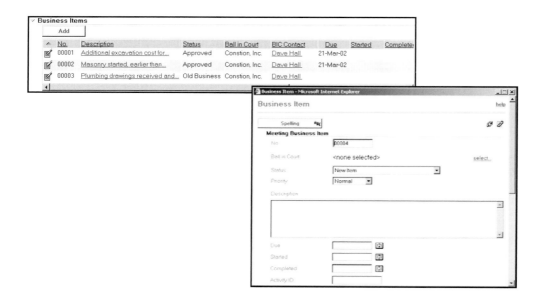

Complete the remaining fields as appropriate. Click Save & Add Another to continue adding business items. When you are finished adding items, click Save & Close. The new item is added to the bottom of the list.

For details on listing primary contacts, see *Setting Up the Company Directory* in the *Planning and Adding a Contract Manager Module Project* chapter.

**Add an attendee**  In the Attendees section of the Meeting Minutes document window, click Add. Select the contact in the Company field. The module automatically fills in the initials and company name of the key contact in the Company Directory. Click Save & Close.

**Link meeting minutes to issues**  Scroll to the Issues section of the Meeting Minutes document window to link meeting minutes to previously identified issues. You can also link business items to issues by scrolling to the Issues section of the Business Item dialog box.

**Attach relevant files to meeting minutes**  Use the Attachments section to easily attach associated documents to your meeting minutes, such as drawings, pictures, or text files.

# Producing an Agenda from the Minutes of the Last Meeting

During a project, meetings are often held at regular intervals; the same people attend and the agenda contains the open items from the previous meeting. You can create a new meeting minutes entry by copying the pertinent information from the minutes of the last meeting.

**Copy meeting minutes information**  From the Meeting Minutes log window, open the meeting document containing the information you want to copy. From the Select an Action drop-down, click Generate Document, and then click Go.

*Select a date for the new meeting.*

*Choose whether to link the new meeting document to the same issues and attachments as the original document.*

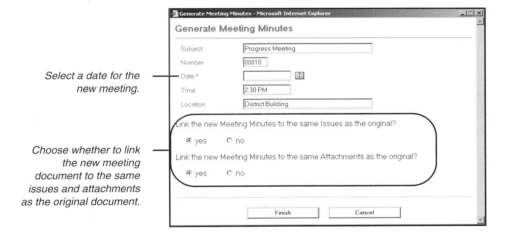

You can print this new document and use it as an instant agenda. After the meeting, update the record with any new information.

■ Business items with an Approved or Closed status are not copied.

■ All New, Open, and Old business items are carried forward, and their status changes to Old. Business items with an Approved or Closed status are not copied.

■ All attendee information in entered in the Attendees tab. You can edit this list.

■ The newly generated meeting is marked as the latest meeting.

# Using the Advanced Print Function

See "Printing Logs, Forms, and Reports"

After you enter the minutes for a meeting, you can print copies and distribute them to the attendees to remind them of their responsibilities. Standard reports, forms, and dunning letters are provided for you to use to print the meeting minutes.

### Select the Meeting Minutes to View or Print

To select Meeting Minutes to view or print, do the following:

1  Open the project, and expand the Communications folder.

2  Click Meeting Minutes.

3  Click the meeting minutes you want to view or print.

4  Click Print at the top right of the screen.

5  On the Print dialog box, click the button next to the type of document you want to print (for example, Reports).

6  Choose the document from the list of documents in the box.

# Working with Contracts, Project Costs, and Changes

*T*his part contains information about using Contract Manager module to help you manage your contracts, purchase orders (POs), requisitions, invoices, changes, and other cost-related documents.

Read the chapters in this part to learn how to set up and use the Cost Worksheet to track budgeted and committed costs; create lump sum and unit price contracts and POs; use trends to track possible cost increases; and record billing information in requisitions and invoices.

You will also learn how to manage complex changes using the change management process, use procurement for tracking bids on labor and materials, and use issues to cross-reference and link documents throughout Contract Manager module so you can retrieve them quickly.

# Setting Up and Using the Cost Worksheet

Keeping track of a budget, the amount actually spent, and the amount the original budget has increased (through changes, for example)—is important to the success of any project.

The Cost Worksheet provides a central location where you can collect and track commitments, budget, and actual information and quickly check the financial status of your project. You can adapt standard cost codes or create your own to help track and report different types of costs.

This chapter explains how to set up the Cost Worksheet, how to distribute costs from different documents, and how to interpret information in the Cost Worksheet.

# How Costs are Tracked

The Cost Worksheet tracks costs distributed from contracts, purchase orders (POs), invoices, requisitions, proposals, trends, and changes. Use the Cost Worksheet to closely track budgeted costs, committed costs, actual expenditures, and budget revisions caused by changes. You can also track costs associated with the documents you defined for your change management work process and see how pending cost changes affect the Cost Worksheet as they occur.

---

 *Using the Cost Worksheet is optional: you can use the cost documents listed above independently. However, if you collect cost information in the Cost Worksheet, use it with all of your cost-related documents.*

---

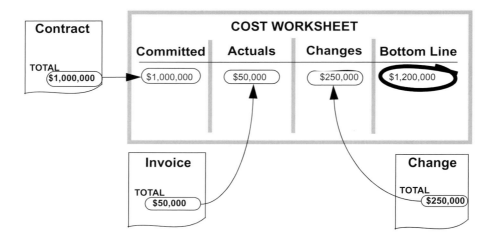

The rest of this chapter shows you how to set up the Cost Worksheet, update it, and review the financial information that's important to you.

# Items the Cost Worksheet Tracks

The Cost Worksheet tracks four categories of cost information:

- **Estimated** includes the procurement estimate, buyout, purchasing buyout, original estimate, estimate accuracy, and estimated gross profit.

- **Budgeted** includes the original budgeted amount, approved revisions to the budget, revised budget amount, pending budget revisions, estimated budget revisions, manual adjustments to the budget, and the projected budget.

- **Committed** includes the original commitment amount, approved revisions to committed costs, the revised commitment, pending revisions to committed costs, estimated revisions to committed costs, the adjusted commitment, and the projected commitment.

- **Actuals** include money you have paid and money you have received.

- **Variance** is the difference between your budgeted and committed costs. Variance includes original variance, approved variance, pending variance, projected variance, budget percent, and commitment percent.

You can use the Order Code field to vary the sort order of your Cost Worksheet from the cost code order.

The chart on the following page shows the main categories of the Cost Worksheet and their subcategories. The bullets indicate where the module places money in the Cost Worksheet when you distribute an amount from a contract, PO, invoice, requisition, trend, change order, or proposed change order.

In the Contracts and POs rows of the chart, the module can distribute the amount to the Original Budget or Original Commitment section of the Cost Worksheet. When you distribute the contract or PO amount, select the Budget or Commitment category, and the Original subcategory is automatically selected.

### Cost Category Distribution

| Type of Document | Budget | | | | | | | Commitment | | | | | | | Estimate | | | | | | Actuals | | | Variance | | | | Funding | | | | | | | |
|---|---|---|---|---|---|---|---|---|---|---|---|---|---|---|---|---|---|---|---|---|---|---|---|---|---|---|---|---|---|---|---|---|---|---|---|
| | Original Budget | Approved Revisions | Revised Budget | Pending Revisions | Estimated Revisions | Adjustments | Projected Budget | Original Commitment | Approved Revisions | Revised Commitment | Pending Revisions | Estimated Revisions | Adjustments | Projected Commitment | Procurement Estimate | Original Estimate | Estimate Accuracy | Estimated Gross Profit | Buyout | Purchasing Buyout | Actuals Received | Actuals Issued | Actuals Expended | Original Variance | Approved Variance | Pending Variance | Projected Variance | Original \<Custom\> | Approved \<Custom\> Revisions | Revised \<Custom\> | Pending \<Custom\> Revisions | Estimated \<Custom\> Revisions | \<Custom\> Adjustments | Projected \<Custom\> | \<Custom\> Percent |
| Column | A | B | C | D | E | F | G | H | I | J | K | L | M | N | O | P | Q | R | S | T | U | V | W | X | Y | Z | a | b | c | d | e | f | g | h | i |
| Contracts | X | | | | | | | X | | | | | | | | | | | | | | | | | | | | X | | | | | | | |
| POs | | | | | | | | X | | | | | | | | | | | | | | | | | | | | X | | | | | | | |
| Proposals | | | | X | | | | | | | X | | | | | | | | | | | | | | | | | | | X | | | | | |
| Change Orders | | X | | X | | | | | X | | X | | | | | | | | | | | | | | | | | | X | X | | | | | |
| Trends | X | X | | X | X | X | | X | X | | X | X | X | | | | | | | | X | X | X | | | | | X | X | | X | X | X | | |
| Invoices | | | | | | | | | | | | | | | | | | | | | * | † | ‡ | | | | | | | | | | | | |
| Procurement | | | | | | | | | | | | | | | X | X | X | X | X | X | | | | | | | | | | | | | | | |
| Requisitions | | | | | | | | | | | | | | | | | | | | | * | † | ‡ | | | | | | | | | | | | |
| Calculated by the module | | | X | | | | X | | | X | | | | X | | X | X | X | X | | | | | X | X | X | X | | X | | | | | X | X |
| Cost Worksheet Column Calculation | | | A+B | | | | A+B+D+E+F | | | H+I | | | | H+I+K+L+M | | P-O | A-P | P-H | O-H | | | | | A-H | (A+B)-(H+I) | (A+B+D)-H-(I-K) | (A+B+D+E+F)-(H+I+K+L+M) | | b+c | | | | | b+c+e+f+g | |

*If Contract/PO is distributed to Committed

†If Contract amount is distributed to Budgeted

‡If Contract is distributed to Funding

# Adding Cost Codes

Use cost codes to break down costs in the Cost Worksheet. Cost codes are similar to categories in a checkbook. For example, if your mortgage payment is $1,000 a month, $400 may apply to principal and $600 to interest. When you record the $1,000 payment in your check register, you may distribute it to principal and interest categories for tax reporting purposes.

Similarly, you may have a lump sum contract for $50,000, of which $25,000 is for rough carpentry and $25,000 is for finish carpentry. To track each carpentry cost separately in the Cost Worksheet, create two codes, Rough and Finish, and distribute $25,000 to each.

You must create cost codes before you can distribute costs to the Cost Worksheet. Consider building meaning into the cost codes. For example, some companies base their cost codes on standard CSI codes.

**Add a cost code**   Click Cost Worksheet in the Contract Information folder. Click Add Cost Code to open the Cost Worksheet dialog box. Type a cost code and a title. Enter an order code if you want to manually sort the cost codes in the Cost Worksheet log window. The order code should correspond to the desired order in the list. The description area can be used to further describe the cost code. Choose to save and close the window or save and add another cost code.

 *You can create cost codes up to 30 characters; they can consist of any combination of letters, numbers, and special characters. You cannot add a cost code named* Not Costed.

*Click Add Cost Code from the Cost Worksheet to create cost codes.*

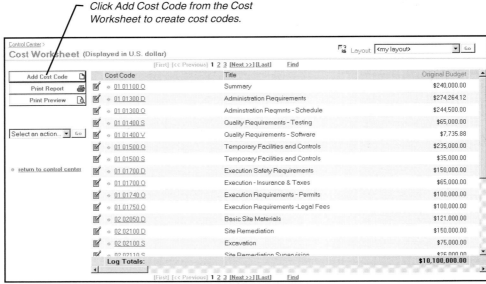

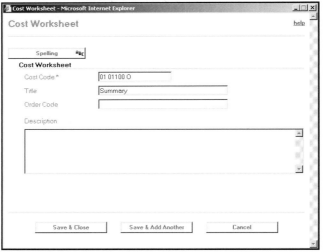

 *Once a cost code is saved, you must have administrator privileges to edit it.*

*Select a cost code line item in the Cost Worksheet log window to display the Cost Worksheet document window, as shown here.*

*Click Edit Cost Code to change a cost code.*

To delete a cost code from the Cost Worksheet, select the cost code, and then choose Delete Cost Code from the Select an Action drop-down list.

# Adding Cost Code Definitions

Cost code definitions enable you to sort and display cost information flexibly in custom reports. For example, if the cost code 06 100 D represents direct costs (D) related to rough carpentry (CSI division 06 100), you need to define this meaning.

*You can use up to 30 characters for each cost code.*

**Add a cost code definition**  Right-click on the top-level folder (All Projects by default), from the Project View and choose Cost Code Definitions. In the Cost Code Definitions dialog box, define your cost codes by entering a name representing a portion of the code, a description of what that portion of the cost code represents, the position where that portion begins in the cost code, and the length of that portion of the code.

In the following example, the first section of the cost code definition, DIVI, (which represents the CSI division) takes up two characters of the code, followed by a space (which is why the next second section starts at 4), and is succeeded by the five-character specification section, followed by a space (which is why the third section starts at 10), and then the one-letter cost category.

The cost codes for this project consist of a CSI division, a CSI subdivision, and a cost category (to track direct, indirect, and vendor costs, for example).

Click a document icon to enter values for each component of

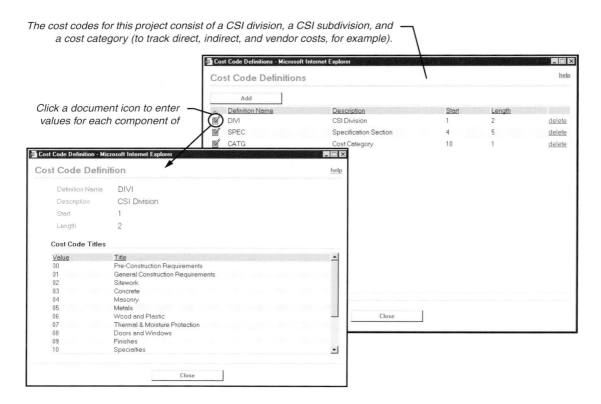

*To define cost code definitions, you must be the only user logged into the Contract Manager module. All other users must be logged out.*

When you add a cost code, you can refer to the definitions created here to properly format the complete cost code.

Breaking down cost codes enables you to use the definitions to customize cost reports by filtering, sorting, and grouping on any part of your definition. For example, the single-character CATG cost code in the preceding example creates a report containing all cost codes that are not Overhead, sorted by cost code and grouped within their categories, with the title for the category from the cost code definitions printed above each section.

# Copying Cost Codes and Titles

Copying the cost codes and titles from one project to another in the same database makes it easy to create closely related or similar projects. Specify the From and To projects and which codes you want to transfer.

 *You cannot copy cost codes to a project that has existing cost codes.*

For information about importing cost codes from other applications, see *Exchanging Contract Manager Module Data with Other Applications*.

**Copy cost codes and titles**   In the Project View, right-click on the project to which you want to copy codes and choose Copy Cost Codes. Select the project from which you want to copy codes. Select a specific cost code then click Add, or click Add All to copy all the cost codes from one project to another. Choose Remove or Remove All if you change your mind about which codes to copy from one project to another. You cannot remove an existing cost code from the "Copy To" project.

*Click to display a list of projects from which to copy codes.*

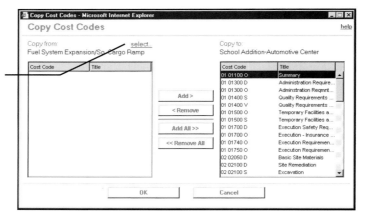

Open the project to which you copied the cost codes, and then open the Cost Worksheet to view the copied information. Cost codes and titles are copied to the project without any of the distributions.

# Distributing Costs to the Cost Worksheet

To break down the value of a contract, PO, invoice, requisition, trend, proposal, or change, distribute the associated costs to one or more cost codes in the Cost Worksheet. This section uses a contract as an example of how to distribute costs; follow the same procedure to distribute costs for any other documents.

**Distribute costs**  Open the document window for the contract for which you want to distribute costs, and then click the Line Items icon at the top of the page or scroll down to the Line Items section. Click either Add Lump Sum or Add Unit Price. Type the amount to distribute in the Lump Amount or Unit Price field. Scroll down to the Costing section and click Add to select the cost code to which to distribute costs. Add as many cost codes as necessary. Enter the amount to distribute in the Distributed field, and then click Add Balance. Click Save & Close to send the data to the Cost Worksheet.

 *Since most documents from which you can distribute costs relate to a specific contract, distribute contract costs first.*

From a Contract or PO document window, values are distributed to either the Budgeted or Committed section of the Cost Worksheet.

The following page illustrates the basic process for distributing costs to the Cost Worksheet.

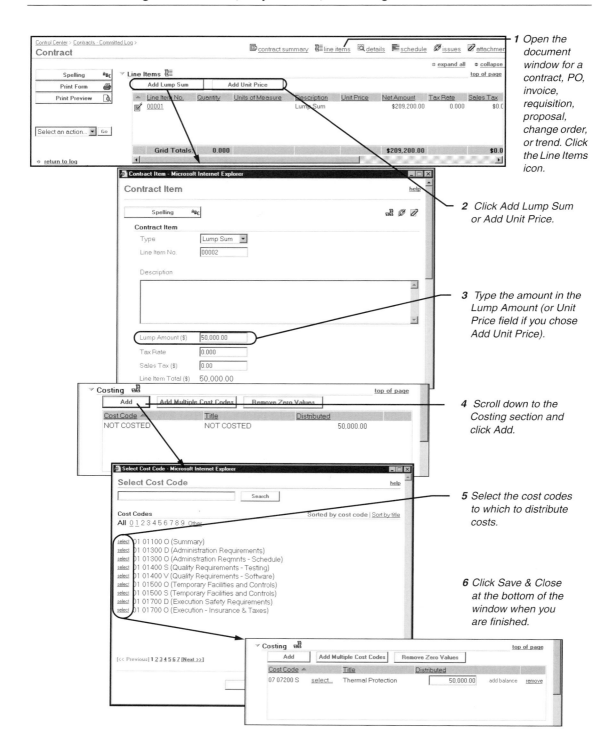

1 Open the document window for a contract, PO, invoice, requisition, proposal, change order, or trend. Click the Line Items icon.

2 Click Add Lump Sum or Add Unit Price.

3 Type the amount in the Lump Amount (or Unit Price field if you chose Add Unit Price).

4 Scroll down to the Costing section and click Add.

5 Select the cost codes to which to distribute costs.

6 Click Save & Close at the bottom of the window when you are finished.

*In Project Settings, if you mark the checkboxes under the Costing section, Document Must be Fully Costed column, you must post the entire balance to existing cost codes.*

**Distributing costs from proposals and change orders**  When you distribute costs from proposals, costs are categorized as pending in the Cost Worksheet. When you distribute costs from change orders, costs are categorized as approved or pending, based on the status code entered in the Status section of the change order. Approved costs have a status of Approved. If the status is anything other than Approved, Closed, or Rejected, costs associated with the change are Pending.

*To access the Status Dictionary, right-click on the top-level folder in the Project View, and then click Dictionaries, Status.*

To ensure that the Cost Worksheet works properly, you must include at least one of each of the following status types in the Status Dictionary: New, Approved, Open, Closed, and Rejected. You cannot delete the last status code for each of these status types. For example, if only one status with a status type of Approved is included in the Status Dictionary, you cannot delete that status.

If you change the status of any change document to Closed or Rejected, the module retains the document's cost distributions but removes this information from the Cost Worksheet and the Contract Summary section.

*For more information about trends, see the Using Trends chapter.*

# Manually Adjusting the Cost Worksheet

Use trends—a manager's expectation of future costs—in conjunction with the Cost Worksheet to track possible cost increases. To add or transfer money within the Cost Worksheet without modifying the original contract or PO or adding a change order, add a Trend document, and then distribute its cost to the Cost Worksheet.

# Distributing Costs Using Change Management

*To access Project Settings, right-click on a project in the Project View.*

Change management is a work process that automatically creates the documents necessary to track a change from the initial request through approval. Change management links the documents for reporting purposes, and updates the Cost Worksheet at each step in the work process according to your specifications. Using the Change Management section in Project Settings (shown as follows), you supply the document type you want to create, and the corresponding column on the Cost Worksheet where you want to distribute change amounts. Each budgeted and committed value creates a document that is then posted to the Cost Worksheet areas you specify.

You can also enable editing previous change management phases and copying cost codes from previous phases.

*Specify document types and cost categories to accommodate your work process for managing changes as they occur.*

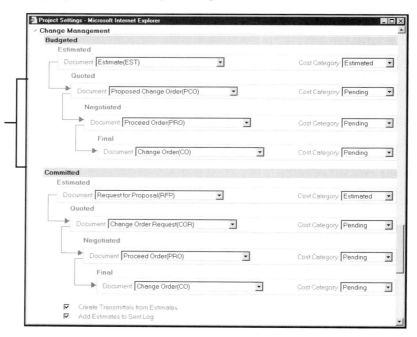

For details about change management, see the *Using Change Management* chapter.

When you add values for one of the phases—Estimated, Quoted, Negotiated, or Final—in a Change Management document, the designated documents are generated based on the information you provide. Click Change Management in the Contract Information folder to access this document type.

*The module automatically assigns cost
codes from the corresponding contract/
PO for the cost distribution.*

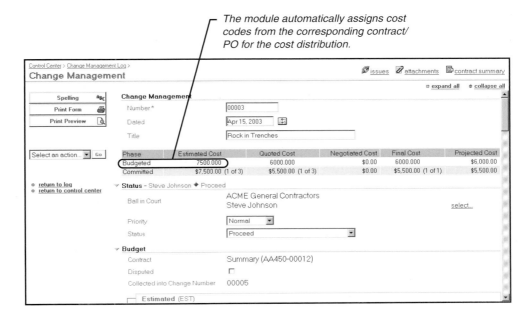

If more than one cost code exists for the originating contract/PO, the
document value is treated as a lump sum value, and it is placed in a cost
code called Not Costed. You can then distribute the value among the
appropriate cost codes.

 *If the contract has only one cost code, the entire document
amount is distributed to that cost code.*

The next time you enter a value in a phase to continue the change
management work process, the cost codes created in the holding table are
based on the prior document in the work process' costing scheme. You
can, however, add cost codes to subsequent documents as necessary in the
work process.

# Getting the Information You Need from the Cost Worksheet

After you set up the Cost Worksheet and distribute costs to it, start using it to monitor your project's financial condition. You can see as much or as little detail as you need.

**For a quick glance at the current status**  Review the totals at the bottom of the Cost Worksheet.

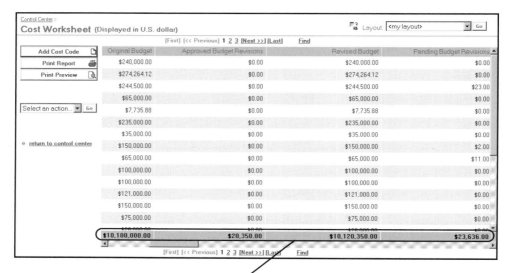

The bottom row of the Cost Worksheet
provides you with a quick summary of
your project costs.

**For a detailed look at the costs associated with a specific cost code**  Click the Cost Code document icon.

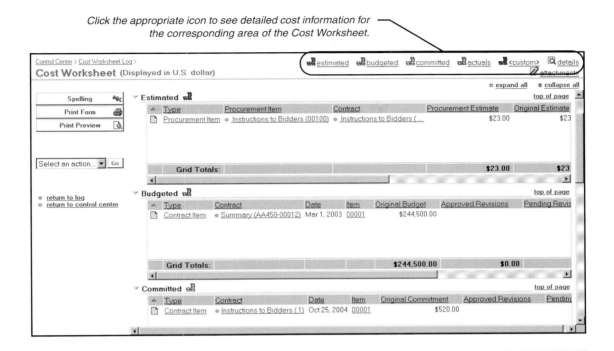

Click the appropriate icon to see detailed cost information for the corresponding area of the Cost Worksheet.

For more information on using these features, see the *Overview* and *Working with Log and Document Windows* chapters.

## Using Other Contract Manager module Features with the Cost Worksheet

Attach word-processor documents, drawings, or other text or picture files to Cost Worksheet log entries. Scroll down the Cost Worksheet to the Attachments section. You may want to attach an electronic version of a CAD drawing or sketch even if you have a printed version.

You can also link costs to issues to track problems or conditions. The module automatically links any documents generated from the cost to the same issues.

You can also use Find, Filter, Sort, and Group to locate and organize costs or assign custom fields to the records to help categorize them for reporting. If you use grouping, you can total the values in each primary group in the Cost Worksheet.

# Using the Custom Cost Worksheet Section

If you need to be able to cost to a third, customizable cost category in the Cost Worksheet, you can use the Custom Cost Worksheet feature. When you enable this feature in the Costing section of the Project Settings dialog box, a new module called Contracts <Custom> appears in the Contract Information folder of the project in the Project View. Several new <Custom> columns also appear in the Cost Worksheet. You can then create new custom contracts as a third cost category customized for your business, and then create any change documents and trends against the custom contract. The custom documents are costed to the Custom columns in the Cost Worksheet.

See *Custom Cost Worksheet Section Overview* in Help for information on the additional columns.

In the Details section of a custom Contract document window, the Cost Category field indicates that this contract is being costed to the Custom columns of the Cost Worksheet. You can change the term <custom> to whatever term that applies to your situation. Use the Folders dialog box to change the name of the Custom Contracts module, and the Customize Text dialog box to change "custom" to another term.

If a change order is linked to a <custom> contract, the change order's Cost Category is set to <Custom>. <Custom> change orders added outside of Change Management collect changes costed to that cost category.

*For trends, the <Custom> option is added below Commitment in the Cost Category drop-down.*

# Cost Worksheet Reports and Forms

Standard reports and forms are provided for you to use to print cost information.

From the Cost Worksheet document window, click Select an Action, and then Advanced Print. Click Go. Select the report or form, and then click Print.

| **ACME General Contractors** | | | | | **School Addition-Automotive Center** |
|---|---|---|---|---|---|

**Budgeted vs. Actual Variance**

| **Job No:   JBAA450** | | | | **Date:** | **4/11/00** |
|---|---|---|---|---|---|
| **Project No: PRJAA450** | | | | **Page:** | **1 of 2** |

| Cost Code | Original Amount | Approved Revisions | Pending Revisions | Actuals Issued | Actuals Revised Variance |
|---|---|---|---|---|---|
| 01 01100 O<br>Summary | $240,000.00 | $0.00 | $0.00 | $240,000.00 | $0.00 |
| 01 01300 D<br>Administration Requirements | $274,264.12 | $0.00 | $0.00 | $274,264.12 | $0.00 |
| 01 01300 O<br>Adminstration Reqmnts - Schedule | $244,500.00 | $0.00 | $0.00 | $244,500.00 | $0.00 |
| 01 01400 S<br>Quality Requirements - Testing | $315,000.00 | $0.00 | $0.00 | $58,500.00 | $256,500.00 |
| 01 01400 V<br>Quality Requirements - Software | $1,007,735.88 | $0.00 | $0.00 | $7,735.88 | $1,000,000.00 |
| 01 01500 O<br>Temporary Facilities and Controls | $235,000.00 | $0.00 | $0.00 | $176,250.00 | $58,750.00 |
| 01 01500 S<br>Temporary Facilities and Controls | $35,000.00 | $0.00 | $0.00 | $35,000.00 | $0.00 |
| 01 01700 D<br>Execution Safety Requirements | $150,000.00 | $0.00 | $0.00 | $112,500.00 | $37,500.00 |
| 01 01700 O<br>Execution - Insurance & Taxes | $65,000.00 | $0.00 | $0.00 | $48,750.00 | $16,250.00 |
| 01 01740 O<br>Execution Requirements - Permits | $100,000.00 | $0.00 | $0.00 | $75,000.00 | $25,000.00 |

# Managing Contracts and Purchase Orders

The Contract Manager module helps you organize and manage contracts and purchase orders (POs) with lump sum and/or unit prices. Once you set up a contract or PO, you can create related submittals, generate materials delivery records and requisitions, track changes, and monitor costs.

Since the information contained in contracts and POs is usually identical or very similar, you process them the same way in the Contract Manager module. For simplicity, this chapter primarily refers to contracts.

# Adding a Contract or Purchase Order

A contract is a written agreement in which one party agrees to perform specialized work for another party for a certain price. Contract work can involve labor only or labor and materials; examples include excavation, plumbing, and landscaping. A contract usually includes a description of the work to be performed, a list of special terms and conditions that apply to the contract, the start and finish dates, and the negotiated price.

Purchase orders (POs) document the purchase of materials or services. The information in a PO includes a description of the items ordered, payment terms, the negotiated price, and the required delivery date.

Use contracts and purchase orders to define the initial terms and amounts associated with a project and the project participants. Later, you can track other documents, such as change orders, against these contracts and POs.

For more information on adding contracts and purchase orders, see *Add a Contract* and *Add a Purchase Order* in Help.

**Add a contract or purchase order**  Click Contracts–Budgeted, Contracts–Committed, or Purchase Orders in the Contract Information folder in the Project View, and then click Add Document. The new contract or purchase order is automatically assigned the next available number. The current date and the default company are automatically entered as the From contact (set in the Set Default Field Values dialog box); you can edit any of these values.

*Click Select to choose the companies bound by the contract.*

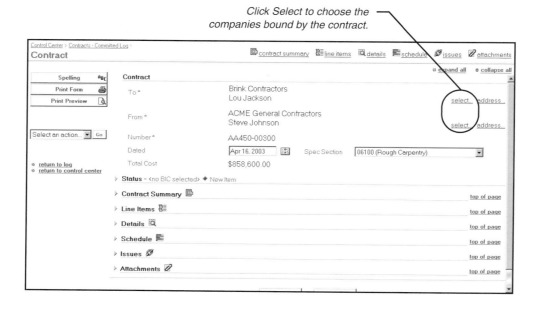

In the Line Items section, you can create either a lump sum or unit price contract/PO. If the contract involves payment of a single lump sum for services, click Add Lump Sum. If the contract contains itemized labor or material costs, click Add Unit Price.

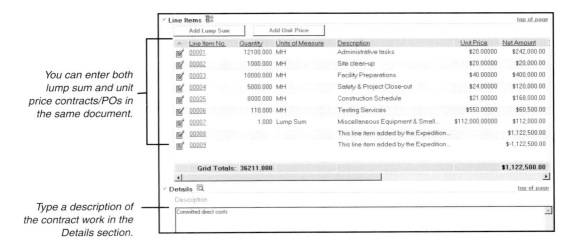

*You can enter both lump sum and unit price contracts/POs in the same document.*

*Type a description of the contract work in the Details section.*

**To create default markup categories for changes**   Use the markup for changes feature. From the Contract or Purchase Order document window, choose Select an Action, Markup for Changes, and then click Go. No calculations are performed here. If you link change orders or proposals to this contract, the values entered in this section will apply to them.

*Click Add Markup to add a new markup value.*

*Type either a markup percentage or a fixed markup amount (not both).*

*Select the cost code to which you want to apply the markup.*

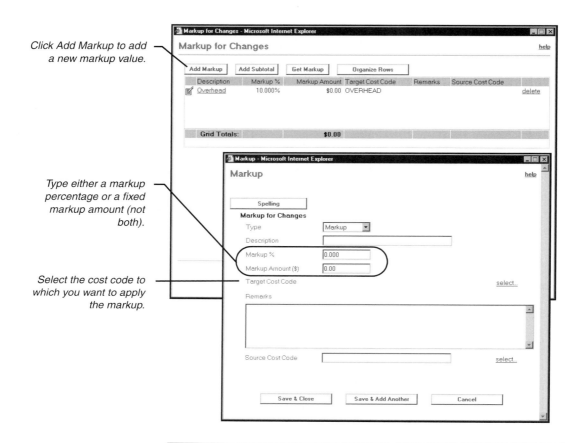

 *If you entered markup values in the Project Settings Markup section (right click on the project and choose Project Settings), when you click Get Markup, the corresponding fields in this section are automatically completed. You can edit this information. The edited values will override the values in the Project Settings Markup section.*

# Using Hammock Activities for Contracts

When associating/updating lump sum contract dates with Contract Manager module schedule dates, use hammock activities for global or master-level analysis. Individual activities are better suited for line item contracts. Since hammocks comprise a group of activities and corresponding resources that are monitored collectively, they can fit easily into the related contract requirements for lump sum payment.

*You can use early or actual start and finish dates of an associated activity from a linked schedule.*

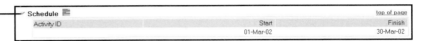

| Schedule | | |
|---|---|---|
| Activity ID | Start | Finish |
| | 01-Mar-02 | 30-Mar-02 |

*For more information, see Distributing Budgeted and Committed Costs to the Cost Worksheet later in this chapter.*

 *If you delete a contract or PO, the related invoice, all Cost Worksheet references to the invoice, all Cost Worksheet references to the contract or PO, and any issue links are also deleted. Materials delivery records, change and request documents, and requisitions related to the contract or PO remain intact.*

 *You cannot delete a contract/PO that has approved change orders against it.*

# Creating Submittals from a Contract or Purchase Order

You can create submittals from a contract or purchase order. Submittals help you ensure contract compliance by tracking who received what and when they received it.

*The date recorded for the generated document is the current date, which is editable.*

**Create a submittal from a contract or purchase order**  From the Contract or Purchase Order document window, click Edit Document and add unit price line items in the Line Items section. In the Submittals section, under the Contract Summary section, click Add to create a new submittal.

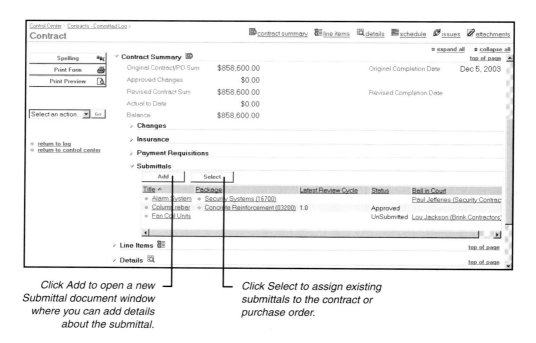

Click Add to open a new Submittal document window where you can add details about the submittal.

Click Select to assign existing submittals to the contract or purchase order.

For more information about submittals, see the *Managing Submittals* chapter.

# Generating Materials Delivery Records from a Contract or Purchase Order

If you use unit price contracts and POs, the module can automatically generate a materials delivery record so you can record materials delivered to the site.

The material code is automatically with the correct line item in the Payment Requisition's Schedule of Values section if you generate both the material and the requisition from the contract. Order of generation is not important.

**Generate a materials delivery record from a contract or purchase order**   From the Contract or Purchase Order document window, click Edit Document. Scroll down to the Line Items section and click Add Unit Price to add the unit price line items. In the Contract Item window, specify a unit price or lump sum, and then scroll down and select a unique material code in the Material Name field (do not choose an existing one). Leave the material code for a line item blank if you don't want to generate a materials delivery record for it. In the Costing section, enter costing information. Click Save and Close when finished. In the Contract or PO document window, choose Select an Action, Generate Materials, and then click Go.

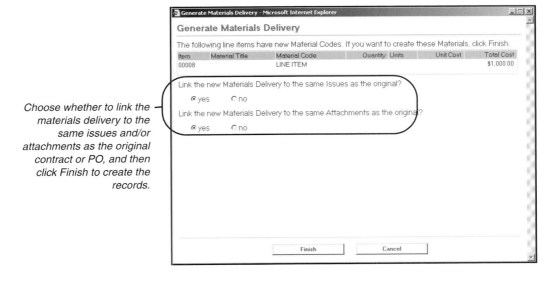

*Choose whether to link the materials delivery to the same issues and/or attachments as the original contract or PO, and then click Finish to create the records.*

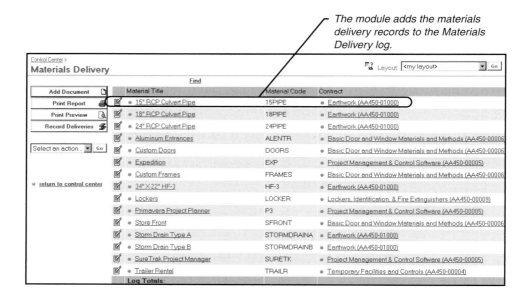

The module adds the materials delivery records to the Materials Delivery log.

For more information about tracking material deliveries, see the *Tracking Materials Deliveries* chapter.

# Generating Requisitions from a Contract or Purchase Order

The module can use lump sum and/or unit price line items from the costed contract/PO to automatically create a requisition and its schedule of values.

*For details on these settings, see the Setting Up Dictionaries and Preferences chapter.*

**Set lump sum/unit price preferences and retainage calculations for new requisitions** If the contract/PO has not yet been created, right-click on the project in the Project View and choose Project Settings. Set the default preferences for requisitions for all new contracts/POs in the Requisitions section.

To configure retainage per existing contract/PO, open the Contract or Purchase Order document window and click Select an Action, Requisition Options, and then click Go.

*These numbers are used to create each line item number in the requisition schedule of values.*

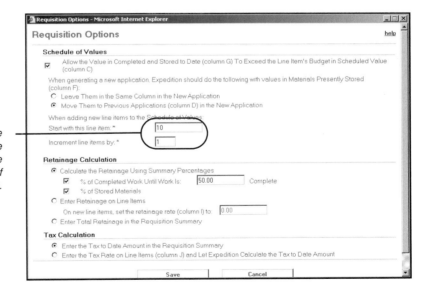

Use the Requisition Summary section in a Requisition document window to specify retainage calculations per individual requisition.

*After you generate the first requisition from the contract/PO, create periodic payment applications from the originating requisition by choosing Select an Action, Generate Requisition from the Requisition document window.*

**Generate the first requisition for a project payment**  Open a Contract or Purchase Order document window; click Select an Action, Generate Requisition, and then click Go. Select the Period To for the requisition, and then choose whether to link the same issues and attachments to it as the contract. Click Finish. Enter the requisition information in the Requisition document window.

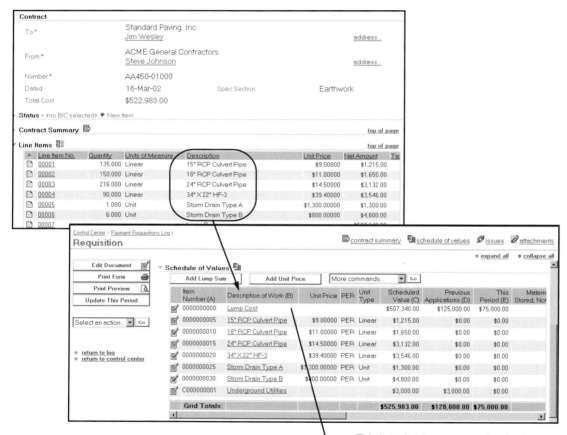

This is both a lump sum and unit price contract, so a Lump Sum line was created in the requisition Schedule of Values in addition to the unit price line items.

# Distributing Budgeted and Committed Costs to the Cost Worksheet

Use the Cost Worksheet to keep detailed records of the money associated with your project, including amounts budgeted, committed, and spent or received, as well as amounts you received or expect to receive as the result of changes.

For more information about cost codes and distributing costs, see the *Setting Up and Using the Cost Worksheet* chapter.

You can distribute contract costs to the Budgeted or Committed section of the Cost Worksheet, and distribute purchase order costs to the Committed section. Use the Budgeted section for the total amount available to spend on the project; use the Committed section for amounts you have agreed to pay someone else.

 *Distributing contract or PO costs is optional. You do not have to use the Cost Worksheet to use a contract or PO. If you use the Cost Worksheet, you should set up cost codes when you first add a project.*

To distribute costs, click Edit Document in the Contract or Purchase Order document window. In the Line Items section, click either Add Lump Sum or Add Unit Price. Insert an amount in the Lump Amount or Unit Price field. In the Costing section, click Add and select a Cost Code to which distribute costs. (You can click Add Multiple Cost Codes to add more than one cost code at a time.) Enter the amount to distribute in the Distributed field, and then click Add Balance. Click Save & Close to distribute the costs to the Cost Worksheet.

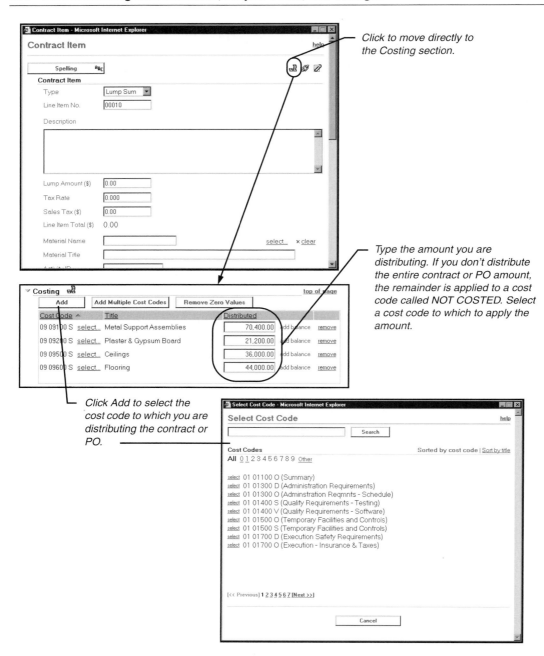

Click to move directly to the Costing section.

Type the amount you are distributing. If you don't distribute the entire contract or PO amount, the remainder is applied to a cost code called NOT COSTED. Select a cost code to which to apply the amount.

Click Add to select the cost code to which you are distributing the contract or PO.

# Reviewing Contract Status

Use the Contract Summary section in a Contract document window to review all pending and approved cost changes associated with a contract, and to see the sum of invoices to date and the remaining balance.

For details on creating change documents, see the *Recording and Tracking Communications* chapter.

Expand the Changes section to view all change documents associated with the contract. Costs associated with each document are listed in either the Approved Changes or Pending Changes column, depending on the document's status. Costs associated with documents that have an Approval status code appear in the Approved Changes column; costs and documents with other status codes are shown in the Pending Changes column. Documents with status codes of Closed or Rejected are not displayed in the Contract Summary section.

Click to jump immediately to the Contract Summary section.

 You can also view all insurance policies, invoices, requisitions, and submittals associated with the contract.

# Contract/Purchase Order Reports and Forms

Standard reports and forms are provided for you to use to print contract/PO information. To print standard reports and forms from a Contract or Purchase Order document

window, click Select an Action, and then Advanced Print. Click Go. Select the report or form, and then click Print.

| ACME General Contractors | | | | | | | | | School Addition-Automotive Center |
|---|---|---|---|---|---|---|---|---|---|

**Contract Log**
**by To Company**

| Job No: | JBAA450 | | | | | | | Date: | 4/11/00 |
|---|---|---|---|---|---|---|---|---|---|
| Project No: PRJAA450 | | | | | | | | Page: | 1 of 1 |

| To | From | Contract No. | Date | Description | Spec Section | Total Cost | Approved Changes | Pending Changes | Revised Contract Sum |
|---|---|---|---|---|---|---|---|---|---|
| ACE Mason Contractors | | | | | | | | | |
| | ACMEGC | AA450-00602 | 4/15/00 | Basic Masonry Materials and Methods | 04050 | $813,150.00 | $9,850.00 | $9,850.00 | $823,000.00 |
| ACME General Contractors | | | | | | | | | |
| | ACMEGC | DIRECT COSTS | 3/1/00 | Summary | 01100 | $1,122,500.00 | $0.00 | $120.00 | $1,122,500.00 |
| | PHILASCH | AA450-00012 | 1/3/00 | Summary | 01100 | $10,000,000.00 | $20,350.00 | $29,904.00 | $10,020,350.00 |
| Brink Contractors | | | | | | | | | |
| | ACMEGC | AA450-00300 | 4/16/00 | Rough Carpentry | 06100 | $858,600.00 | $0.00 | $0.00 | $858,600.00 |
| Button Paint & Paper | | | | | | | | | |
| | ACMEGC | AA450-00400 | 6/1/00 | Basic Finish Materials and Methods | 09050 | $209,200.00 | $0.00 | $0.00 | $209,200.00 |
| CPM Consultants | | | | | | | | | |
| | ACMEGC | AA450-00500 | 3/16/00 | Price and Payment Procedures | 01200 | $45,000.00 | $0.00 | $0.00 | $45,000.00 |
| Finish Ceilings, Inc. | | | | | | | | | |
| | ACMEGC | AA450-01300 | 6/1/00 | Ceilings | 09500 | $171,600.00 | $0.00 | $0.00 | $171,600.00 |

# Using Trends

With the Contract Manager module, you can record an anticipated cost that is not documented in another area. For example, you can record a preliminary agreement amount before you create a contract.

This chapter describes how to use the Trends feature to record anticipated costs, items, adjustments, revisions, estimates, or actuals "on the fly" as they occur during the contract life cycle. You can also distribute these costs to the Cost Worksheet to track possible cost increases or decreases.

# Why Use Trends?

Changes are inevitable in any phase of a project—from the outset, as design deliberations and associated budget amounts are negotiated, through final payment approval as work is completed. Most participants in the process—owner and subcontractor alike—will be presented with expected revisions. Trends are provided as a place to record expectations of future costs or other items that will most likely affect budgeted costs in the near future. You can place these values in trends, then incorporate them in the project as they occur; you can also use trends to perform "what-if" analysis on a backup of the project so you can see how they affect costs.

Keep in mind that trends are usually not definite changes (although they can be), unlike those you record in change documents; they typically represent probable future costs. For example, if the pipe you will be ordering for delivery at a construction site costs $10 per foot at the time your bid is submitted, but the same pipe is expected to increase to $12 per foot when your bid will be accepted, you can expect the pipe will be $12 per foot when you place the order. Trends can be used to represent adjustments, revisions, estimates, or actuals—they can be as flexible as you require.

Once you record a trend, you can add it to the Cost Worksheet by distributing its cost to a cost code and assigning the amount to a column used for revisions or adjustments to the original budget, or for any other cost area. You can then track these possible cost changes and fine-tune your budget.

# Adding a Trend

Use trends to add and track anticipated costs that may change the project scope as they occur.

**Add a trend** In the Contract Information folder, click Trends to open the Trends log window, then Add Document. The new trend is automatically assigned the next available number. The module also enters the current date, and your user name in the Entered By field.

*You can cost the trend amount to this cost category on the Cost Worksheet.*

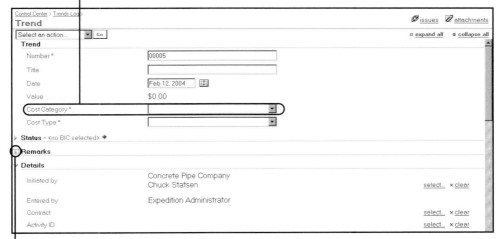

*Click to expand or collapse any section; the module saves your settings.*

You can also create a new trend from an existing trend. See the next section for more details.

**Viewing or changing Trend details** Expand the Status section to view or change the ball in court contact, priority, or status of the trend. Use the Remarks section to enter comments about the trend. Open the Details section to view additional information, such as who initiated the trend, an associated activity ID, and other schedule and change details. Expand the Line Items section when you want to enter itemized costs for the trend. Attach related issues or attachments to any trend document.

# Generating a Trend

If you want to create a trend that is similar to one that already exists, use the Generate Trend feature to create a new trend with copied information.

**Generate a trend**   From the Trends log window, select the trend you want to copy. Click Select an Action, Generate Trend, then click Go.

*The module supplies a number for the trend, which you can use or change.*

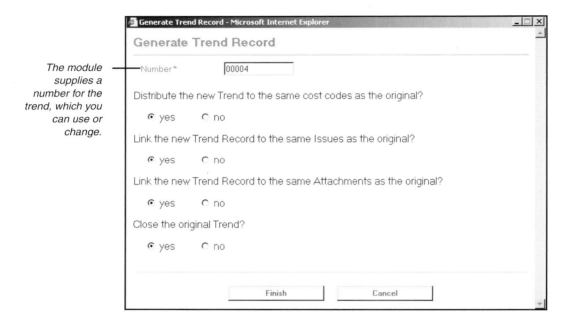

Choose whether you want to distribute the new trend to the same cost codes as the original, link the new trend to the same issues and attachments as the original, or close out the original trend. Click Finish to generate the new trend.

# Distributing Costs to the Cost Worksheet

The Cost Worksheet provides a central location for tracking all project costs. You can compare budget and committed costs to actual costs for each work element. Open the Cost Worksheet log from the Contract Information folder. Costs are organized by cost codes, which represent various categories of project work. Using Project Settings, you can distribute most cost documents.

To add or transfer money within the Cost Worksheet without modifying the original contract or PO, or without using change management, add a Trend document, then distribute its cost to the Cost Worksheet.

**To distribute costs**  Open the document window for the trend for which you want to distribute costs. Expand the Line Items section.

*Click either Add Lump Sum or Add Unit Price.*

*Insert an amount in the Unit Price (or Line Item Total) field.*

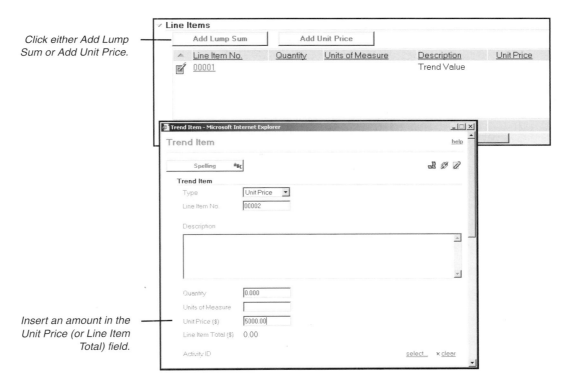

*Scroll to the Costing section and click Add.*

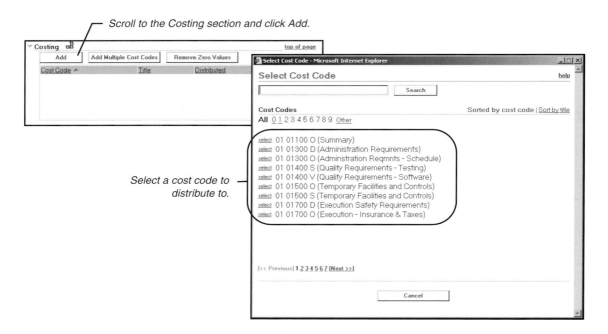

*Select a cost code to distribute to.*

You can add as many cost codes as necessary.

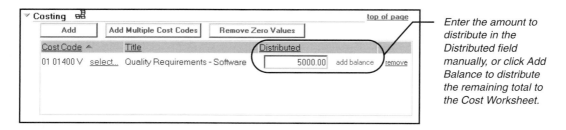

*Enter the amount to distribute in the Distributed field manually, or click Add Balance to distribute the remaining total to the Cost Worksheet.*

Click Save & Close to send the information to the Cost Worksheet.

Values are distributed to any section of the Cost Worksheet. Using Project Settings, you can set options to ensure that the entire amount of the item must be distributed to defined cost codes.

# Trends Reports and Forms

Standard reports and forms are provided for you to use to print a list of trends and details about a selected trend, including cost distributions.

From the Trend document window, click Select an Action, then Advanced Print. Click Go. Select the report or form, then click Print.

| ACME General Contractors | | | | | | School Addition-Automotive Center | |
|---|---|---|---|---|---|---|---|
| | | | **Trends** | | | | |
| Job No: | JBAA450 | | | | | Date: | 4/11/00 |
| Project No: PRJAA450 | | | | | | Page: | 1 of 1 |

| Date | Number | Title | Status | Entered By | | Value |
|---|---|---|---|---|---|---|
| 4/16/00 | 00001 | Administrative Cost Hit | OUT | Steve | | $2,760.00 |
| 5/1/00 | 00002 | Fuel Increase - Budget Allocation | OUT | Steve | | $1,750.00 |
| 5/1/00 | 00003 | Fuel increase - Expected Sub Claims | OUT | Steve | | $11,750.00 |
| | | | | | Total: | $16,260.00 |

# Preparing Requisitions for Payment

Contracts usually require partial payments at regular intervals, based on the amount of work accomplished and materials installed. If you use requisitions for payment, you probably use them in association with your contracts or POs. Contracts are used in the examples in this chapter.

The contract price is subdivided into a list of component prices or work items, so that progress can be measured more precisely. This list, called a schedule of values, accompanies each requisition for payment. At the end of each period, a requisition is submitted that shows the value of work performed and materials installed since the last payment.

This chapter explains the process of submitting requests for payment, or requisitions.

# Process Overview

Requisitions, or formal requests for payment, are usually issued by general contractors (GCs) to the owner on a monthly basis as portions of work on a project are completed. Subcontractors or vendors submit requisitions to the GC for their portions of the work. Once the initial requisition with line items is established at intervals determined by the pay cycle established between the contract parties, an application for payment based on the original requisition is updated, certified, and sent. This requisition update/issuing cycle continues until the work is completed and the GC and subcontractors have been paid in full in accordance with the contract agreement. The following diagram illustrates a typical cycle.

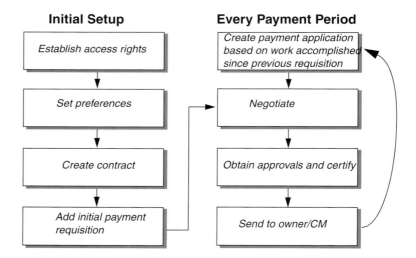

Materials for delivery and approved change orders applicable to each period are collected and added to the corresponding requisition. In addition, the contracting parties usually withhold a percentage of each payment, called retainage, until all the work is completed or until they are satisfied that work is progressing as planned. This retainage is applied to the current amount due, on a line item or percent complete basis.

Requisitions are based on a contract or purchase order established in the Contract Manager module for the project and parallel industry standard certification for payment forms. The module can use lump sum and/or unit price line items from the contract/PO to automatically create the requisition schedule of values. You negotiate the line item or lump sum costs until a payment agreement is reached and the requisition is approved and certified.

# Setting Up Requisitions

You can create requisitions for all project contracts. Depending on your role, you may issue payment requests or receive payment requests. For example, if you are a GC, you receive requisitions from subcontractors and you issue requisitions to the owner. You can distribute requisition amounts to the Cost Worksheet's Actuals Issued or Actuals Received column(s), then compare the actual costs to the budgeted or committed costs for various work items.

For details on steps 1 and 2, see the *Planning and Adding a Contract Manager Module Project* and *Setting Up Dictionaries and Preferences* chapters.

Follow these steps to set up the first requisition for each contract/PO:

1 Set access rights to requisitions and for certifying them.

2 Set lump sum/line item preferences and retainage calculations in the Requisitions section in the Project Settings dialog box.

3 Create the requisition and schedule of values.

4 Negotiate the payment amount.

5 Approve and certify the requisition.

6 Start the cycle beginning with step 3 for the next payment period, based on work completed since the previous requisition was issued.

*If you use both requisitions and invoices, you typically generate requisitions from contracts and invoices from POs.*

Assuming requisition access rights have been set and preference defaults are being used in generating requisitions (steps 1 and 2), this section discusses step 3 in the process—creating a requisition.

**APPLICATION AND CERTIFICATE FOR PAYMENT**   AIA DOCUMENT G702   PAGE ONE OF   PAG

TO OWNER:
2400 Chestnut St
Philadelphia, PA 19049

PROJECT: School Addition-Automotive Cente

FROM CONTRACTOR:
15 Rockhill Road
Bala Cynwyd, PA 19004

VIA ARCHITECT: Design Group
1215 Ventnor Ave
Philadelphia, PA 19000

APPLICATION NO: 00002
PERIOD TO:   5/1/03
PROJECT NOS.:   PRJAA450

CONTRACT DATE: 1/3/03

CONTRACT FOR:

Distribution to:
☐ OWNER
☐ ARCHITECT
☐ CONTRACTC
☐
☐

**CONTRACTOR'S APPLICATION FOR PAYMENT**

Application is made for payment, as shown below, in connection with the contract.
Continuation Sheet, AIA Document G703, is attached.

| | |
|---|---|
| 1. ORIGINAL CONTRACT SUM | $10,000,000.00 |
| 2. Net change by Change Orders | $3,300.00 |
| 3. CONTRACT SUM TO DATE (Line 1 ± 2) | $10,003,300.00 |
| 4. TOTAL COMPLETED && STORED TO DATE (Column G on G703) | $1,037,675.00 |
| 5. RETAINAGE: | |
| a. 10.000 % of Completed Work (Columns D + E on G703) | $103,767.50 |
| b. 10.000 % of Stored Material (Columns F on G703) | $0.00 |

The undersigned Contractor certifies that to the best of the Contractor's knowledge, inf
mation and belief the Work covered by this application for Payment has been comple
in accordance with the Contract Documents, that all amounts have been paid by
Contractor for Work for which previous Certificates for Payment were issued and p
ments received from the Owner, and that current payment shown herein is now d

CONTRACTOR: ACME General Contractors

By: _____   Date: _____
        Charlie Jones                            5/15/03

State of:
County of:
Subscribed and sworn to before
me this        day of
Notary Public:
My Commission expires:

*Sample Requisition Summary Page*

**Create the first requisition for a project payment**   Click one of the Contracts folders or the Purchase Orders folder under Contract Information in the Project View to open its log window. To generate a requisition, open the contract/PO document you want to generate a requisition for, then click Select an Action and choose Generate Requisition, then click Go.

The module sequentially numbers requisitions that refer to the same contract/PO, starting with 00001 (you can change this number). It also copies the total amount from the specified contract/PO to the Original Contract Sum field on the requisition.

*You can also click Add Document to add a new requisition while in the Payment Requisitions log or Requisition document window (in View mode).*

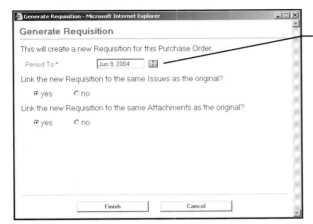

You can change the default Period To date
to issue a payment application for a
different timeframe; click on the calendar to
select a date.

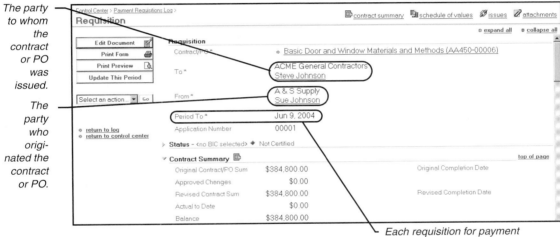

The party
to whom
the
contract
or PO
was
issued.

The
party
who
origi-
nated the
contract
or PO.

Each requisition for payment
covers the time period between
Period To dates for the last requisition
and the current requisition.

**Create a schedule of values or add line items to an uncertified
requisition** Expand the Schedule of Values section to view the items
transferred from the contract/PO. This section consists of columns A
through K.

One of the following is used to create each line item number:

■   The Start with this Line Item number and the Increment Line Items
    By value specified in the Requisition Options dialog box (accessed
    from the Select an Action drop-down list for the Contract/Purchase
    Order document window for the existing contract/purchase order).

- The Requisitions section in the Project Settings dialog box for a new contract/PO.

If a unit tax amount per line item or a lump tax per lump sum exists for the originating contract/PO, the entire amount is totaled and placed on a separate line called Total Tax.

**Add a line item in lump sum, unit price, headers, subtotal, or blank line item format** While working in the Schedule of Values section for an uncertified requisition, you can create five types of line items: unit price, lump sum, subtotal, header, or blank line. Click Add Unit Price for material line items; click Add Lump Sum for the line items involving labor.

The other three line item types, headers, subtotals, and blank lines (located in the More Commands drop-down), organize the information in the Schedule of Values section. Headers organize line items by work package or cost category. Subtotals total a group of items. Blank lines separate lines for better organization.

Line items are listed numerically. To group the line items by a general category and then calculate subtotals for each group, enter appropriate item numbers for the header and subtotal. In the following example, the heading PIPE is changed to line item number 2 and the SUBTOTAL is changed to number 4. The line item, and any additional items placed between 2 and 4 are categorized as pipes. To arrange the data in the order you want, click the document icon next to the line item you want to edit. Change the Item Number and click Save & Close to view the changes.

*Click to select other types of items to add to the schedule of values. You can add a subtotal, header or blank line item.*

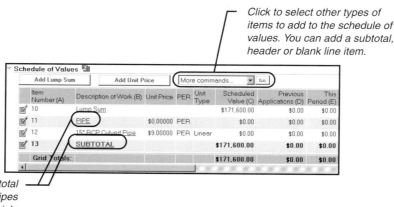

*This header and subtotal categorize and total pipes used for the job.*

Headers are not required to calculate subtotals. If you enter items and subtotals only, all line items are summarized between subtotals.

You can also use the blank line item type to separate and group items in the schedule of values. The next sequential item number is used, but all other columns are blank for this item type. Blank lines do not affect subtotals.

When you finish creating line items and entering the scheduled values, the grand total for the Scheduled Value column (column C) should equal the Original Contract Sum in the Contract Summary section. The module notifies you if these numbers do not match when you attempt to close the Requisition document window, and it displays the amount needed to balance the two numbers. Adjust the schedule of values for existing line items, or create new line items and schedule values to balance the totals.

**All applicable parties approve the requisition**  The requisition is certified by the last approver and returned to the appropriate contact via any of the following: e-mail, a remote access program, regular mail, or fax.

**Costs are distributed**  Costs are calculated (including retainage), and line items or lump sum costs are distributed to the Cost Worksheet in the Actuals Issued (owner's committed costs), Actuals Received (the general contractor's budgeted costs), and Actuals Expended (the funded costs) columns.

**Create periodic payment requisitions based on the previous requisition for the contract/PO**  Use a filter to separate requisitions received from those sent from the Payment Requisitions log. Open the previous month's certified requisition for the contract/PO. Choose Select an Action, Generate Requisition, then click Go. Follow the steps in the Generate Requisition wizard to create the current requisition. Click Get Approved Changes to "get" approved change orders for delivery for the current requisition.

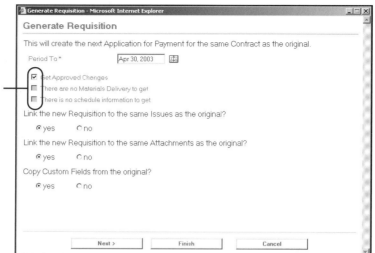

*Mark to "get" approved change orders, materials for delivery, and schedule information for the current requisition.*

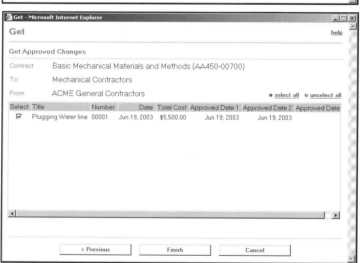

For details on certifying a requisition, see *Certifying a Requisition* later in this chapter.

**Update the current requisition**  In the Schedule of Values section, edit each line item to change the value for This Period or Percent Complete based on work completed this period, then go to the Status section and certify the requisition. If you associated Contract Manager module schedule activities with requisition line items or with the contract/ PO, mark the Get Schedule checkbox in the Generate Requisitions wizard to update the total percentage of work completed for the period to date (%G/C column) in the schedule of values using the activities' percent complete.

Click the docume nt icon to edit the line item.

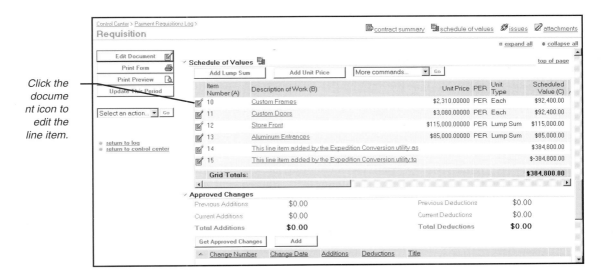

# Adding a Requisition

Requisitions must be linked to a contract/PO. You should create your contract/PO and establish its requisition options, then generate the first requisition for payment from the contract/PO.

You can also add a requisition from the Payment Requisitions log. Click Add Document. In the Add Requisition wizard, select the contract/PO to which to link the requisition, then select a To contact (for example, the GC receiving the request for payment) and the From contact (for example, the subcontractor submitting the requisition for payment). The module uses the current date for the Period To, which you can change. Click Finish to create the new requisition for payment.

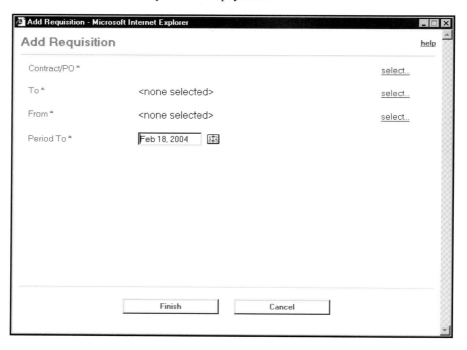

# Recording Progress

Follow these general steps to complete monthly requisitions:

1   Generate the current requisition from the previous month's requisition.

2   "Get" materials delivered during the current period and approved change orders that increase or decrease the contract sum. The module prompts you to get this information when you generate requisitions. Or you can select Get Approved Changes or Get Materials Delivery in the More Commands drop-down list, then click Go, in the Schedule of Values section. You can then follow the Add Change Orders and/or Material Deliveries wizard instructions.

3   Enter values for the following items:

- Work completed this period

- Stored materials

- Retainage amount

- Sales tax

Throughout the project, only one requisition for payment should be active (uncertified) for each contract. If you try to add a new requisition before certifying the previous application, the module reminds you about the previous uncertified requisition but will accept a new one.

When "getting" a change order into a requisition, the cost distribution is copied to the new line item in the requisition. The value of each cost distribution in the requisition will be set to zero.

Use the Not Certified or Is the Latest=Y standard filter to easily locate the requisition you want in the log. Select Customize Layouts in the Layouts drop-down list from Payment Requisitions log window. Edit or add a new layout to assign one of these standard filters to the layout, or create your own to include other selection parameters.

**Update a requisition**  With the previous month's certified requisition selected, choose Select an Action, Generate Requisition, then click Go. You can enter the scheduled value for the new requisition. You can also cost the scheduled value to the same cost codes without having to distribute costs again.

In the Generate Requisition wizard, mark the Get Approved Changes checkbox to show the associated approved change order costs in the Requisition Summary section and automatically record them in the Approved Changes and Schedule of Values sections for the new requisition.

If you want to associate Project Management module schedule activities with requisition line items or with the contract/PO, mark the checkbox to Get Schedule Information to update the total percentage of work completed for all periods to date in the schedule of values (%G/C column) using the current schedule activities' percent complete.

If a delivery is linked to a lump sum item, the total value of the delivery is copied to the This Period column (column E). If the delivery is linked to a unit price item, the module calculates the column E value by multiplying the quantity delivered by the unit price added in the Schedule of Values section.

*This field is recalculated to equal the sum of all approved change orders and the original contract sum.*

Make sure you have Primavera "get" change orders for the requisition using the Generate Requisition wizard (or select Get Change Orders and/ or Get Materials Delivery from the More Commands drop-down list in the Schedule of Values section); otherwise, the grand total for the Scheduled Value column (column C) may not match the Contract Sum to Date column. The requisition cannot be certified until these amounts are equal.

**Record progress**  In the Schedule of Values section, click the document icon to edit the line item in the Requisition Detail dialog box. Type the value of completed work for the current period in the This Period (E) field. If you don't know the actual amount, enter the percentage of work completed in the % Complete, G/C field. The percentage represents work completed and stored materials for all periods to date, not just the current period.

*Columns E and %G/C are linked. When you update one field in the Requisition Detail dialog box, Primavera calculates the value for the other.*

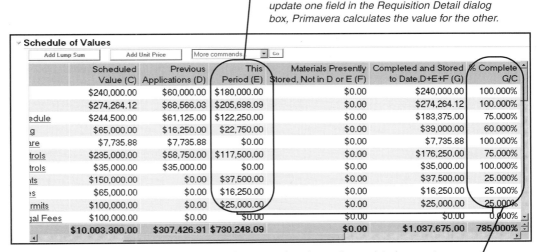

| | Scheduled Value (C) | Previous Applications (D) | This Period (E) | Materials Presently Stored, Not in D or E (F) | Completed and Stored to Date, D+E+F (G) | % Complete G/C |
|---|---|---|---|---|---|---|
| | $240,000.00 | $60,000.00 | $180,000.00 | $0.00 | $240,000.00 | 100.000% |
| | $274,264.12 | $68,566.03 | $205,698.09 | $0.00 | $274,264.12 | 100.000% |
| edule | $244,500.00 | $61,125.00 | $122,250.00 | $0.00 | $183,375.00 | 75.000% |
| g | $65,000.00 | $16,250.00 | $22,750.00 | $0.00 | $39,000.00 | 60.000% |
| are | $7,735.88 | $7,735.88 | $0.00 | $0.00 | $7,735.88 | 100.000% |
| trols | $235,000.00 | $58,750.00 | $117,500.00 | $0.00 | $176,250.00 | 75.000% |
| trols | $35,000.00 | $35,000.00 | $0.00 | $0.00 | $35,000.00 | 100.000% |
| its | $150,000.00 | $0.00 | $37,500.00 | $0.00 | $37,500.00 | 25.000% |
| s | $65,000.00 | $0.00 | $16,250.00 | $0.00 | $16,250.00 | 25.000% |
| rmits | $100,000.00 | $0.00 | $25,000.00 | $0.00 | $25,000.00 | 25.000% |
| al Fees | $100,000.00 | $0.00 | $0.00 | $0.00 | $0.00 | 0.000% |
| | **$10,003,300.00** | **$307,426.91** | **$730,248.09** | **$0.00** | **$1,037,675.00** | **785.000%** |

*You can update the work completed percentages with the Primavera schedule activity percent complete values associated with each line item.*

If you enter a value for This Period (column E), Primavera calculates the progress percentage by dividing the value in the Completed and Stored to Date D+E+F field (column G) by the value in the Scheduled Value field (column C).

If you enter a percentage for column G, Primavera calculates the value in column E by multiplying the percentage by the column C value, then subtracting from this value the sum of all Previous Applications column (column D):

**Column E = (column G% x column C) – column D**

Columns E and %G/C are linked. If a new percentage is added, the formula above is used and column E is updated.

**Update stored materials**  In the Schedule of Values section, click the document icon to edit the line item in the Requisition Detail dialog box. In the column F field (Materials Presently Stored, Not in D or E), enter the value of stored materials for the project. When you change the value in column F, Primavera recalculates both the cost and percentage values in column G.

**Calculate retainage**  Retainage is the amount withheld from each progress payment. First, select a default method for recording retainage by selecting Requisition Options from the Select an Action drop-down list of the Contract/Purchase Order document window for an existing contract/PO, or use the Requisitions section in the Project Settings dialog box for new contracts/POs. Then, specify calculations per requisition in the Requisition Summary section in the Requisition document window.

You can enter retainage values one of three ways for requisitions in the Requisitions Summary and Schedule of Values sections, as illustrated in the following examples.

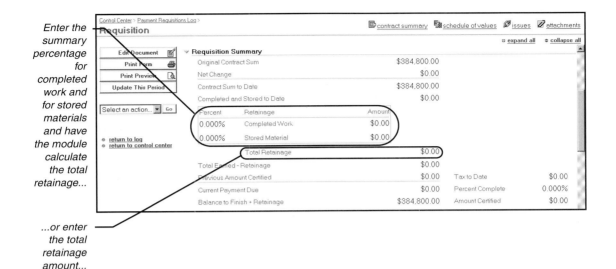

Enter the summary percentage for completed work and for stored materials and have the module calculate the total retainage...

...or enter the total retainage amount...

...or enter retainage for each line item, if retainage percentages vary among line items.

If you record retainage by entering summary percentages in the Requisition Summary section, Primavera calculates the retainage for completed work and stored materials. If you record retainage in the Total Retainage field in the Requisition Summary section, be sure that the value you enter includes completed work and stored materials for all periods to date. If you record retainage by editing each line item in the Schedule of Values section (click the document icon to open the Requisition Detail dialog box), enter the total retainage for stored materials and completed work or enter a percentage for the Retain % column (column I).

The two column I values are linked. If you enter a currency value, Primavera calculates the percentage. If you enter a percentage, Primavera calculates the value by multiplying the percentage by the column G value (Completed and Stored to Date, D+E+F).

Primavera adds the values in column I and displays the total in the Total Retainage field in the Requisition Summary section (if the Enter Retainage on Line Items option is chosen in the Requisition Options dialog box). Primavera does not calculate a separate retainage value for stored materials.

**Calculate tax amounts**  If you marked the Use Line Item % to Calculate Tax checkbox in the Requisition Options dialog box (choose Select an Action, Requisition Options from the Contract/Purchase Order document window), or the Requisitions section in Project Settings for a new contract/PO, you can enter the tax percentage for each edited line item in the Tax Rate field (column J) in the Schedule of Values section. Primavera calculates the tax amount by multiplying the percentage by the value in column G (sum of completed work and stored materials for all periods to date). Primavera displays the sum of all tax amounts in the Tax to Date field in the Requisition Summary section.

## Using Other Features with Requisitions

For more information on how to use these features, see the *Creating and Tracking Issues* chapter and Part 2, *Working with a Project.*

Primavera asks if you want to link to the same issues and attachments when generating a new payment requisition from an existing requisition or contract/PO. If you choose to link to the same issues, the requisition is then included when you organize and cross-reference project documents by issues. You can also use custom fields to provide additional information about each line item on the schedule of values. Custom fields represent categories of information, such as project phase or responsible manager, or provide additional date, cost, or quantity information about an item. You can also use Search, Filter, Sort, and Group to locate and organize your requisitions.

# Certifying a Requisition

You should review the values in the Requisition Summary and Schedule of Values sections before certifying a requisition. A requisition cannot be certified if the grand total for scheduled values does not equal the value in the Contract Sum to Date field.

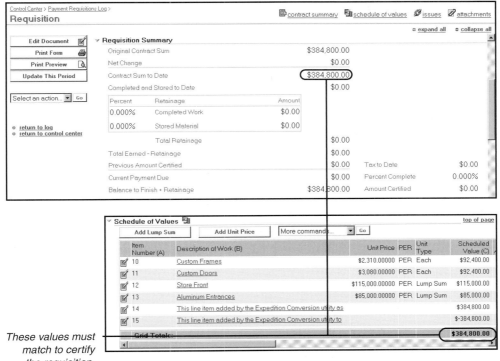

*These values must match to certify the requisition.*

**Enter approval names and dates**  Primavera enters the contract's To and From contact names in the Contractor and Certified areas in the Status section; you can change these names.

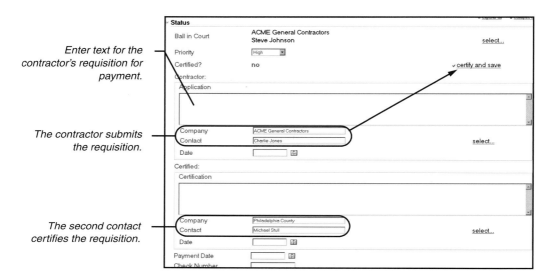

*Enter text for the contractor's requisition for payment.*

*The contractor submits the requisition.*

*The second contact certifies the requisition.*

**Certify payment for the current period**  Certify the requisition to close it out for the current period. Each approver enters the applicable approval date by his/her name in the Certification area of the Status section (or one approver can enter names and dates to save time); the last approver also clicks Certify and Save in the Status section of the Requisition document window, then confirms the certification when prompted.

In general, you should not edit a certified requisition—it has already been approved. Also, the values in a certified requisition form the basis of payment for the next period. When you add a new requisition for payment, Primavera rolls forward summary and detailed cost information from the previous requisition. If you change values in a previously certified requisition, you may have to manually update each subsequent requisition.

# Transferring Information to New Requisitions

When you generate the next requisition, Primavera copies all information from the previous requisition to the new one. Primavera makes the following changes in the Schedule of Values and Requisition Summary sections of the new requisition:

- Primavera assigns the new requisition the next sequential number. You can change this number.

- In the Period To field, Primavera enters the date that is one month later than the previous requisition's Period To date. It assumes progress payments are made monthly. You can enter a different date.

- Contract Manager copies all line items and values from the previous requisition to the new requisition's Schedule of Values section. All This Period (column E) values are set to zero.

- Contract Manager adds all This Period and Materials Presently Stored values from the previous requisition to the sum of all Previous Applications column (column D) if you cleared the % of Stored Materials checkbox in the Requisition Options dialog box (available from the Select an Action drop-down list in the Contract/Purchase Order document window, or the Requisitions section in Project Settings for a new contract/PO).

  To instruct Contract Manager to retain costs for materials stored in the Materials Presently Stored, Not in D or E column (column F) in the Schedule of Values when generating a new requisition, mark the Leave "Them in the Same Column in the New Application checkbox in the Requisition Options dialog box.

- The Previous Amount Certified value in the Requisition Summary section now includes the amount certified in the previous requisition. The Amount Certified field equals zero.

# Distributing Actual Costs to the Cost Worksheet

Use the Requisition Detail dialog box to distribute the amounts recorded for work completed this period (column E in the Schedule of Values section) to the Actuals section of the Cost Worksheet. To open the Requisition Detail dialog box, click a line item in the Requisition document window's Schedule of Values section. If you distributed costs from the originating contract or PO, Contract Manager automatically supplies the corresponding costs codes, titles, and amounts in the Requisition Detail dialog box for the requisition unit item or lump sum.

*Distribute the value of work completed this period to one or more cost codes.*

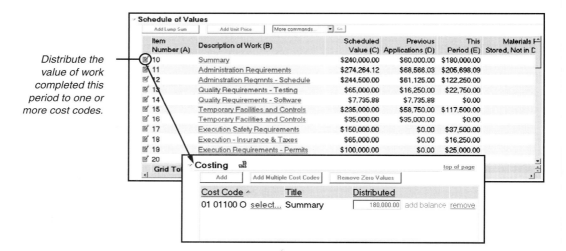

Distribute amounts to the same cost codes used to distribute the original contract sum. Refer to the Costing section in the Requisition Detail dialog box to see which cost codes were used. If you attempt to close the Requisition Detail dialog box without distributing the entire amount, Contract Manager distributes the remaining amount to a cost code called Not Costed (if you marked the Default Invoice Amount to Contract/PO Balance checkbox in the Contracts/POs section of the Project Settings dialog box, but cleared the checkboxes to force documents to be fully distributed to valid costs codes in the Project Settings dialog box Costing section).

Contract Manager automatically distributes revenue (to the contractor, as a result of being paid), or costs (to the owner/contract manager, as a result of paying the contractor the requisition amount) in the Costing section in the Requisition Detail dialog box.

For instructions on how to set up cost codes, see the *Setting Up and Using the Cost Worksheet* chapter.

If the contract shown at the top of the Requisition document window was distributed to the Original Budget column, Contract Manager automatically distributes the requisition amounts to the Actuals Issued column (to represent the owner's costs) in the Cost Worksheet. If the contract amount was distributed to the Original Commitment column, Contract Manager automatically distributes the requisition amounts to the Actuals Received column (to represent the contractor's paid amount).

The Cost Worksheet tracks the actual costs recorded in requisitions and invoices.

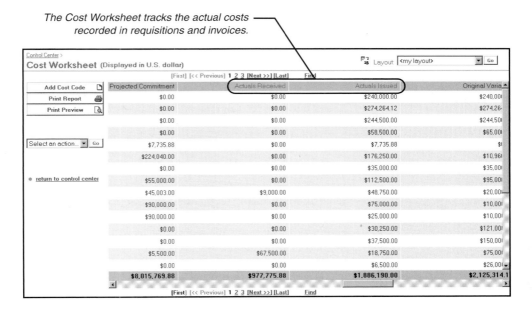

# Sending a Requisition

After a requisition is submitted, the contracting parties negotiate and eventually agree on an amount. The requisition is then certified, and you (the contractor) can submit it to the owner for payment. The method you use to relay the requisition depends on your physical location and interaction with the database server on which the project resides.

For details on how to prepare Contract Manager to exchange documents with local and remote users, see *Setting Up the Inbox* in the *Sending Contract Manager Module Documents to Other Users* chapter.

You can use the Send to Inbox feature or E-mail Form feature to send correspondence to the owner/construction manager.

**Send a requisition to a local user's Inbox**  Send the certified requisition to the construction manager's Inbox; from the requisition you want to send, click Select an Action, choose Send to InBox, then click Go. Select the Send to recipient, add comments, and click Send. When the addressee opens his/her Inbox, it contains an entry for the requisition you sent. When the addressee clicks the Inbox document, Primavera opens it.

**Send a requisition to a non-Primavera user via email**  Suppose you are working in a trailer at the job site and you need to send a certified requisition. From the requisition, click Select an Action, choose E-mail Form, then click Go. Select a contact, add comments, then click OK. The addressee will receive the requisition as a PDF attachment, and will include a link to the document.

# Requisition Reports and Forms

Standard reports and forms are provided for you to use to print requisition information. From the Requisition log or document window, click Select an Action, and then click Advanced Print.

Click Go. Select the report or form, then click Print.

| ACME General Contractors | | | | | | | School Addition-Automotive Center | |
|---|---|---|---|---|---|---|---|---|

**Requisition Summary Totals**
**By Contract**

| Job No: | JBAA450 | | | | | | Date: | 4/11/00 |
|---|---|---|---|---|---|---|---|---|
| Project No: | PRJAA450 | | | | | | Page: | 1 of 1 |

| To | From | Number | Scheduled Value | Previous Application | This Period | Total Stored To Date | Retainage | Balance To Finish + Retain. |
|---|---|---|---|---|---|---|---|---|
| ACMEGC | PHILASCH | AA450-00012 | | | | | | |
| | | 00001 | $10,000,000.00 | $0.00 | $307,426.91 | $307,426.91 | $30,742.69 | $9,723,315.78 |
| | | 00002 | $10,003,300.00 | $307,426.91 | $730,248.09 | $1,037,675.00 | $103,767.50 | $9,069,392.50 |
| | | 00003 | $10,013,150.00 | $933,907.50 | $440,475.00 | $1,478,150.00 | $147,815.00 | $8,682,815.00 |
| | | 00004 | $10,013,150.00 | $933,907.50 | $0.00 | $1,478,150.00 | $147,815.00 | $8,690,015.00 |
| | | 00005 | $10,013,150.00 | $933,907.50 | $0.00 | $1,478,150.00 | $147,815.00 | $8,690,015.00 |
| CPM | ACMEGC | AA450-00500 | | | | | | |
| | | 00001 | $45,000.00 | $0.00 | $4,500.00 | $4,500.00 | $450.00 | $40,950.00 |
| | | 00002 | $45,000.00 | $4,050.00 | $4,500.00 | $9,000.00 | $900.00 | $36,900.00 |
| STDPAV | ACMEGC | AA450-01000 | | | | | | |
| | | 00001 | $522,983.00 | $0.00 | $25,000.00 | $25,000.00 | $2,500.00 | $500,483.00 |
| | | 00002 | $525,983.00 | $22,500.00 | $103,000.00 | $128,000.00 | $12,800.00 | $410,783.00 |
| | | 00003 | $525,983.00 | $115,200.00 | $75,000.00 | $203,000.00 | $20,300.00 | $343,283.00 |
| | | 00004 | $525,983.00 | $182,700.00 | $0.00 | $203,000.00 | $20,300.00 | $343,283.00 |

# Recording Invoices

This chapter describes how to add invoices to Contracts or Purchase Orders (POs) and distribute actual costs to the Cost Worksheet. The Contract Management module can automate this process by supplying the same cost codes and distribution amounts from the originating contract/PO. However, you can distribute costs to other cost codes as well.

# Adding Invoices to a Contract/PO

You can use the Invoices section of a contract or purchase order document to record bills that have been issued or received relating to the selected contract or PO.

 *You can use either invoices or requisitions with contracts/POs, not both. If the contract/PO has a requisition against it, invoices will not be available.*

Each time you record a payment in an invoice, the balance on the contract or PO changes immediately. Although you can distribute the amount of an invoice to multiple cost codes, you cannot include individual line items or retainage in an invoice. Use a requisition instead of an invoice if you need to include a list of the items covered by a particular payment, or if you want to withhold a portion of the payment until work is completed.

**Set project settings for invoices**  The Default Invoice Amount to Contract/PO Balance checkbox in the Contracts/POs section of the Project Settings dialog box determines how the Amount field is used in new invoices. It also specifies whether to automatically use the cost codes from the associated PO to distribute the amount to the Cost Worksheet. From the Project View, right-click the project you are working with, then choose Project Settings.

*Mark this checkbox to have the module fill the Amount field with the balance of the PO when you create a new invoice. Click Save at the bottom of the Project Settings dialog box.*

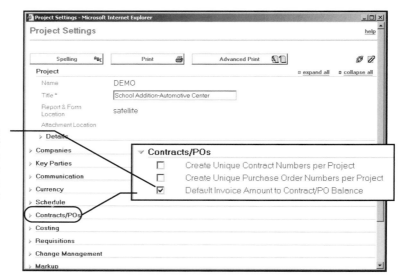

The module also distributes the value in the Amount field using cost codes from the associated PO. If necessary, you can change the value in the Amount field, then redistribute the new value to the cost codes as necessary.

**Close out a PO using one invoice**  From the Contract Information folder, click Purchase Orders. Open the Purchase Order you want to work with, then click Edit Document (if you are not in Edit mode). Scroll down to the Contract Summary section and expand the Invoices section.

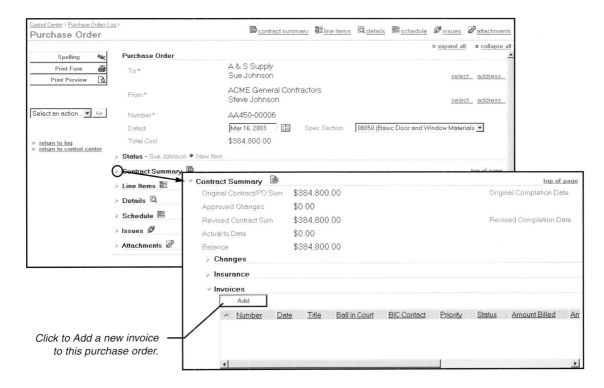

*Click to Add a new invoice to this purchase order.*

A unique invoice number is created, the current date is entered as the invoice date, and the specification section from the PO is used as the invoice title. Enter the payment date, check number, status, and activity ID (if applicable), then click Save.

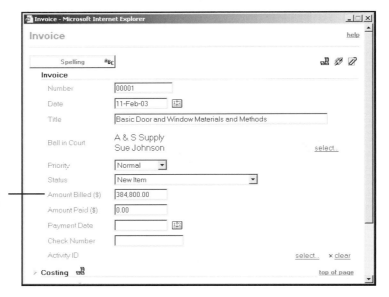

*If you change the invoice amount, you must redistribute costs.*

Scroll down and expand the Costing section to add one or most cost codes to be associated with the invoice.

*Click to assign cost codes to which you are distributing the amount.*

**Close out a PO using multiple invoices**  If you want to distribute invoices using the cost codes assigned to the PO, mark the Default Invoice Amount to Contract/PO Balance checkbox in the Contracts/ POs section of the Project Settings dialog box. In the Contract Information folder, click Purchase Orders. Open the PO to which you want to attach an invoice. From the Contract Summary section, expand the Invoices section.

Click Add. The next invoice number is created, the current date becomes the invoice date, and the specification section from the PO becomes the invoice title.

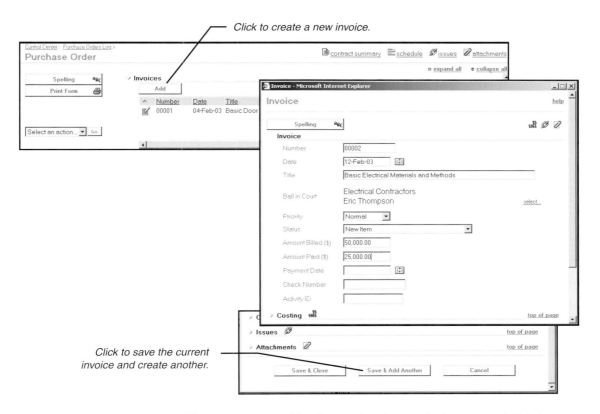

The amount entered for the new invoice equals the contract/PO balance. The module uses the value in the Amount Billed field, and creates cost distributions based on the cost codes assigned to all line items in the contract/PO. These values are automatically posted to the Cost Worksheet. If necessary, change the value in the Amount Paid field, and change the invoice title to accurately describe the content of the invoice. Enter the payment date, check number, status, and activity ID, then save the invoice document. Click Save & Add Another. Modify the fields as needed, then click Save & Close when you are finished adding invoices.

**Delete an invoice entry**  To delete an invoice, open the contract or PO that contains the invoice you want to delete. From the Contract Summary section of the document, expand the Invoices section, drag the scrollbar to the far right and click Delete for the row that contains the invoice you want to remove.

*When you delete an invoice, the module  also deletes any cost distributions associated with that invoice and adjusts the balance on the PO.*

| y | Status | Amount Billed | Amount Paid | Payment Date | Check Number | Activity ID | |
|---|--------|---------------|-------------|--------------|--------------|-------------|---|
| al | New Item | $384,800.00 | $0.00 | | | | delete |
| al | New Item | $0.00 | $0.00 | | | | delete |

Invoices / Add

# Distributing Actual Costs to the Cost Worksheet

The Cost Worksheet provides a central location for tracking all project costs. You can compare budgeted and committed costs to actual costs for each work element. Open the Cost Worksheet log window from the Contract Information folder.

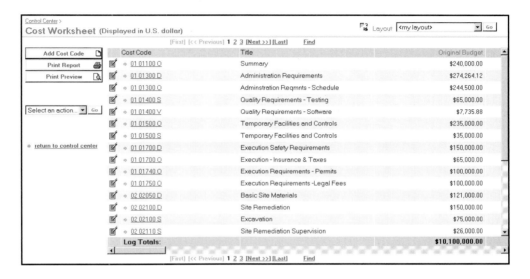

Costs are organized by cost codes, which represent various categories of project work. To specify how cost documents are distributed, right-click on the project name, and select Project Settings. Expand the Costing section and make your selections, then click Save.

For more information about distribution preferences and distributing costs to the Cost Worksheet, see the *Setting Up and Using the Cost Worksheet* chapter.

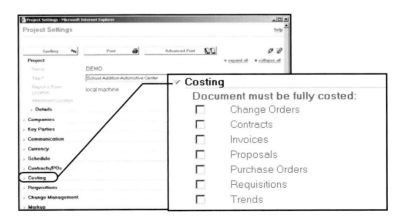

Once you record the payment in the Invoice dialog box, you can distribute it to the Actuals side of the Cost Worksheet by using the invoice's Costing section.

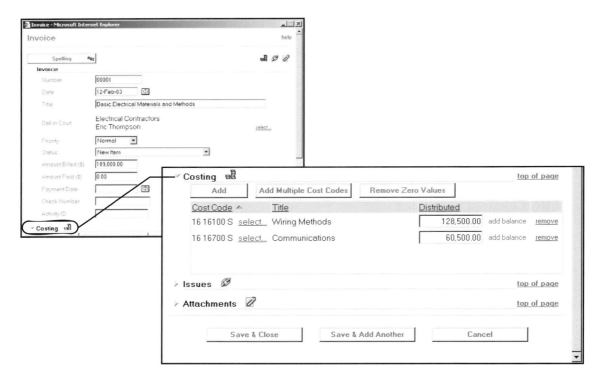

Invoices for a contract you originally distributed to Budget are distributed to Actuals Issued. Invoices for a contract (or PO) you originally distributed to Committed are distributed to Actuals Received.

Costing out your invoices is optional. You do not have to use the Cost Worksheet to use invoices or requisitions.

If you know you'll be using the Cost Worksheet, there are three ways to add cost codes:

- Create a project template that contains your standard cost codes.

- Add cost codes to the cost worksheet.

- Right-click a project that you want to copy costs codes to, then select Copy Cost Codes.

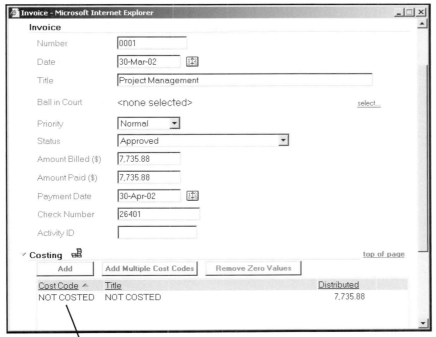

If you do not distribute the entire amount of the invoice, the non-distributed amount is applied to a cost code called Not Costed.

Using the Project Settings dialog box (right-click on the project name and choose Project Settings), you can specify that the entire amount of the invoice must be distributed to defined cost codes.

# Invoice Reports and Forms

Standard reports and forms are provided for you to use to print invoices and related costing information.

From the Invoice dialog box (accessed from contracts and POs), click Advanced Print. Select the report or form, then click Print.

| ACME General Contractors | | | | | | | School Addition-Automotive Center | | |
|---|---|---|---|---|---|---|---|---|---|
| | | **Invoices** | | | | | | | |
| Job No: JBAA450 | | | | | | | Date: | | 4/11/00 |
| Project No: PRJAA450 | | | | | | | Page: | | 1 of 1 |

| Type Invoice Number | Title | To | Check Number | From | Invoice Date | Payment Date | Amount | Con/PO No. | Paid |
|---|---|---|---|---|---|---|---|---|---|
| Contract | | ACE Mason Contractors | | ACME General Contractors | | | | AA450-00602 | |
| 0001 | Masonry Work | | 27109 | | 5/18/00 | 6/16/00 | $100,000.00 | | $100,000.00 |
| 0002 | Masonry Work | | | | 6/16/00 | | $100,000.00 | | $0.00 |
| | | | | | | Subtotals: | $200,000.00 | | $100,000.00 |
| Contract | | ACME General Contractors | | ACME General Contractors | | | | DIRECT COSTS | |
| 0001 | Administrative Costs | | | | 4/15/00 | 4/15/00 | $250,000.00 | | $90,000.00 |
| 0002 | Administrative Costs | | | | 5/15/00 | 5/15/00 | $275,000.00 | | $140,000.00 |
| | | | | | | Subtotals: | $525,000.00 | | $230,000.00 |
| Contract | | ACME General Contractors | | Philadelphia County | | | | AA450-00012 | |
| 0001 | General Construction | | 60555 | | 4/30/00 | 5/30/00 | $115,000.00 | | $150,000.00 |
| 0002 | General Construction | | 62789 | | 5/30/00 | 6/16/00 | $153,040.00 | | $153,040.00 |
| 0003 | Construction Facilities | | 62793 | | 5/30/00 | 6/16/00 | $140,000.00 | | $140,000.00 |
| 0004 | General Construction | | | | 5/30/00 | | $200,000.00 | | $0.00 |
| | | | | | | Subtotals: | $608,040.00 | | $443,040.00 |
| Purchase Order | | Gelco Space | | ACME General Contractors | | | | AA450-00004 | |
| 0001 | Construction Setup | | 2678 | | 3/16/00 | 4/15/00 | $3,040.00 | | $3,040.00 |

# Using Change Management

Contracts and purchase orders (POs) often change as a result of modifications to the scope of work, site conditions, or project schedule. Change management automates the change process according to your work process requirements, organizing and reducing the amount of work involved.

This chapter describes the change management process in the Contract Manager module and explains how you can use it to track changes to your projects.

# The Change Management Process

For more information, see *Change Management Overview* in Help.

Controlling changes involves notifying and coordinating affected project participants as well as containing costs and the schedule for the project. Change management provides an overview, from estimate to final approval for budgeted costs in the Budget Contract Summary section of each Change Management document window. Since the change process in a project differs according to the nature of each change and the methods a company employs for recording and tracking changes, the Contract Manager module change management process enables you to create a customized work process to meet your company's needs for tracking and resolving changes.

Change management provides one location where you enter all necessary contract, contractor, and costing information about a change. At any stage of the process, you can see the current status of the change, including estimates, costs, documents, and responsibilities of all parties.

Change management enables you to cost all generated documents and post generated documents to any portion of the Cost Worksheet. Another benefit is that change management effectively closes changes when the process finishes.

Construction managers (CMs) or general contractors (GCs) are responsible for coordinating all the construction work and disseminating change information to all affected parties. They must notify the owner of any changes that might affect the schedule or value of the budget contract, control quotes from contractors, negotiate with both the owner and contractors to properly compensate the affected parties, and circulate approval notices to all affected parties once the change is approved.

The following diagram illustrates the typical change management process for Construction Managers or General Contractors.

## Construction Manager
## or
## General Contractor

For details on setting project access, see *Setting Access Rights (Project Access)* in the *Planning and Adding a Contract Manager*

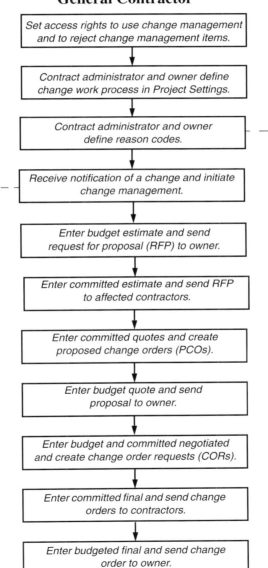

Set access rights to use change management and to reject change management items.

Contract administrator and owner define change work process in Project Settings.

Contract administrator and owner define reason codes.

Use reason codes to categorize and report on changes.

Receive notification of a change and initiate change management.

Notification of a change may come from many sources: a bulletin or notice, a telephone call, or a meeting.

Enter budget estimate and send request for proposal (RFP) to owner.

Enter committed estimate and send RFP to affected contractors.

Enter committed quotes and create proposed change orders (PCOs).

Enter budget quote and send proposal to owner.

Enter budget and committed negotiated and create change order requests (CORs).

Enter committed final and send change orders to contractors.

Enter budgeted final and send change order to owner.

# Specifying Change Management Project Settings

Change management preferences enable you to define the change management work process. Typically, the contract administrator and the owner determine the change management work process required for the project soon after the contract is awarded.

For details on setting up change management data, see the *Setting Up Dictionaries and Preferences* chapter.

**Create the change management work process**  From the Project View, right-click a project, then choose Project Settings. Scroll down to the Change Management section.

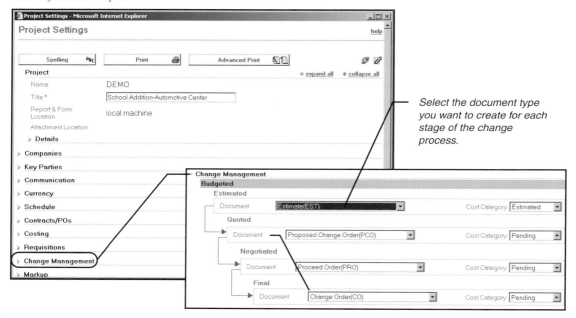

Select the document type you want to create for each stage of the change process.

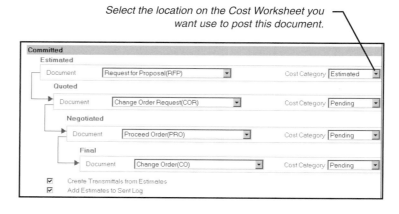

Select the location on the Cost Worksheet you want use to post this document.

For more information about customizing documents, see *Choosing Acronyms and Descriptions* in the *Customizing Log and Document Windows* chapter.

Specify the document type you want to create and the corresponding column on the Cost Worksheet where you want to distribute costs when you use change management. When you finish making changes, scroll to the bottom of the window and click Save.

You can customize the change management work process even further by customizing blank change types, or proposal types, and including them in your change management work process.

**Modify the change management work process** You can modify your change management project settings at any time; however, the changes apply only to new documents generated from change management. Any documents already created from change management remain unchanged.

To change the document type of an existing document, select the Change Management document and then click Clear Phase. Click Yes to confirm.

**Restrict access to change management information** If you use the module in a multiuser environment and exchange information with project participants, you must ensure that other users cannot alter the change management work process set in the Project Settings dialog box or see your budget information in Change Management documents. To prevent project participants from viewing your budget information, you can restrict access to the project by contact. To set access rights, right-click the project in which you want to restrict access to change management, then choose Project Access. Click the icon for the user whose access rights you want to configure, then set the rights in the Change Management section of the User Project Access dialog box. Click Save & Close when finished.

# Defining Reason Codes

You can assign a reason code to each change estimate in change management, which enables you to categorize changes and determine the factors that are causing changes during the project. The module includes several predefined reason codes. You can add or delete reason codes at any time, but it is a good idea to define them in conjunction with the owner and contract administrator before you begin using change management.

For details on setting up reason codes, see the *Setting Up Dictionaries and Preferences* chapter.

**Define reason codes** Right-click the top-level folder in the Project View and choose Dictionaries, Change Reason Codes. Click Add to add a new reason code. To delete a reason code, click Delete in the row that contains the code you want to remove. All of the projects in a database share defined reason codes.

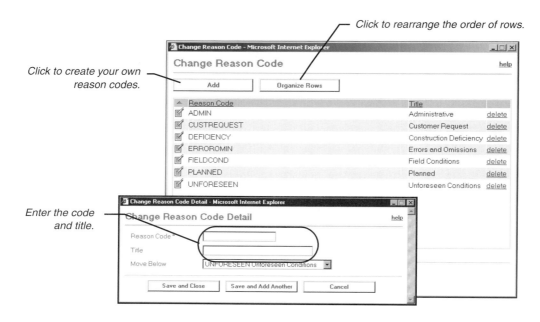

Click to rearrange the order of rows.

Click to create your own reason codes.

Enter the code and title.

# Initiating Change Management from Other Documents

You can initiate change management from many documents in the module, including notices, meeting minutes, requests for information (RFIs), punchlists, daily reports, notepads, correspondence received, noncompliance notices, and contract summaries.

**Initiate change management**  From the Project View, open the Communication folder and click the module you want to use. Add a new document, such as a notice, from which you want to create a Change Management document.

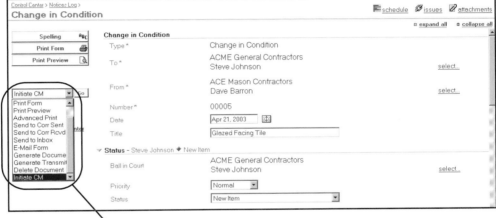

Click Select an Action, Initiate
CM (Change Management).

The module creates a new Change Management document and completes the following fields using information from the original document: Title, Date, Ball in Court, Status (set to New Item), Reference Document, Activity ID, Scope (defaults to Out of Scope), Remarks, and Issues. A link is created from the initiating document to the Change Management document, and a link is created from the Change Management document to the initiating document.

 *When you initiate change management from an RFI that has a question and answer, the question and answer are copied to the Remarks section of the Change Management document window.*

# Adding Change Documents

For more information, see *change management* in Help.

In the Contract Information folder in the Project View, click Change Management.

The Change Management log window provides a central location to view information on Change Management documents.

Click to add a new document

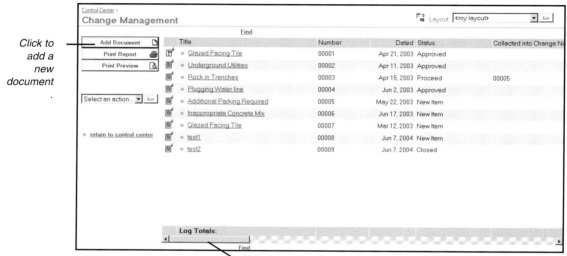

Drag the scrollbar to the right to view all columns associated with each change management document.

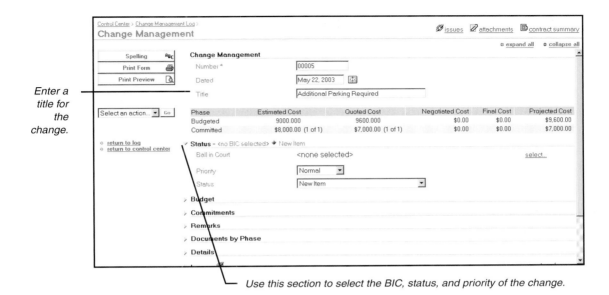

*Enter a title for the change.*

*Use this section to select the BIC, status, and priority of the change.*

After you enter the basic information for the change, you can begin generating documents using the remaining sections of the document window. Click Save at the bottom of the window when you are finished adding information to the document.

*The Budget section generates change documents for the budgeted contract.*

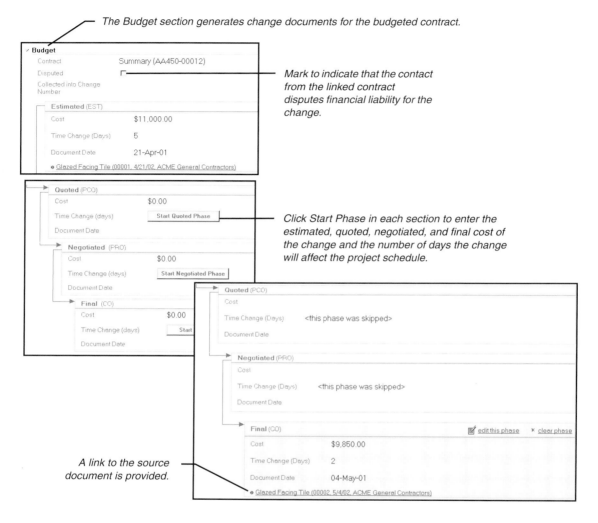

*Mark to indicate that the contact from the linked contract disputes financial liability for the change.*

*Click Start Phase in each section to enter the estimated, quoted, negotiated, and final cost of the change and the number of days the change will affect the project schedule.*

*A link to the source document is provided.*

*This section displays a summary of the costs associated with the contract this change is linked to. This section is not editable.*

*Use the Commitments section to generate change documents for committed contracts and POs.*

**Commitments**

| Add | Add Multiple Estimates | | Total Included Commitments:$7,000.00 | Copy Commitments to Budget |

| | Include | Contract/PO | Estimated (RFP) Cost | Time | Date | Quoted (COR) Cost | Time | Date |
|---|---|---|---|---|---|---|---|---|
| | ✔ | Standard Paving, Inc. (AA450-01000) | $8,000.00 | 0 | 23-May-02 | $7,000.00 | 0 | 23-May |
| | | **Total Included:** | **$8,000.00** | | | **$7,000.00** | | |

*The Remarks section enables you to include additional information about the change.*

**Remarks**

Due to the substitution of facing tile, the new base selected will not flush with the CMU walls.  To correct this we will need to wait until the specified facing tile is available.  Fortunately it is now in stock, we anticipate receipt within 5 days of ordering.

Please respond regarding any cost and anticipated delays to your project schedule.

*This section displays documents associated with the change. Click the links to open the documents.*

*The document acronym for each phase is displayed.*

**Documents by Phase**

**Commitments**

☐ Display Only Included Commitments

| Title | Required Date | Current Status | Include | Cost |
|---|---|---|---|---|
| **Commitments Estimated (RFP)** | | | | |
| Additional Parking Required (00003, 5/23/02, Standard Paving, Inc.) | 30-May-02 | CLO | ✔ | $8,000.00 |
| | | | **Total Included:** | **$8,000.00** |
| **Commitments Quoted (COR)** | | | | |
| Additional Parking Required (00001, 5/23/02, Standard Paving, Inc.) | 30-May-02 | NEW | ✔ | $7,000.00 |
| | | | **Total Included:** | **$7,000.00** |

**Budget**

| Title | Required Date | Current Status | | Cost |
|---|---|---|---|---|
| **Budget Estimated (EST)** | | | | |
| Additional Parking Required (00006, 5/23/02, ACME General Contractors) | 30-May-02 | CLO | | $9,000.00 |
| | | | **Total Included:** | **$9,000.00** |
| **Budget Quoted (PCO)** | | | | |
| Additional Parking Required (00006, 5/23/02, ACME General Contractors) | 30-May-02 | NEW | | $9,600.00 |
| | | | **Total Included:** | **$9,600.00** |

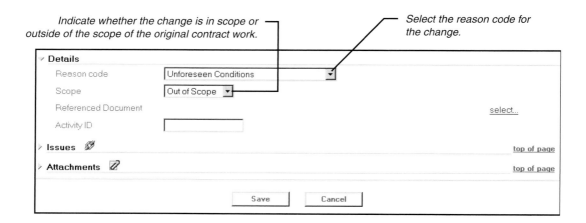

Indicate whether the change is in scope or outside of the scope of the original contract work.

Select the reason code for the change.

# Proposals and Change Orders

**Proposals**  The Proposals module includes proposed change orders (PCOs), change order requests (CORs), estimates (ESTs), and requests for proposals (RFPs). Click Proposals in the Contract Information folder from the Project View to review proposals. These documents solicit a bid to perform a specific activity or outline the cost and duration of a specific change. You can edit existing proposals from the Proposals log. To create new proposal documents, you must use Change Management.

*From the log window, click a proposal to review its details.*

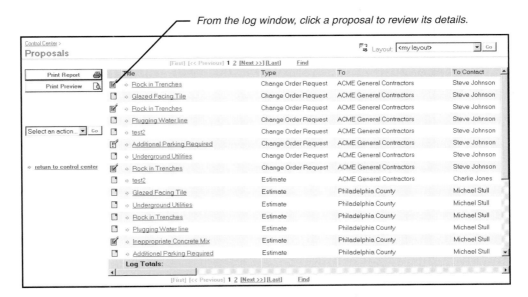

*A change order request, which is one type of proposal, contains To and From information and details about the status.*

*Scroll down to review contract summary information. The relevant data is automatically entered when you specify the contract number at the top of the document.*

The Line Items section contains information about itemized changes.

The Details section contains remarks about the proposal, as well as change management information and important dates.

Use the Markup for Changes section to create markup categories for this proposal.

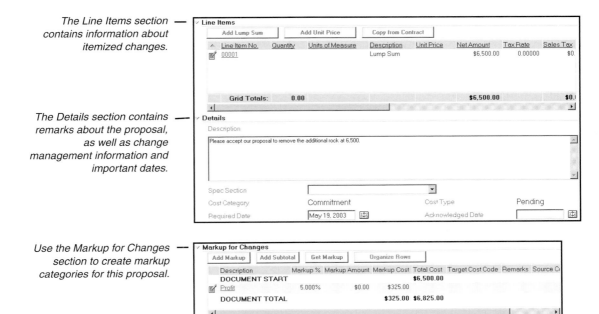

**Change orders** Click Change Management in the Contract Information folder to add or review change orders. Change orders specify a redirection of plans or introduce new items to the schedule. Change orders also show any approved increases or decreases in costs and contract item allowances.

 *Change orders are typically generated from change management, but if you want to be able to collect other change orders into a change order, you must add it from the Change Orders log (not from Change Management).*

Use the Change Order document window to review or add details about the change order.

The Status section contains approving authorities.

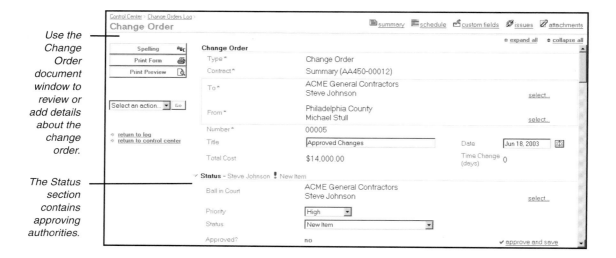

Scroll down to review contract summary information.

Use this section to create markup categories for the change order.

Click Get Markup to copy markup values from the contract.

The Line Items section itemizes changes. Click Add Lump Sum to add a new line item row.

The Details section contains a description of the change order, as well as change management information and important dates.

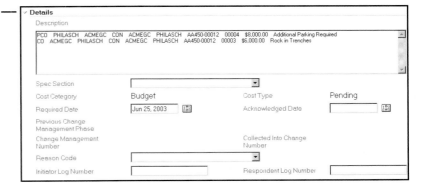

Each custom field assigned to the change orders table is shown with applicable values. Custom fields enable you to define additional information about a project.

Custom Fields

Drawing Reference

Location

OSHA Reference

Proceed

Spec Reference

top of page

# Applying Markup

A project's success requires effectively managing change during a project. Change management is designed to help you track the change process more accurately; you can also manage overhead and profit by using markup in change documents.

For more information on markup, see *markup* in Help.

Markup allows you to add overhead, profit, or any other markup categories you create to change documents.

You can set default values or percentages for overhead, profit, and other markup categories by using the Markup section of the contract/PO the change is written against. The default values are then used for all markup calculations for changes to that contract.

You can set different markup values for individual contracts and purchase orders (POs). When applying overhead, you may need to change the percentage in certain situations. You can have different markup values based on total labor, material, and equipment costs. You can apply markup to your budgeted costs or direct costs, as well as to the total committed costs.

**Markup forms**   Markup provides you with a comprehensive method for managing changes from the initial estimate to the final approval, including reporting to compare the total of initial change costs plus the total markup for changes and the combined costs for changes. There is a form for proposals and change documents with markups, which you can print.

**Where markup is used**   You can apply markup to change orders and proposals in the Change Order/Proposal document windows and in change management.

You can generate a budgeted change from the existing changes in the Change Management document window Commitment section. You can add the markup to the commitment changes and produce a budgeted change for that total.

### What you can do with markup

- You can set default markup values for overhead, profit, and other markup categories that you create. The default values are used in all markup calculations for that contract/PO.

- You can set separate markup values for different contracts and purchase orders. When applying overhead, you may need to change the percentage. You can apply markup to your budgeted costs and committed costs.

- You can have different markup values based on total labor, material, and equipment costs.

- You can set default values for overhead and profit, and you can also add additional markup values for each document.

- You can assign markup categories using a percentage rate or a flat amount.

- You can specify the target cost code to which you want to apply the markup amount.

- You can set the order in which markup categories are applied.

- You can specify a source cost code, which allows you to break down costs into individual components.

**Create default markup values using the Project Settings dialog box Markup section**  The Project Settings dialog box Markup section contains fields in which you can enter any description, percent, or fixed amount you want. The Target Cost Code column contains all cost codes. Right-click on a project in the Project View, then choose Project Settings. Scroll down to the Markup section.

When adding a new contract or PO, the module pulls the markup defaults that you enter here and uses them in the contract/PO.

 *Even if you enter default markup values, you can modify the markup values on a per contract/PO basis.*

*Select the order in which to apply the markup categories.*                *Select the cost code to which you want to apply the markup.*

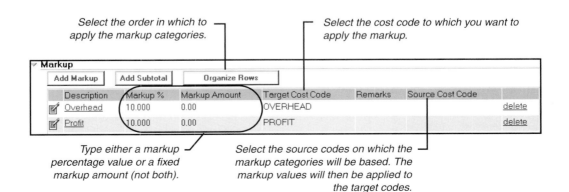

*Type either a markup percentage value or a fixed markup amount (not both).*                *Select the source codes on which the markup categories will be based. The markup values will then be applied to the target codes.*

For more information on setting markup preferences, see *Specifying Project Settings* in the *Setting Up Dictionaries and Preferences* chapter.

Using source cost codes allows you to break down costs into individual components. Instead of basing markup on one lump sum (such as overall cost), you can divide the cost into labor, materials, and bond, and apply markup categories to each of those. The module calculates the amount of markup that is applied from the distributed value of all cost distributions that match the specific cost code.

You can use wildcards in the Source Cost Code field. Use a question mark (?) to replace one letter or an asterisk (*) to replace multiple letters. For example, if you have cost codes A1B and A2B, and you enter A?B, both cost codes will be found. Similarly, if you use A*, all cost codes that begin with A will be found.

**Apply markup values to change orders and proposals** If you do not want to use the default markup values, you can apply separate values to individual change documents. the new values will apply only to the change document to which they are applied. Click Change Orders in the Contract Information folder in the Project View, then choose Add Document. The module enters the current date. Select the document's type, the to and from parties, and any other information relevant to the change order. Scroll down to the Markup for Changes section.

*Click to add a new row below the current row.*

*Click to update the markup amounts based on any changes that have been made to the document value and/or cost distributions.*

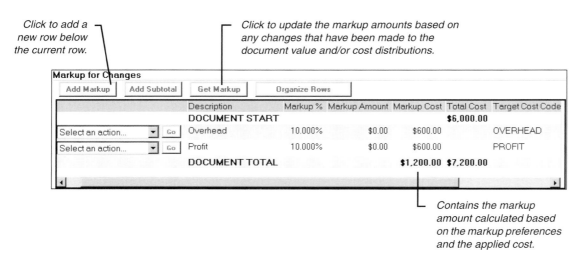

*Contains the markup amount calculated based on the markup preferences and the applied cost.*

**Use subtotals** Subtotals are cumulative. When you click Add Subtotal, a Subtotal row is added to the bottom of the list. Use Organize Rows to move the new row to the desired location. If you use Markup %, the markup cost is taken from the Total Cost column, or the previous Subtotal Total Cost column, and calculated in the Markup Amount column.

# Collecting into Change Orders

When you create a change order independently of change management, you can collect costs from pending change orders. Use this feature to combine multiple changes for one contract into a single change order; this reduces the number of documents to track and update.

**Collect into a change order**   From the Change Orders log window, add or generate a new change order. Scroll down to the Line Items section and click Collect from Changes. The module searches the database for pending change orders involving the same PO or contract referenced in the current change order. The module marks the collected change orders CLO (closed), and adds a line for each change order collected to the Collected Changes section on the change order.

 *The change orders being collected must not have been collected into another change order, and cannot have an approved, closed, or rejected status.*

*In the Change Order document window, scroll down to the Line Items section. Click Collect from Changes.*

*You are prompted to select the change orders to collect.*

*Choose Yes to link the new change to the same issues and/or attachments as the collected documents.*

*The module adds collected documents to the Collected Changes section on the change order.*

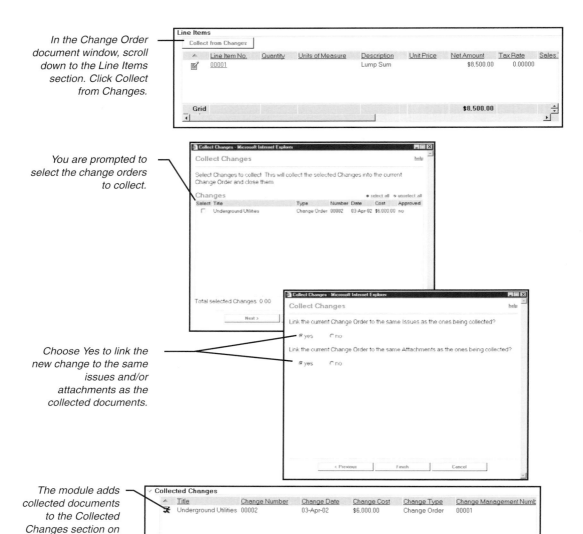

 *The status of change orders collected into another change order is changed to Closed.*

# Approving Change Orders

The final step in the change process is approving the change order. The change order Summary section summarizes the contract history to date.

**Approve a change order**  From the document window for the selected change order, scroll down to the Status section. Choose the date the change order was approved by the contract parties in each Date field; you must enter the first two dates before you can approve the change order. Click Approve and Save and confirm that you want to approve the change order. The status of the change order is changed to Approved.

If you use the Cost Worksheet, The change order cost distributions are transferred from the Pending Revisions column to the Approved Revisions column.

In the Change Order document window, scroll down to the Status section. Click Approve and Save to approve the change order.

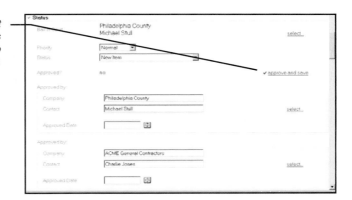

The Contract Summary section summarizes the contract history to date.

Mark this checkbox to include both pending and approved changes in the Net Amount of Previous Changes field.

# Generating Change Documents from Change Management

The process of generating documents is essentially the same for each document type in the work process.

### Prepare to generate document from change management

Before you generate documents, you should specify contract information in the Budget section. In the Budget section, click Select and choose the contract; in the Commitments section, click Add and choose the phase. You will choose the contract when you start the first phase.

---

*If only one budgeted contract/PO exists, it is automatically selected in the Budget section.*

*In the Budget section, you can only select contracts that are distributed to the Budgeted side of the Cost Worksheet. In the Commitments section, you can select any committed contract/PO.*

---

**Generate a document**   From the Budget or Commitments section, click the appropriate button for the phase from which you want to start: Start Estimated Phase, Start Quoted Phase, Start Negotiated Phase, or Start Final Phase.

---

*If there is no value for a phase, no document exists for that phase. A $0.00 value may have documents.*

---

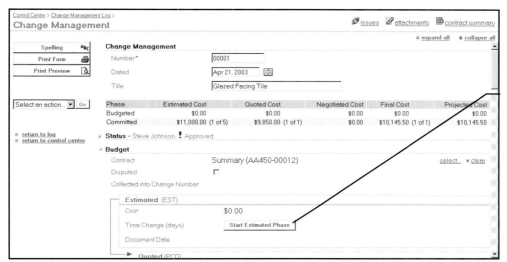

*1.* To generate budgeted change documents, expand the Budget section and then click Start Estimated Phase.

*2.* Enter the estimate information, then click Save. Click the Return to Change Management link.

In the Commitments section, you can add rows for as many contractors as the change requires. Click Add to create a row for the contractor. Select the phase, then select the contract. You can also click Add Multiple Estimates to include multiple rows if you are obtaining bids from several contractors for the same work.

**Delete generated documents**  While you can review a change document from the associated log after change management generates it, you cannot delete the document from any log or document window other than change management. For example, if you generate an RFP from change management, you can open that document in the Proposals log, but you cannot delete it from there. You must delete the document using change management.

Click Clear Phase to delete a generated document. You cannot delete a document from a phase if there are later phases that have generated documents. For example, if you want to delete the Budget Estimate document, but you generated a Budget Quoted document, you must delete the Budget Quoted document before you can delete the Budget Estimate document.

**Delete change management documents**  To delete a change management document, open the document you want to delete, then click Delete Document from the Select an Action drop-down.

Deleting a change management document deletes all the documents that were generated from it and removes any information posted to the Cost Worksheet.

# Costing Generated Documents

Costing information is assigned to generated documents based on the contract (for the first generated document) or the last generated document. When you start the first phase on the budgeted or committed side, click Copy from Contract in the Line Items section to copy line items and costing from the contract to this document. For subsequent phases, line items and costing are copied from the previous phase.

Change management enables you to post to the portion of the cost worksheet that best suits your company's needs. Amounts from the generated documents are automatically posted to the cost worksheet when you assign cost distributions, except when you clear the Include checkbox for commitments.

**Use costing for a contractor in the Cost Worksheet** To add commitments to the cost worksheet, mark the Include checkbox in the Commitment dialog box (while in Edit mode). To remove commitments from the cost worksheet, clear the Include checkbox; costing information is removed from the cost worksheet.

 *Costing information is retained for documents for which you did not mark the Include checkbox, but the values are not posted in the cost worksheet.*

 *You can mark the Include checkbox for more than one of the same contractor type. However, if you mark the Include checkbox for multiple contractors who are bidding on the same work, all checked contractors will be posted to the cost worksheet.*

**Using multiple rounds of negotiations** Through change management, you can perform multiple rounds of negotiations in the negotiated phase for both budget and commitments.

**Copy commitments into a budget** Using change management, you can copy multiple commitments for a particular phase into one document on the budget side for any phase, and you can carry over the cost codes.

# Adding Multiple Commitment Documents to the Estimated Phase

Using change management, you can add multiple commitment documents from companies that have committed contracts to the estimated phase.

**Add multiple commitments documents**  In the Change Management document window, click the Commitments section, then click Add Multiple Estimates.

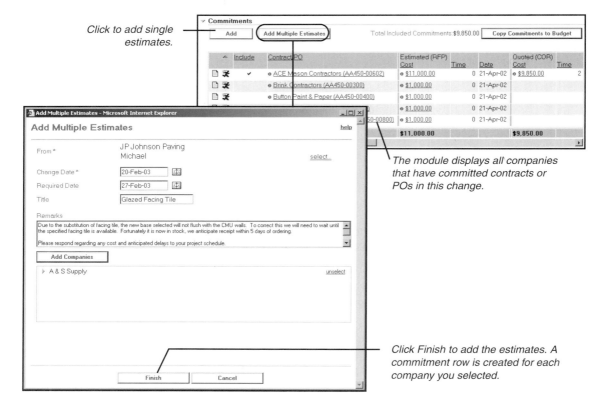

*Click to add single estimates.*

*The module displays all companies that have committed contracts or POs in this change.*

*Click Finish to add the estimates. A commitment row is created for each company you selected.*

Select the From contact. The module enters the change date (the current date), enters the required date (the current date plus seven days), and copies the title and remarks from the Change Management document.

# Change Management Reports and Forms

Standard reports and forms are provided for you to use to print change estimates by reason code, scope, issue, or status.

From the Change Management document window, click Select an Action, then Advanced Print. Click Go. Select the report or form, then click Print.

**ACME General Contractors**                                                                                     **School Addition-Automotive Center**

| | | | | | | **All Change Documents** | | | | |
| Job No: | **JBAA450** | | | | | **By Change Management Number** | | | Date: | **4/11/00** |
| Project No: **PRJAA450** | | | | | | | | | Page: | **1 of 2** |

Change Management Number :   00001

| Type | Issue | To Vendor | From Vendor | Number | Date | Title | Contract Number | Status | Spec Section | Cost |
|------|-------|-----------|-------------|--------|------|-------|-----------------|--------|--------------|------|
| CO | TILE | MASON | ACMEGC | 00001 | 5/4/00 | Glazed Facing Tile | AA450-00602 | APP | | $9,850.00 |
| COR | TILE | ACMEGC | MASON | 00001 | 4/30/00 | Glazed Facing Tile | AA450-00602 | CLO | | $9,850.00 |
| RFP | TILE | BUTTON | ACMEGC | 00001 | 4/21/00 | Glazed Facing Tile | AA450-00400 | CLO | | $1,000.00 |
| CO | TILE | ACMEGC | PHILASCH | 00002 | 5/4/00 | Glazed Facing Tile | AA450-00012 | APP | | $9,850.00 |
| RFP | TILE | SMITH | ACMEGC | 00001 | 4/21/00 | Glazed Facing Tile | AA450-00800 | CLO | | $1,000.00 |
| RFP | TILE | MASON | ACMEGC | 00001 | 4/21/00 | Glazed Facing Tile | AA450-00602 | CLO | | $11,000.00 |
| RFP | TILE | FINISH | ACMEGC | 00001 | 4/21/00 | Glazed Facing Tile | AA450-01300 | CLO | | $1,000.00 |
| RFP | TILE | BRINK | ACMEGC | 00001 | 4/21/00 | Glazed Facing Tile | AA450-00300 | CLO | | $1,000.00 |
| EST | TILE | PHILASCH | ACMEGC | 00001 | 4/21/00 | Glazed Facing Tile | AA450-00012 | CLO | | $11,000.00 |

Change Management Number :   00002

| Type | Issue | To Vendor | From Vendor | Number | Date | Title | Contract Number | Status | Spec Section | Cost |
|------|-------|-----------|-------------|--------|------|-------|-----------------|--------|--------------|------|
| COR | UTIL | ACMEGC | STDPAV | 00001 | 4/22/00 | Underground Utilities | AA450-01000 | CLO | | $3,000.00 |
| CO | UTIL | STDPAV | ACMEGC | 00001 | 4/30/00 | Underground Utilities | AA450-01000 | APP | | $3,000.00 |
| PCO | UTIL | PHILASCH | ACMEGC | 00001 | 4/24/00 | Underground Utilities | AA450-00012 | CLO | | $3,300.00 |
| EST | UTIL | PHILASCH | ACMEGC | 00001 | 4/22/00 | Underground Utilities | AA450-00012 | CLO | | $4,000.00 |
| CO | UTIL | ACMEGC | PHILASCH | 00001 | 4/28/00 | Underground Utilities | AA450-00012 | APP | | $3,300.00 |
| RFP | UTIL | STDPAV | ACMEGC | 00001 | 4/22/00 | Underground Utilities | AA450-01000 | CLO | | $4,000.00 |

# Using Procurement

Use the Procurement module to enter and track information for procurement items, and then award a contract to the winning bidder.

This chapter describes the procurement process, and explains how you can use it for estimating, bid tracking, and contract award.

# The Procurement Process

For more information, see *Procurement* in Help.

The procurement section enables you to enter and track information for procurement items and the related scope items that make up the procurement item. Use this module if you need to procure materials or labor.

During the procurement process, you can request bids from contractors on materials that you require, or a job you need done. Once the item is open for bid, you can track who is bidding, how much they bid for each procurement item and its scope items, and then award the procurement item to a contract or purchase order for the winning bidder.

 The Procurement module covers the bidding process and contract award within the bidding process.

You can enter and track information per procurement item. When the bidding is complete, you can award the procurement item to a contract or purchase order, and you can also generate materials. You can also view statistics on bidders, including how much they bid on various items, and which items they have been awarded.

Costing is done at the scope item level (one level below the procurement item level), and the contract/PO award can be done at the procurement item level or the scope item level.

Any user with access rights can enter data in a procurement document. You can set the security options to prevent users from viewing and entering data that you don't want them to have access to. This allows you to prevent users from seeing information in this module.

# Initiating Procurement

Once you know the details of the materials you require or the job you need done, create a new procurement item document in which you will enter all bids and other relevant information.

You can create a log of procurement item documents in the following two ways: You can import existing items from an estimating package, or you can enter them manually.

**Import procurement item documents**  To save time, you can import documents from an estimating package. To import, you must know the name of the file, and the file must be properly formatted. From the Procurement Items log window, choose Select an Action, Import, then click Go to open the Import dialog box. Click Browse to locate the file, then click Import. The items appear in the log.

**Create a new procurement item document**  From the Project View, open the Contract Information folder and click Procurement Items. Click Add Document to open a new Procurement Item document window.

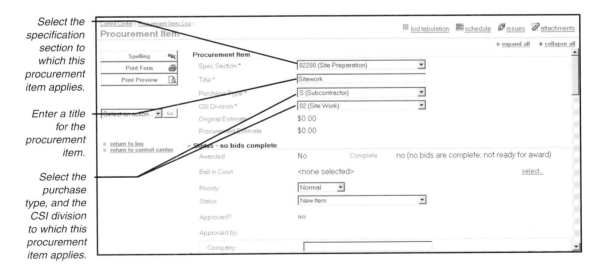

Select the specification section to which this procurement item applies.

Enter a title for the procurement item.

Select the purchase type, and the CSI division to which this procurement item applies.

**Add scope items to the procurement item**  You should first add the individual components (scope items) that make up the procurement item up for bid. Scroll down to the Bid Tabulation section and click the Add button next to Scope Items.

*Click to add scope items.*

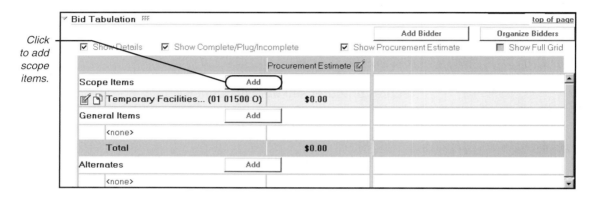

In the Add Scope Item dialog box, enter the details for the scope item.

*Enter quantity and unit price information.*

*Click to add sub-items to the scope item.*

*Click to add more scope items to the procurement item. Click Save and Close when finished.*

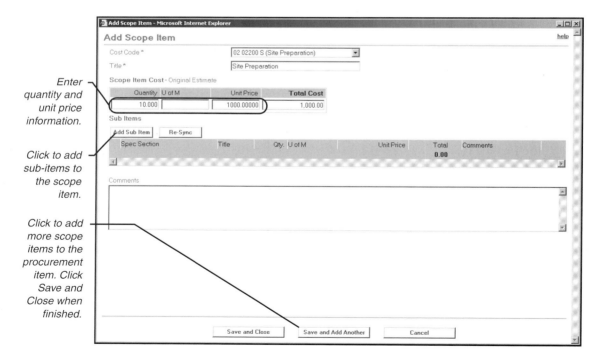

The scope items appear in the left column of the Bid Tabulation section. You can add as many scope items as necessary to the procurement item.

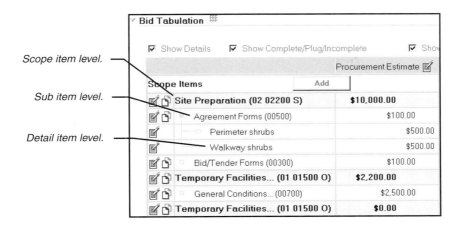

Scope item level.

Sub item level.

Detail item level.

**Add sub items to scope items**   You can add a second level below scope items, called sub items, to break down the scope items into more specific components. In the Add Scope Item dialog box, click Add Sub Item to add a sub item row, then enter the required information. The sub item will appear indented below the scope item in the Bid Tabulation section of the Procurement Item document window.

 *You can assign a specification section to a sub item.*

 *You can also press F7 to add a sub item row from the Add/Edit Scope Item dialog box.*

**Add detail items to sub items**   You can add a third level, which will fall below sub items, called detail items, to make bidding even more specific. In the Add Scope Item dialog box, click the icon to the left of the sub item to which you want to add a detail item, or press F8. Enter the required information. The row will appear indented below the sub item in the Bid Tabulation section of the Procurement Item document window.

 *You can also add sub and detail items directly in the Bid Tabulation section by clicking the respective icons next to the scope and sub item rows, as shown here.*

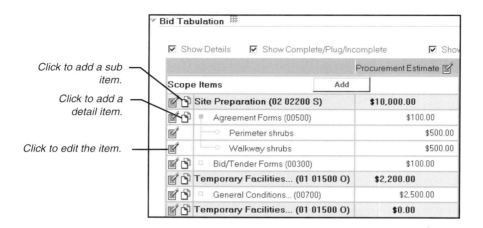

Click to add a sub item.

Click to add a detail item.

Click to edit the item.

**Add alternate items**   You can add alternate items that don't belong with scope items. For example, if you want elm trees, but you know they probably won't be available, use the Alternates section to add maple trees as an alternate item. Click the Add button next to Alternates in the Bid Tabulation section.

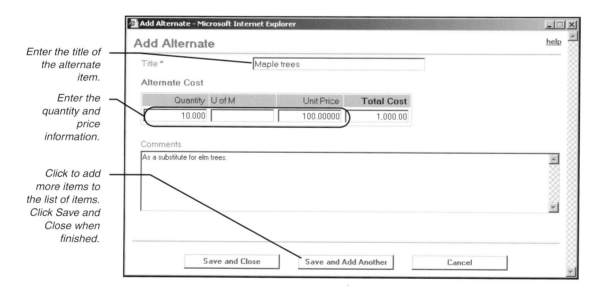

Enter the title of the alternate item.

Enter the quantity and price information.

Click to add more items to the list of items. Click Save and Close when finished.

*Alternate items are not included in the total amount of the procurement item. Scope and general items are included. If you use an alternate item and want to award it, you must move the item to either the Scope Items or General Items section.*

**Add general items**  You can add general items that don't belong with scope items. General items are costed similarly to scope items, but cannot be broken down into sub and detail items. For example, you might consider some costs, such as freight or taxes, as general, rather than scope items. Click the Add button next to General Items in the Bid Tabulation section. You are required to select a cost code for general items.

Select a cost code for the general item.

Enter the quantity and price information.

Click to add more items to the list of items. Click Save and Close when finished.

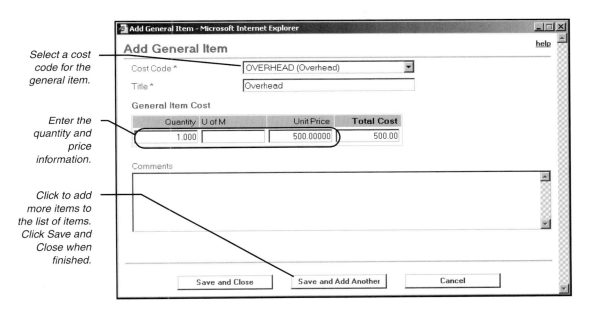

The alternate items appear in the Alternates section, and the general items appear in the General Items section.

General item

Alternate item

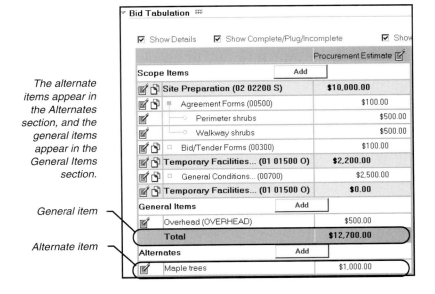

**Edit the original and procurement estimates**   After you have added scope and other items, you can edit the original and procurement estimates. The values you enter when you first add scope, sub, detail, general, or alternate items are the original estimate values. If you edit the estimates after they are entered, the procurement estimate values are edited, not the original.

 *You can edit original estimates if you have access rights to do so, and only in the Edit Estimate Worksheet dialog box. The access rights are set in the Project Access dialog box.*

*Click to open the Edit Estimate Worksheet dialog box, in which you can edit original and procurement estimates.*

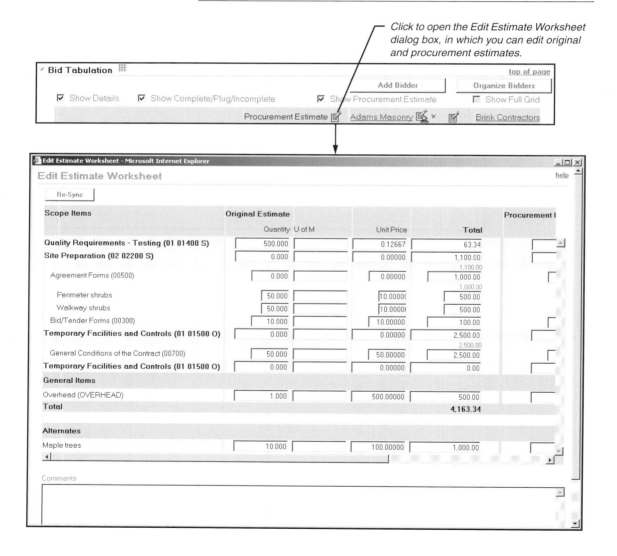

**Add bidders**  In the Bid Tabulation section, click Add Bidder to add the names of contacts who have made or will make bids on the items.

Bidders
appear
in the
right
columns

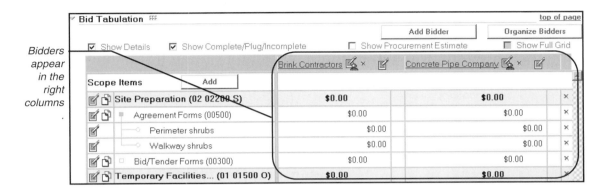

In the Add Bidder dialog box, enter details about the bidder.

Click to insert
the name of the
bidder.

Click Select to
insert the names
of the contacts
who received the
bids.

Enter the
names of any
witnesses who
saw the bid.

Click to add
more bidders.
Click Save and
Close when
finished.

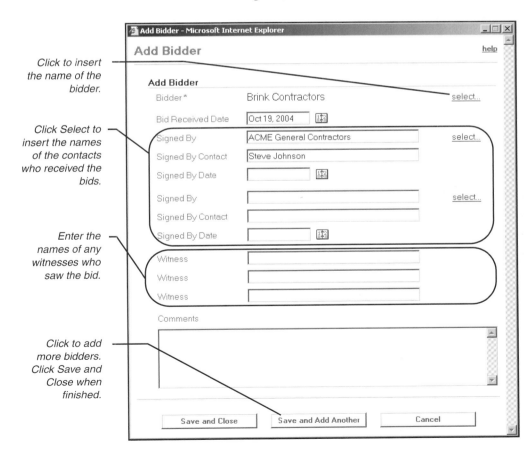

**Enter and edit bids**  Once you have added bidders, you can enter their bids in the Bid Tabulation section.

*Click to open the Edit Bid Worksheet dialog box, in which you can enter bids for the selected bidder.*

*Enter the bids from this bidder, including quantity and unit price, or total.*

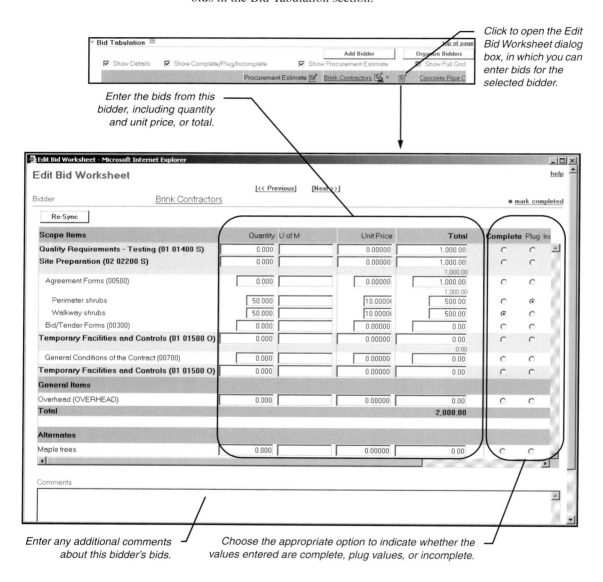

*Enter any additional comments about this bidder's bids.*

*Choose the appropriate option to indicate whether the values entered are complete, plug values, or incomplete.*

 *See* Edit Bid Worksheet dialog box *in Help for information on the Re-Sync feature, the Complete/Plug/Incomplete options, and other detailed information for the dialog box above.*

Click Save and Close when finished.

**Add new bidders and edit bids simultaneously**  Use the Record Bid feature to add a bidder and enter bids in one step. Choose Select an Action, Record Bid, then click Go to open the Record Bid dialog box.

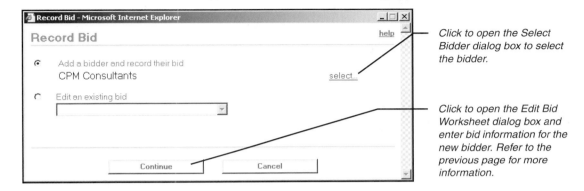

*Click to open the Select Bidder dialog box to select the bidder.*

*Click to open the Edit Bid Worksheet dialog box and enter bid information for the new bidder. Refer to the previous page for more information.*

**Add any other relevant information**  You can add any other necessary information in the Status, Scope of Work, Schedule, and Details sections, and link the procurement item to issues and attach files to it in the respective sections.

*Enter details about the scope of the work*

*Enter scheduling information*

*Enter additional information in the Comments field.*

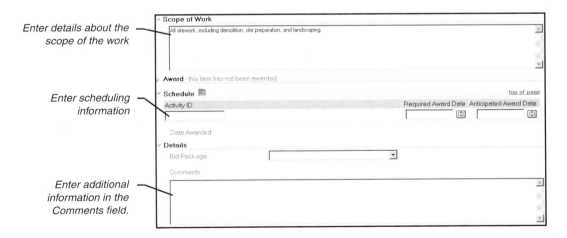

**View procurement log statistics**  You can view awarded percentages and other general statistics about all documents in the procurement log. From the Procurement Items log window, click Select an Action, View Log Stats, then click Go to open the Procurement Statistics dialog box.

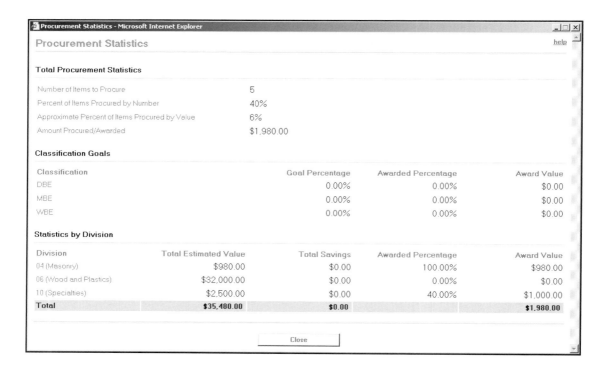

 *For information on each field, refer to Procurement Statistics dialog box in Help.*

**View bidder statistics**  You can view statistics about any bidder who has made bids on items in the procurement log. From the Procurement Items log window, click Select an Action, View Bidder Stats, then click Go to open the Bidder Statistics dialog box.

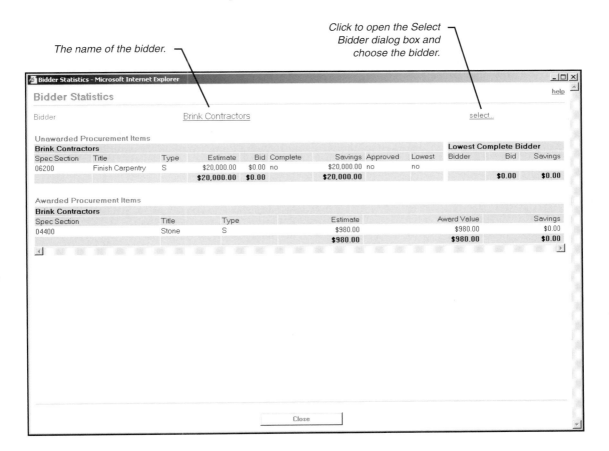

*The name of the bidder.*

*Click to open the Select Bidder dialog box and choose the bidder.*

# Reports and Forms

Standard reports and forms are provided for you to use to print information about procurement items.

From the Procurement Item document window, click Select an Action, then Advanced Print. Click Go. Select the report or form, then click Print.

# Award Procurement Items to a Bidder

Once all bids are in and marked as complete, you can award a contract or purchase order to a bidder. You can award multiple items to a bidder at one time, or a single item to a bidder.

*Only procurement items that are complete can be awarded.*

*Generally, a contract is awarded for materials and labor; a purchase order is awarded for materials only.*

**Award multiple procurement items to one bidder** If you want to award multiple procurement items to one bidder, and the bids have been marked as complete, click Award Items from the Procurement Items log window to open the Award wizard.

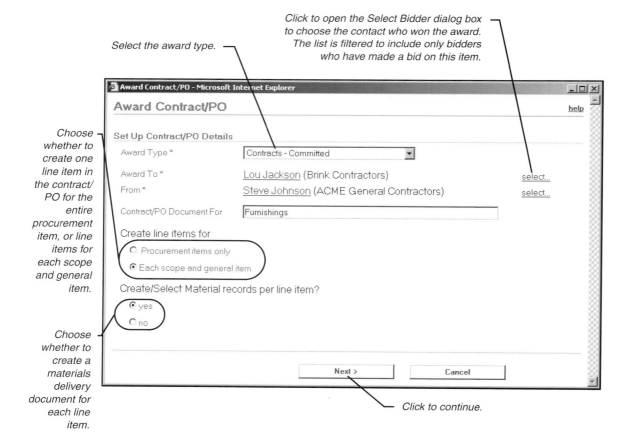

*Select the award type.*

*Click to open the Select Bidder dialog box to choose the contact who won the award. The list is filtered to include only bidders who have made a bid on this item.*

*Choose whether to create one line item in the contract/ PO for the entire procurement item, or line items for each scope and general item.*

*Choose whether to create a materials delivery document for each line item.*

*Click to continue.*

Mark the checkboxes for the items
you want to award to this bidder

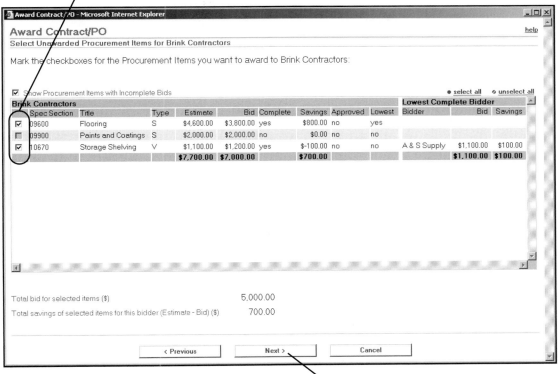

Click to continue.

If you have any scope or general items that are not costed, the following screen appears, in which you must choose a cost code for each item.

 *The following screen appears only if the contracts or purchase orders checkboxes are marked as must be fully costed in the Costing section of the Project Settings dialog box. If the checkboxes are cleared, the following screen will not appear.*

*Click to open the Select Cost Code dialog box to choose a cost code.*

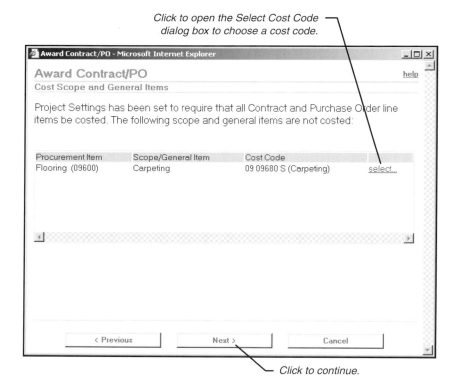

*Click to continue.*

If you chose to create line items for each scope and general item, and to create a materials delivery document for each line item, the scope and general items appear as line items in the next screen.

 *The following screen will not appear if you chose not to create/ select materials records per line item in the first Award screen.*

*Select the specification section for each item, if applicable.*

*Click to open the Select Material dialog box to choose the material to which to apply the item. Or...*

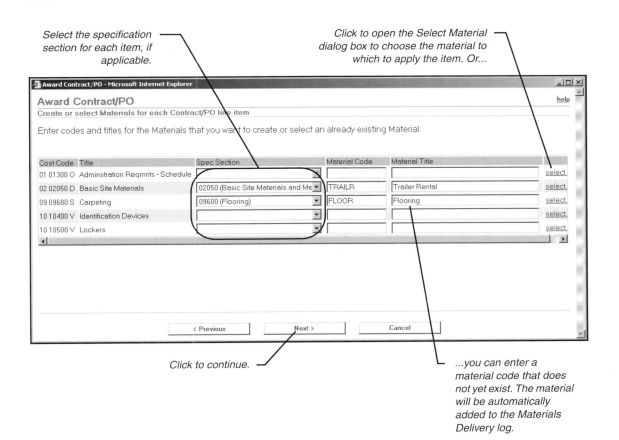

*Click to continue.*

*...you can enter a material code that does not yet exist. The material will be automatically added to the Materials Delivery log.*

*Review the information. If everything is correct, click Finish to award the contract/PO to the winning bidder.*

The new Contract or Purchase Order document window opens, and is added to the respective log window. Line items for each scope and general item appear in the Line Items section, or one line item for the entire procurement item, depending on which option you chose in the first award screen.

The cost of the contract or purchase order is assigned to the Original Commitment or Original Budget column in the Cost Worksheet, depending on which option you chose in the first award screen. (Purchase Orders are applied to the Original Commitment column.)

**Award a single procurement item to a bidder**  When you are ready to award a single procurement item, and have determined which bidder it is being awarded to, open its document window and mark the bid as complete. Scroll down to the Bid Tabulation section and click Award This Item to open the Award wizard.

*Click to open the Select Bidder dialog box to choose the contact who won the award. The list is filtered to include only bidders who have made a bid on this item.*

*Select the award type.*

*Choose whether to create one line item in the contract/PO for the entire procurement item, or line items for each scope and general item.*

*Choose whether to create a materials delivery document for each line item.*

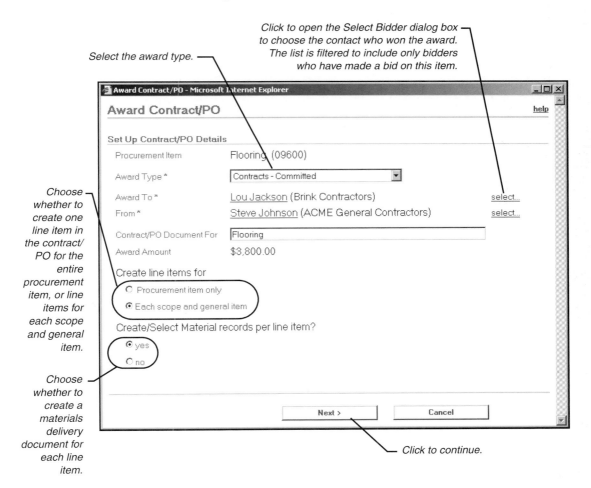

*Click to continue.*

If you have any scope or general items that are not costed, the following screen appears, in which you must choose a cost code for each item.

 *The following screen appears only if the contracts or purchase orders checkboxes are marked as must be fully costed in the Costing section of the Project Settings dialog box. If the checkboxes are cleared, the following screen will not appear.*

*Click to open the Select Cost Code dialog box to choose a cost code.*

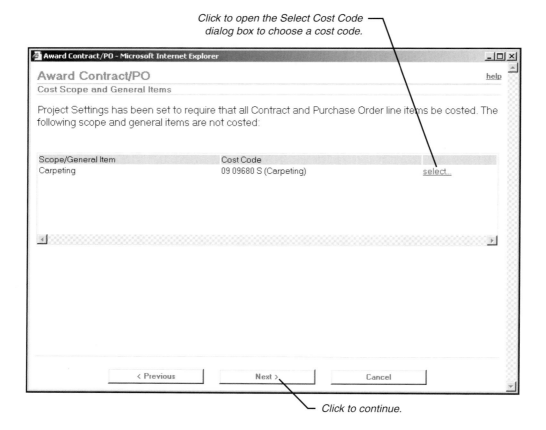

*Click to continue.*

If you chose to create line items for each scope and general item, and to create a materials delivery document for each line item, the scope and general items appear as line items in the next screen.

 *The following screen will not appear if you chose not to create/select materials records per line item in the first Award screen.*

Select the specification section for each item, if applicable.

Click to open the Select Material dialog box to choose the material to which to apply the item. Or...

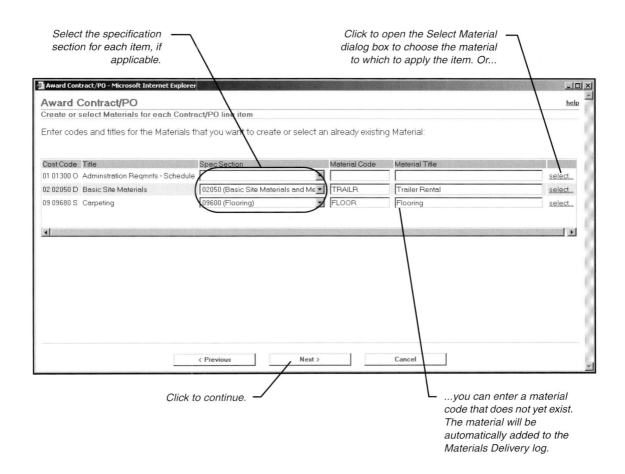

Click to continue.

...you can enter a material code that does not yet exist. The material will be automatically added to the Materials Delivery log.

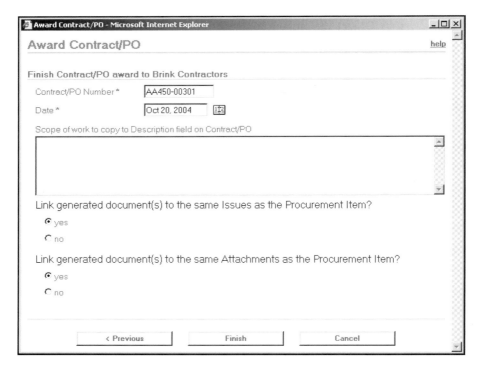

*Review the information. If everything is correct, click Finish to award the contract/PO to the winning bidder.*

The new Contract or Purchase Order document window opens, and is added to the respective log window. Line items for each scope and general item appear in the Line Items section, or one line item for the entire procurement item, depending on which option you chose in the first award screen.

The cost of the contract or purchase order is assigned to the Original Commitment or Original Budget column in the Cost Worksheet, depending on which option you chose in the first award screen. (Purchase Orders are applied to the Original Commitment column.)

**Unaward a procurement item**   To unaward a procurement item, you can either delete the associated contract or PO that was generated during the award process, or delete all line items in that contract or PO.

**Delete a procurement item**   Only unawarded procurement item documents can be deleted. If the procurement item has been awarded, you must first delete the contract or PO as described above to unaward the item. Next, from the procurement item you want to delete, choose Select an Action, Delete Document, then click Go.

# Creating and Tracking Issues

After your project is underway, problems can arise that you want to track and document because they may lead to contract changes or claims. The Issues feature functions like a "file cabinet" where you can organize all project documents related to an identified subject or situation in one easily accessible place.

This chapter describes how you can create an issue from any Contract Manager module document, at any time during the project; link any data item to one or more existing issues; and have the module build an issue automatically.

# Linking Contract Manager Module Documents Using Issues

An issue can be a problem that must be resolved before the project can be completed, or a condition that can lead to contract changes or claims. Organizing project information by issues enables you to quickly review each problem that may affect the project schedule or completion cost.

An issue can link several documents of any type, such as a contract, drawing, meeting minute, or change order. You may want to create an issue to

- Gather relevant documents quickly when you are involved in a claim

- Track every piece of information relating to a company when you experience ongoing problems with that company

- Group different documents related to a topic that led to a formal change order, such as meeting minutes, records of telephone calls, and change documents

You can establish an issue at any point during a project and link documents to it as the project progresses. For example, if a labor shortage is noted in a daily report, create an issue named Labor and link the daily report to it. You can also link other items to the issue, such as the original labor contract, relevant meeting minutes, discussion items, and change and request documents. You can also link several existing documents to an issue at the same time. Use the Build Issue feature to automatically search for, and link, related documents.

You can link an issue to any Contract Manager module document except the Cost Worksheet and other issues (you can't link one issue to another issue). You can also link some items within documents to issues. For example, meeting-minute business items can be linked to different issues than the meeting minute document that contains them. Other items that can be linked to issues include contract/purchase order (PO) items; requisition schedule of value line items; change and proposal line items; daily report visitors, equipment, and labor; submittal revisions; drawing revisions; punch list items; notepad items; and materials delivery tickets.

**Add an issue**  From the Project Information folder in the Project View, click Issues, then Add Document. Enter a title and code for the issue. Add any other information about the issue as necessary, including a linked contract, the status, priority, ball in court, and any attachments.

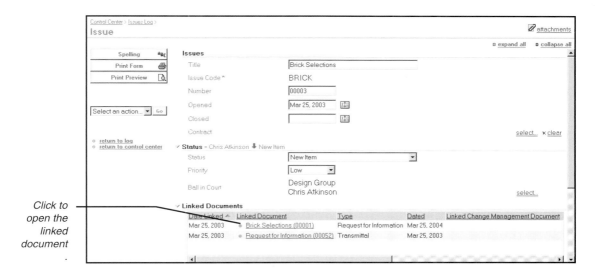

Click to
open the
linked
document

**Link a document to an existing issue**  You can link various documents and items to an issue. Open the document you want to link to an issue. Scroll down to the Issues section, or click the Link icon at the top of the page.

Click to select the issue you want to link the document to.

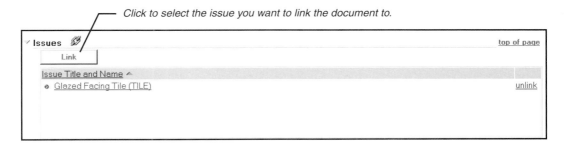

 *If you want to open the issue document window, click the issue's link in the Issue Title and Name column.*

**Display a document linked to an issue**  From the Issues log, click the document icon for the issue you want to open. A list of all the documents attached to that issue is displayed in the Linked Documents section. Click the title in the Linked Document column to open the document.

 *When you edit a document linked to an issue, the issue is automatically updated when you save or close the document.*

**Remove a document link from an issue**  Click Issues in the Project Information folder to open the Issues log window. Open the issue from which you want to remove a linked document. Scroll down to the Linked Documents section and scroll to the right. Click Unlink for the document you want to remove from the issue.

# Searching for Documents to Build Issues

During a project you may decide to link several documents to an issue at the same time. For example, you may have completed Phase 1, and want to link all Phase 1 documents to an issue to keep track of them. The Search feature does this for you quickly and automatically.

Select a project in the Project View. Click Search in the upper right corner of the Workspace to open the Search window.

*Enter the keywords relating to the documents that you want to search for, then click Search.*

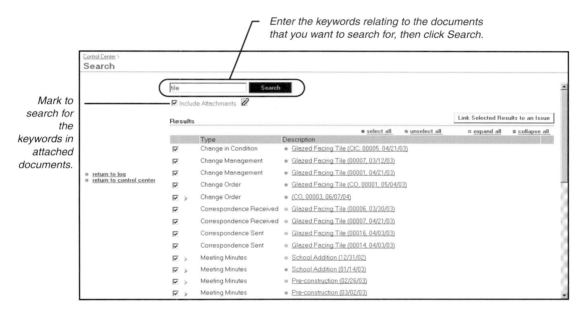

*Mark to search for the keywords in attached documents.*

Refer to *Search* in Help for detailed information on this feature.

To search for multiple words in one field, use a space between words, for example, Insurance Liability. The documents are listed that contain both of the words.

All documents are selected to be included in the issue by default. To prevent documents from being linked to an issue, clear the checkboxes for the respective documents.

Click Link Selected Results to an Issue to open the Select Issue dialog box.

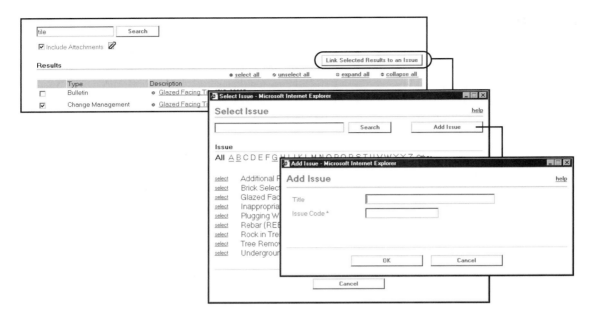

Choose whether to link the documents to an existing issue (click Select next to the issue), or to create a new issue. For a new issue, click Add Issue and enter a code and a descriptive title. Click OK when finished. The selected documents are linked to the issue.

# Issues Reports and Forms

Standard reports and forms are provided for you to use to print Issues. From the Issue document window, click Select an Action, and then Advanced Print. Click Go. Select the report or form, then click Print.

| ACME General Contractors | | | | | | | | School Addition-Automotive Center | |
|---|---|---|---|---|---|---|---|---|---|

**Issue History**
**by To Company**

| Job No: | JBAA450 | | | | | | | Date: | 4/11/00 |
|---|---|---|---|---|---|---|---|---|---|
| Project No: PRJAA450 | | | | | | | | Page: | 1 of 3 |

| To | Issue | Dated | Item | From | Number | Description | Spec Section | Status | Value |
|---|---|---|---|---|---|---|---|---|---|
| ACE Mason Contractors | | | | | MASON | Ball In Court:  DESIGN CA | | | |
| | TILE | 4/21/00 | RFP | ACMEGC | 00001 | Glazed Facing Tile | | CLO | 11000.00 |
| | | 5/4/00 | CO | ACMEGC | 00001 | Glazed Facing Tile | | APP | 9850.00 |
| ACME General Contractors | | | | | ACMEGC | Ball In Court:  DESIGN CA | | | |
| | BRICK | 4/28/00 | CO | PHILASCH | 00001 | Underground Utilities | | APP | 3300.00 |
| | PARK | 5/22/00 | CM | PHILASCH | 00005 | Additional Parking Required | | NEW | 0 |
| | | 5/22/00 | RFI | ACMEGC | 00003 | Additional Parking Required | | CLO | 0 |
| | | 5/23/00 | COR | STDPAV | 00001 | Additional Parking Required | 02000 | NEW | 7000.00 |
| | | 5/23/00 | RFP | STDPAV | 00003 | Additional Parking Required | 02000 | CLO | 8000.00 |
| | | 6/11/00 | COR | STDPAV | 00004 | Additional Parking Required | | NEW | 7000.00 |
| | | 6/11/00 | REC | STDPAV | 00014 | | | CLO | 7000.00 |
| | | 6/18/00 | CO | PHILASCH | 00005 | Approved Changes | | NEW | 14000.00 |
| | ROCK | 4/15/00 | CIC | STDPAV | 00003 | Rock in Trenches | | CLO | 0 |
| | | 4/15/00 | CM | PHILASCH | 00003 | Rock in Trenches | | PRO | 0 |
| | | 5/12/00 | COR | MOORE | 00001 | Rock in Trenches | | OPN | 6500.00 |
| | | 5/18/00 | COR | JOHNSON | 00001 | Rock in Trenches | | NEW | 7000.00 |
| | | 5/18/00 | COR | STDPAV | 00002 | Rock in Trenches | | CLO | 5500.00 |

# Part 5

# Logging and Tracking Information

**In this part**

Tracking Drawings

Managing Submittals

Tracking Materials Deliveries

Using Daily Reports

Tracking Insurance Certificates

Producing Punch Lists

*L*ogging and tracking information accurately is an important aspect of managing a successful project. This part describes how the Contract Manager module can help you more easily and effectively manage these functions.

*Tracking Drawings* explains how the module helps you identify and maintain contract drawings received and sent, while *Managing Submittals* describes how to log and track submittals through multiple reviewers and review cycles.

Read *Tracking Materials Deliveries* and *Using Daily Reports* to learn how the module enables you to track daily project events at the site, so you can identify reasons for problems and delays.

Review *Tracking Insurance Certificates* to see how all project participants can use the Insurance log. Logging and tracking lists of items that each project participant must complete before the project can be finished are described in *Producing Punch Lists*.

# Tracking Drawings

The Drawings log serves as a central location for tracking the numerous drawings and revisions participants use during a contract life cycle, while the Drawing Sets log groups new revisions for related drawings.

This chapter provides an overview of the two Drawing logs and explains how you can use them to track project drawings, specifications, other contract documents, and drawing revisions through the distribution cycle.

# Drawings Overview

The primary function of the Drawings log and Drawing Sets log is to expedite the distribution of documents.

You can use the Drawings and Drawing Sets logs to

- Log new drawings

- Group drawings by set with the Drawing Sets log

- Distribute drawings by creating distribution lists for mass distribution

- Review drawing history via drawing revisions

- Generate transmittals

Drawing development and control are handled by various project participants in the distribution phase of the contract process. Once drawings are approved for construction, the construction work can begin, signaling the start of the distribution phase. At this point, the contract is awarded, and the construction manager (CM), general contractor (GC), or subcontractor becomes involved in this phase of the drawing process. The CM or GC is responsible for coordinating all construction work and disseminating drawings to the mechanical, electrical, plumbing, and other subcontractors and vendors for construction or procurement and submittal processing.

Through the Drawings log and the Drawing Sets log, the Contract Manager module helps you perform the following functions for drawings submitted for bid, approval, construction, or other contract requirements/ negotiations.

- Maintain an accurate history of revisions to see who changed what and why

- Determine and maintain distribution lists for drawing implementation and coordination

- Identify how many copies are being sent and to whom

- Reduce data entry by automatically creating transmittals for each revision

The following diagram provides a workflow of the general stages of the design review and distribution cycles. The distribution cycle is supported.

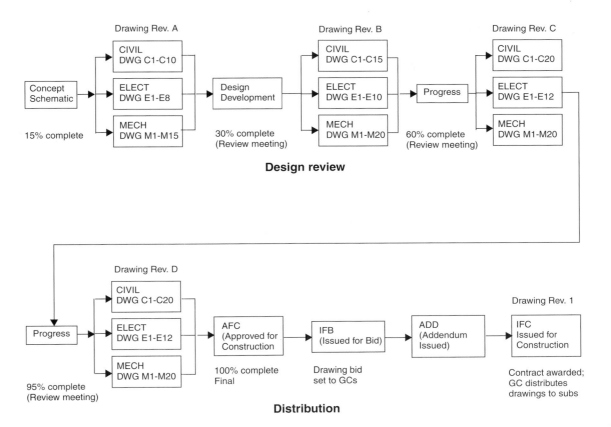

**Design review**

**Distribution**

*Design* development and review coordinates and tracks each piece of the design in the Issued For Design (IFD) phase (30%, 60%, 90% to 100% complete).

*Distribution* occurs when construction is underway—Issued For Bid (IFB) and Issued For Construction (IFC) phase—to keep all parties informed.

**Distribution**

Create distribution lists for distribution

Log contract drawings /documents

Generate a set of drawings and add drawings for distribution

Assign distribution list and individuals

Create transmittals and print reproduction order

Update log with dates

# Setting Up Drawing Data

Start by setting up the standard data used to categorize and identify drawings.

**Distribution lists**  contain the names of individuals you want to include when distributing drawings. The Company Directory should already contain information for these individuals, since the distribution lists are based on company information. You can use defined distribution lists in any project in the same database. Distribution lists are established per project using the project contact list or globally for all projects in the same database using the group contact list.

**Drawing phases**  identify the purpose for the issued drawing, such as Issued for Bid or Issued for Construction. To define drawing phases, right-click on the top level folder in the Project View, then choose Dictionaries, Drawings, Drawing Phases.

**Drawing disciplines**  categorize drawings and drawing sets by discipline, such as electrical, mechanical, or civil, for easier tracking. Standard categories are supplied or you can define your own (right-click on the top level folder in the Project View, then choose Dictionaries, Drawings, Disciplines). You can use discipline categories to sort, filter, group, and report drawing information.

**Drawing areas**  identify the various areas associated with a drawing, such as Foyer or Entry, or even a building designation, such as Lot A or Bldg B, for easier reference, filtering, sorting, and grouping. To define drawing areas, right-click on a project in the Project View, then choose Dictionaries, Drawing Areas.

*You can include paper size and number of copies per contact when you set up the Company Directory. Then, when you set up distribution lists for drawings or drawing sets, the paper size and number of copies are included for the corresponding contacts on your list.*

**Paper sizes**  enable you to identify the standard paper sizes associated with issued drawing types. For example, architectural drawings can be various sizes: A through E, and so on. Once paper sizes are defined, you can specify them for individual drawings or drawing sets when reproducing and sending multiple copies for distribution. To define paper sizes, right-click on the top level folder in the Project View, then choose Dictionaries, Drawings, Paper Sizes.

**Bid packages** help you track all drawings and corresponding revisions issued by defining a bid package for each contractor, then logging the drawings by bid package in the Drawings log. You can modify this list if additional contractors require drawings for bid. When logging drawings, the bid packages you define are available from the Latest Bid Package field. You can also filter, sort, and group by bid package, and you can assign a bid package to a drawing set. To define bid packages, right-click on the top level folder in the Project View, then choose Dictionaries, Drawings, Bid Packages.

**File numbers** define the numbers corresponding to the filing system set up specifically for drawings in your organization. You can select the appropriate file number when you log drawings. To define file numbers, right-click on the top level folder in the Project View, then choose Dictionaries, Drawings, File Numbers.

# Adding Drawing Documents

Use the Drawings log to identify and track drawings, specifications, and other supporting documentation to meet contractual requirements and ensure completion of work-site obligations. Tracking drawings through the Drawings log enables you to maintain a list of drawing revisions for the distribution cycle; review the drawing's current status—latest revision date and sent date; and review sets that contain the drawing. Typically, distribution revisions are added when a set is created, but you can also add them using the Drawings log.

**Adding drawing documents in the Drawings log**  Click Drawings in the Logs folder in the Project View, then click Add Document. Enter a Drawing Number, Title, and Issued Date, then click Select to choose the Designer. Enter any other pertinent information in the Status and Details sections.

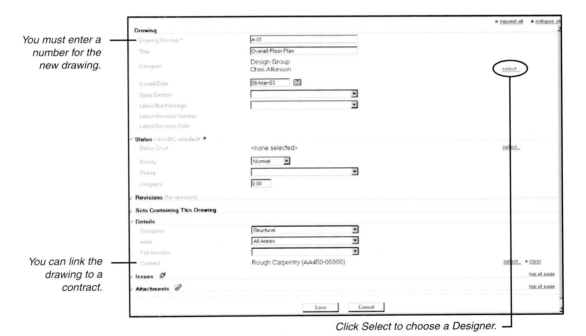

*You must enter a number for the new drawing.*

*You can link the drawing to a contract.*

*Click Select to choose a Designer.*

**Create revisions for a drawing**  In the Drawing document window, click Add in the Revisions section. Enter the revision number and title and select a revision date.

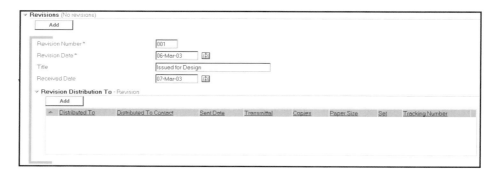

After you enter the basic information for the revision, select the contacts to receive it. Click Add in the Revision Distribution To section. Click Select in the Add Distribution dialog box and select the contacts who will receive the revision. When you finish selecting the contacts to receive the revision, click Save. Type the number of copies and choose the paper size for each contact, then click Save.

*The module enters this information as configured in the Company Directory, but you can change it at any time.*

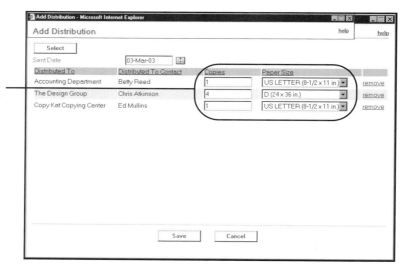

**Review drawing sets** The Sets Containing this Drawing section enables you to see all information about the drawing sets to which this drawing belongs, including the revision number, set title, its phase, progress, and creation date. If this section does not contain any information, the drawing is not part of a set.

*Indicates the revision number of the drawing when it was added to the set: it is not the latest revision number.*

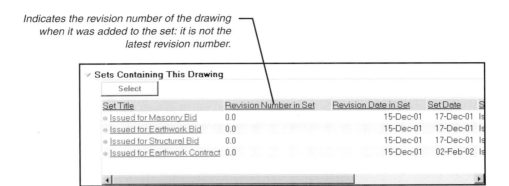

| Set Title | Revision Number in Set | Revision Date in Set | Set Date | S |
|---|---|---|---|---|
| Issued for Masonry Bid | 0.0 | 15-Dec-01 | 17-Dec-01 | Is |
| Issued for Earthwork Bid | 0.0 | 15-Dec-01 | 17-Dec-01 | Is |
| Issued for Structural Bid | 0.0 | 15-Dec-01 | 17-Dec-01 | Is |
| Issued for Earthwork Contract | 0.0 | 15-Dec-01 | 02-Feb-02 | Is |

For information about drawing sets, see *Creating Drawing Sets* later in this chapter.

**Generate multiple drawings**   The easiest way to create a master list of all drawings related to a project is to add one drawing for each discipline, then click Generate Document to create the remaining drawings. After the master list is complete in the Drawings log, you can create a set by discipline or phase in the Drawing Sets log.

Open the drawing you want to copy, then click Generate Document. Type the number of drawings you need to create, and type the drawing number to assign to the first of the new drawings. The other generated drawings will be automatically numbered sequentially using this number. All attributes of the original drawing, such as title, phase, and discipline, are copied to the new one; existing revisions are also copied. You can change any of these items within each generated drawing.

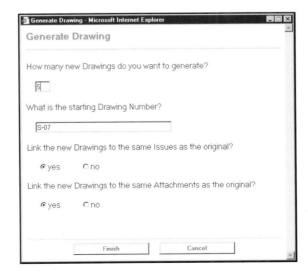

# Creating Drawing Sets

Drawings are often contained in sets for easy distribution and record keeping. Typically, sets correspond to phases such as Schematic, Issued For Bid, and Issued For Construction, and can be part of a change order, bulletin, or request for information (RFI). You can create sets from the Drawing Sets log, and then distribute the drawings to obtain a bid for work or to inform the recipient of the approved construction design. Since the recipients do not return these drawings to the originating person, you only need to track the names of persons to whom the drawings were sent and the dates they were sent.

**Create a drawing set**  Click Drawing Sets in the Logs folder in the Project View, then click Add Document. Type a name and title for the set and enter the date on which the set was received.

*Click Select to choose the person responsible for the drawing set.*

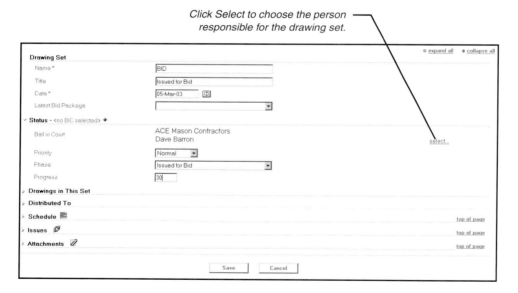

**Add drawings to a set**  In the Drawings in This Set section, click Record. Click Select in the Record Drawings dialog box. The Select Drawing dialog box lists all drawings defined in the Drawings log that have at least one revision. Click Select next to each drawing you want to include in the set, then click Save.

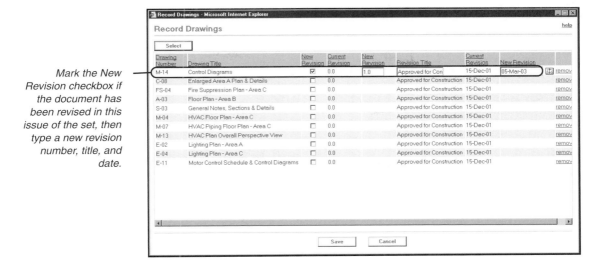

*Mark the New Revision checkbox if the document has been revised in this issue of the set, then type a new revision number, title, and date.*

**Define distribution lists for a set** In the Distributed To section, click Copy from Drawings to copy the names from the distribution lists of drawings recorded with new revisions. The module does not copy distribution lists from drawings added to the set using existing revisions. You can add additional names to the distribution list for the set by clicking Add.

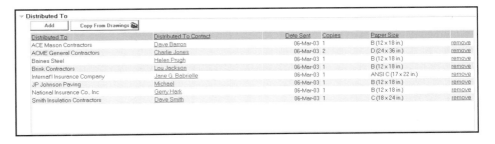

**Generate a set** After the revisions are tracked, the set may need to be reissued to the distribution list. In the Drawing Set document window, click Generate Document.

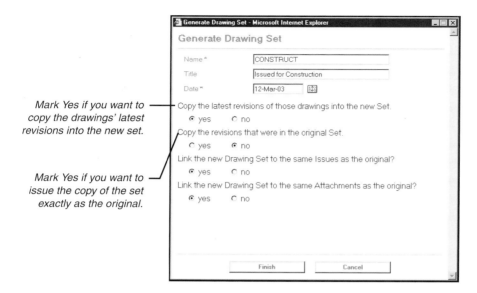

Mark Yes if you want to copy the drawings' latest revisions into the new set.

Mark Yes if you want to issue the copy of the set exactly as the original.

**Create transmittals for drawing sets**  When you create a drawing set, entries are created in the Transmittal Queue for each contact you specified for distribution. To set this preference, mark the Create Transmittals from Distribution List checkbox in the Communication section in Project Settings (right-click on the project in the Project View).

To view the Transmittal Queue, open any module log, then click the Transmittal Queue icon in the upper right side of the header.

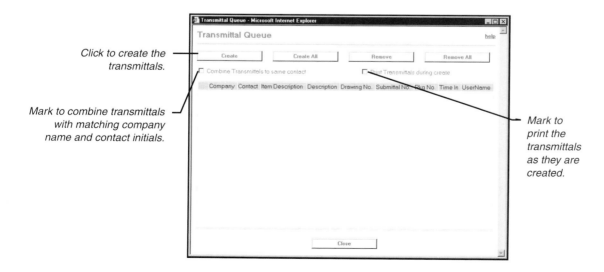

Click to create the transmittals.

Mark to combine transmittals with matching company name and contact initials.

Mark to print the transmittals as they are created.

# Drawings Reports and Forms

Standard reports are provided for you to use to print drawings. From the Drawing or Drawing Set document window, click

Select an Action, then Advanced Print. Click Go. Select a report or form, then click Print.

| ACME General Contractors | | | | | | | | | | School Addition-Automotive Center | |
|---|---|---|---|---|---|---|---|---|---|---|---|
| | | | | **Drawing Log** | | | | | | | |
| **Job No:** | **JBAA450** | | | **by Drawing Number** | | | | | **Date:** | **12/24/01** | |
| **Project No: PRJAA450** | | | | **Latest Revision** | | | | | **Page:** | **1 of 2** | |
| Drawing Number | Latest Rev. No. | Title | Area | Discipline | Phase | Bid Package | Percent Progress | Received | Sent | Designer | |
| A-01 | 0.0 | Overall Floor Plan | ALL | ARCH | IFB | BP-AR.01 | 100 | 12/17/99 | 12/17/99 | DESIGN | CA |
| A-02 | 0.0 | Floor Plan - Area A | A | ARCH | IFB | BP-AR.01 | 100 | 12/17/99 | 12/17/99 | DESIGN | CA |
| A-03 | 0.0 | Floor Plan - Area B | B | ARCH | IFB | BP-AR.01 | 100 | 12/17/99 | 12/17/99 | DESIGN | CA |
| A-04 | 0.0 | Floor Plan - Area C | C | ARCH | IFB | BP-AR.01 | 100 | 12/17/99 | 12/17/99 | DESIGN | CA |
| A-05 | 0.0 | Restroom Plan | ALL | ARCH | IFB | BP-PLB.11 | 100 | 12/17/99 | 12/17/99 | DESIGN | CA |
| A-06 | 0.0 | Reflected Ceiling Plan | ALL | ARCH | IFB | BP-FIN.06 | 100 | 12/17/99 | 12/17/99 | DESIGN | CA |
| A-07 | 0.0 | Roof Plan | ALL | ARCH | IFB | BP-RF.05 | 100 | 12/17/99 | 12/17/99 | DESIGN | CA |
| A-08 | 0.0 | Roof Details | ALL | ARCH | IFB | BP-RF.05 | 100 | 12/17/99 | 12/17/99 | DESIGN | CA |
| A-09 | 0.0 | Elevations | ALL | ARCH | IFB | BP-RF.05 | 100 | 12/17/99 | 12/17/99 | DESIGN | CA |
| A-10 | 0.0 | Building Sections | ALL | ARCH | IFB | BP-MAS.04 | 100 | 12/17/99 | 12/17/99 | DESIGN | CA |
| A-11 | 0.0 | Door / Room Finish Schedule | ALL | ARCH | IFB | BP-FIN.06 | 100 | 12/17/99 | 12/17/99 | DESIGN | CA |
| A-12 | 0.0 | Door Details | ALL | ARCH | IFB | BP-FIN.06 | 100 | 12/17/99 | 12/17/99 | DESIGN | CA |
| A-13 | 0.0 | Window Schedule & Details | ALL | ARCH | IFB | BP-GL.07 | 100 | 12/17/99 | 12/17/99 | DESIGN | CA |
| A-14 | 0.0 | Window Details | ALL | ARCH | IFB | BP-GL.07 | 100 | 12/17/99 | 12/17/99 | DESIGN | CA |
| AS-1 | 0.0 | Architectural Site & Landscape Plan | ALL | ARCH | IFB | BP-UTIL.02 | 100 | 12/17/99 | 12/17/99 | DESIGN | CA |
| C-01 | 1.0 | Site Utilities Removal Plan | ALL | CIVL | IFB | BP-UTIL.02 | 100 | 4/22/00 | 4/22/00 | DESIGN | CA |
| C-02 | 1.0 | Site Utilities Plan | ALL | CIVL | IFB | BP-UTIL.02 | 100 | 4/22/00 | 4/22/00 | DESIGN | CA |
| C-03 | 1.0 | Site Utilities Details | ALL | CIVL | IFB | BP-UTIL.02 | 100 | 4/22/00 | 4/22/00 | DESIGN | CA |
| C-04 | 0.0 | Existing Site/Removal Plan | ALL | CIVL | IFB | BP-UTIL.02 | 100 | 12/17/99 | 12/17/99 | DESIGN | CA |
| C-05 | 0.0 | Site Layout Plan | ALL | CIVL | IFB | BP-UTIL.02 | 100 | 12/17/99 | 12/17/99 | DESIGN | CA |

# Managing Submittals

During a project, managing submittals can be one of the most time-consuming tasks. This chapter describes how the Contract Manager module streamlines the submittals process by enabling you to track each stage of the review cycle and update submittal dates using activities from a linked Contract Manager module schedule.

No matter how many times a submittal is revised, you will always know who received it and when; which submittals were approved and which are pending; which are overdue and by how many days; and, most important, who is currently responsible.

The module also provides distribution copies, transmittals, and dunning letters.

# The Submittal Process

The following steps provide an overview of the typical process for entering a submittal package and tracking its progress. The rest of this chapter explains how to perform each step.

1   Add a submittal package.

2   Add submittals.

3   Record each review cycle.

4   Specify distribution.

5   Establish the schedule.

6   Track status.

7   Update the submittal when necessary.

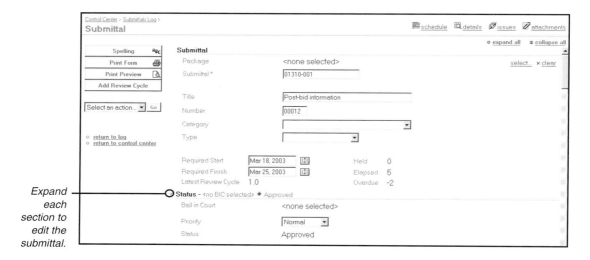

Expand each section to edit the submittal.

# Adding a Submittal Package

Group related submittals into packages for better organization. For example, assemble a submittal package for all submittals pertaining to a specific supplier, floor of a building, or area of work.

**Add a submittal package**  Click Submittal Packages in the Logs folder in the Project View, then click Add Document. In the Submittal Package document window, type a package number.

*The Package Number field is required. One way to structure package number codes is to use CSI codes. You can compile a comprehensive list of packages and submittals at the beginning of a project before you identify reviewers.*

Specify the title, status, priority, and ball in court for the submittal package. Select the company or the corresponding contact for the persons responsible for acting on the submittal package in the Received From, Sent To, Returned By, and Forwarded To fields in the Workflow section.

*You can use Project Settings to specify a default Submittal Coordinator to receive and review submittals. Right-click on the project name in the Project View and choose Project Settings. In the Key Parties section, click Select to specify a contact person.*

The module calculates the value for this field— the percentage of approved items.

Expand to view the submittals in the submittal package.

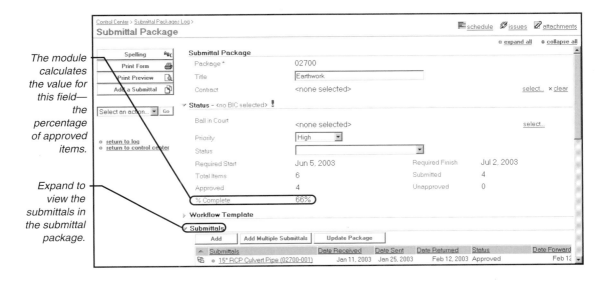

For details on adding a submittal, see *Adding a Submittal* in later in this section.

**Add a new submittal to a submittal package**  Scroll down to the Submittals section and click Add to open a new Submittal document window. The submittal are automatically added to the package, as indicated in the Package field.

To add multiple new submittals at once, click Add Multiple Submittals to open the Add Multiple Submittals wizard. Enter the number of new submittals you want to add, and the starting number. Click Next, then enter the titles, categories, and types for the new submittals. Click Finish to create the new submittals.

**Add an existing submittal to a submittal package**  To add an existing submittal to a package, open the Submittal document window and select a package number in the Package field.

**Remove a submittal from a submittal package**  To remove a submittal from a package, open the Submittal document window in Edit mode and click the Clear link located to the right of the Package field. This deletes the package number. The module then lists the item by itself in the Submittals log.

# Adding a Submittal

The Submittals log window lists all of your submittals, both individual and those in packages. Use the Submittals log to add a submittal.

**Add a submittal**  Click Submittals in the Logs folder in the Project View, then click Add Document. In the Submittal field, type a unique code, up to 15 characters, to identify the submittal. A sequential number that you can change is automatically assigned to the submittal. To add the submittal to an existing package, click Select to open the Select Submittal Package window.

Select a Category for the submittal. Use the Type field to assign a type to the submittal. You can define different submittal types in the Submittal Type dialog box (with no projects open, right-click the top-level folder in the Project View, select Dictionaries, Submittal, Types). You can do the same for categories.

Click the calendars to specify the date range for the submittal using the Required Start and Required Finish date fields. If a date is not selected, the module automatically calculates the required start and required finish based on the Submittal Preparation Start date and the Approval Period Finish date respectively. To do this, in the Schedule section, you must pick a successor activity, specify the lead times for the two activities, and click Update from Lead Time.

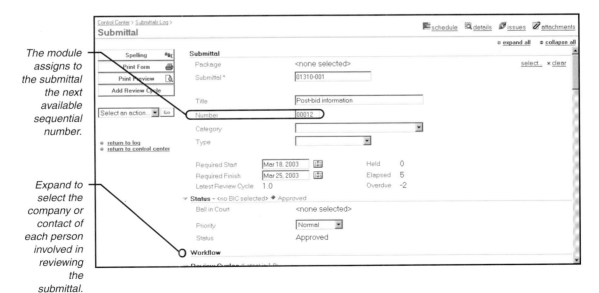

The module assigns to the submittal the next available sequential number.

Expand to select the company or contact of each person involved in reviewing the submittal.

**Delete a submittal**  You can delete a submittal from the Submittal document window. Open the submittal from the Submittal log window. Click Select an Action, Delete Submittal, then click Go.

**Delete a submittal package**  To delete a submittal package, open the package from the Submittal Package log window. Click Select an Action, Delete Package, then click Go. IMPORTANT: When you delete a package,  all submittals in the package are also deleted.

# Copying a Submittal

A submittal package often contains several similar items. To reduce data entry, use the Generate Submittals command to create multiple copies of a submittal, then edit each copy to reflect any differences.

*You can also generate submittals from contracts and purchase orders. For instructions, see* Generating Submittals from a Contract or Purchase Order *in the* Managing Contracts and Purchase Orders *chapter.*

**Copy a submittal**  Click Submittals in the Logs folder in the Project View. Open the submittal you want to copy. Click Select an Action, Generate Submittal, then click Go. Specify the number of new submittals you need, and choose whether to link the new submittals to the same issues as the submittal being copied. Click Finish to create the new submittals.

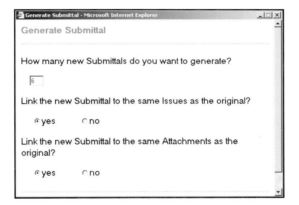

The module numbers the copies with the next available sequential numbers. For example, if the number of a submittal being copied is 16600-0003, you make three copies, and 16600-0003 is the last number assigned in that series, the module numbers the copies 16600-0004 through 16600-0006.

# Tracking and Updating a Submittal Using Review Cycles

The Review Cycles section in the Submittal document window shows the complete history for a submittal, starting with the first revision. If you are linked to a Contract Manager module schedule, and are using its activities in the Schedule section, the module automatically updates submittal schedule activities when you update dates in the Review Cycles section of the Submittal document window.

*For more information about using a schedule in the Contract Manager module, see Exchanging Contract Manager Module Data.*

**Record a review cycle**   Click Submittals in the Logs folder in the Project View, then click the submittal title to open the selected submittal. Click Add Review Cycle. The revisions will be automatically numbered sequentially, beginning with 001. Type a description of this review cycle, then enter the dates when the submittal changed hands. For example, for the first review cycle in the following figure, the submittal was received from Dave Smith on 16-Apr-02 and sent to Chris Atkinson on 22-Apr-02; Chris Atkinson rejected and returned it on 23-Apr-02, and it was forwarded to Dave Smith so it could be updated for another review.

*The review cycle begins when a date is entered in the Received field.*

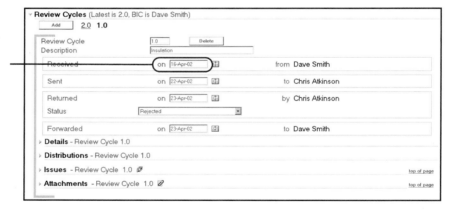

The following steps outline the process for updating submittal schedule dates from review cycle dates:

### To update from the first review cycle

1   When you enter a submittal received date in the Review Cycles area, the start date for the Submittal Preparation activity is updated and the checkbox next to the date is marked to indicate an actual start for this activity in the Schedule section of the Submittal document.

2   When you enter a sent date indicating when you sent the submittal for review in the Review Cycles section, the finish date for the Submittal Preparation activity is updated and the checkbox next to the finish date is marked in the Schedule section of the submittal document to indicate an actual finish. In addition, one day is added to this sent date to update the start date of the Approval Period activity; the checkbox next to the start date is also marked to indicate that this activity has started.

3   When you enter a submittal returned date, the finish date for the Approval Period activity is updated and the checkbox next to the date is marked to indicate an actual finish for this activity in the Schedule section of the submittal document. The status of this revision does not need to be approved for this to happen.

4   If this review cycle is approved, the Resubmit start and finish dates in the Schedule section of the submittal document remain blank. If the review cycle is rejected or has a status other than Approved, all current schedule dates on the submittal Schedule section are retained. If rejected, you would normally start a new review cycle. This process can be continued until you finally approve the submittal.

### To update from any subsequent review cycle

1   When you enter a submittal received date, the module updates the start date for the Resubmit activity in the Schedule section of the submittal document with the received date in this revision; the Start checkbox is also marked to indicate that the next submittal cycle has started, as long as the finish date for an Approval Period activity is marked. The module sets the Schedule section dates using the next lowest revision number in the Review Cycles section.

2   When you enter a submittal returned date and change the status to Approved, if the finish date for an Approval Period activity is entered, the finish date for the Resubmit activity is updated in the Schedule section with the returned date in this revision and marks it as an actual finish. This process occurs for any review cycle after the first cycle.

3   If a review cycle after the first cycle is rejected, you would normally start a new review cycle. Any changes to review dates or status will update the Schedule section of the submittal document using the same conditions listed above. If you clear a review date, the Schedule section dates related to that date are also cleared.

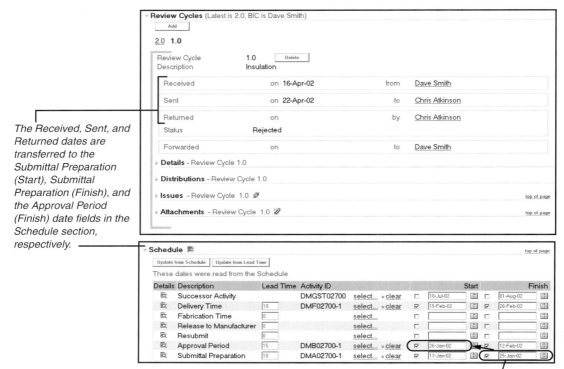

The Received, Sent, and Returned dates are transferred to the Submittal Preparation (Start), Submittal Preparation (Finish), and the Approval Period (Finish) date fields in the Schedule section, respectively.

This date plus one day creates the actual start of the Approval Period activity.

For details on exporting Contract Manager module data to Project Management module schedules, see the *Exchanging Contract Manager Module Data with a Project Management Module Schedule* chapter.

You can also export this data to a Contract Manager module schedule to create or update the activities in the related Project Management module schedule.

# Tracking Multiple Reviewers

Sometimes you want more than one person to review a submittal. When two or more participants review a submittal at the same time, their review information is treated as a "set." When calculating status, a set of reviewers is treated as one revision.

**Enter a set of reviewers** Mark the Multiple Reviewers checkbox in the Workflow section in the Submittal document window. (This option is available only before a review cycle is added.) Add a review cycle, scroll to the Multiple Reviewers section and click Add. In the Revision Set window, select a reviewer. Enter information about the reviewer, the status, description, dates, and any remarks noted by the reviewer for the revision. Click Save & Add Another to add more reviewers.

For any revision that consists of a multiple reviews, the module determines the most critical record in the set and displays those dates in the Review Cycles section. The most critical record is the one with the fewest dates entered, indicating that responses for this revision have not been received, sent, returned, or forwarded by the appropriate ball-in-court (BIC) on time, causing a significant delay in the submittal process. If the number of dates for more than one reviewer is the same, the row with the earliest date farthest to the right is used.

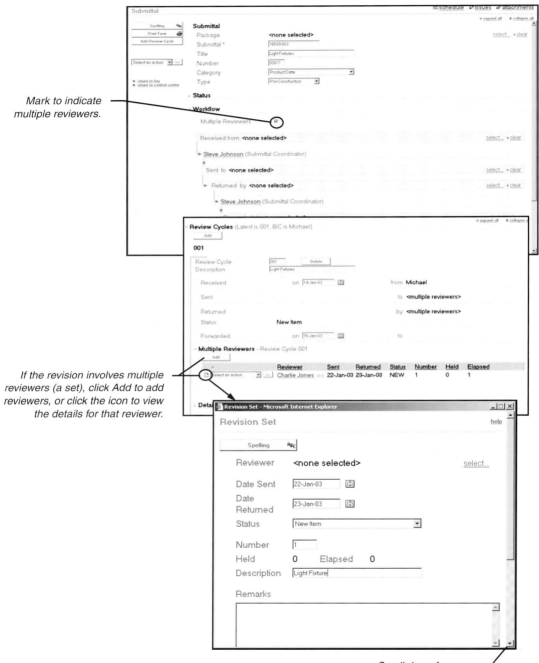

*Mark to indicate multiple reviewers.*

*If the revision involves multiple reviewers (a set), click Add to add reviewers, or click the icon to view the details for that reviewer.*

*Scroll down for more information.*

# Updating Submittals from a Package

To assign a status for several submittals in a package at one time, open a Submittal Package document window, then click Update Package in the Submittals section. This speeds the update process when you receive several submittals in a package from a contractor on the same day.

*Mark each submittal for which you want to change status and/or dates. Click Next.*

*Enter the dates with which you want to update the submittals you selected, and select a status for the submittals.*

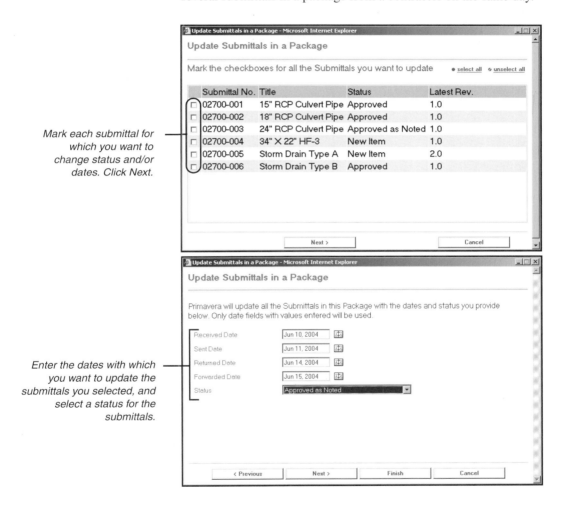

*If you enter a returned date, the module prompts you for the contact who returned the submittal package. Click Select to select a contact or company.*

*The module prompts you to make sure you want to update submittals already approved and to add new revisions to accommodate dates you entered.*

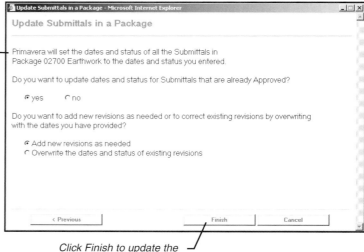

*Click Finish to update the submittals you selected.*

# Using Schedule Activities for Reference and to Update Submittals

If you use the Project Management module to schedule projects, you can use the Schedule section in the submittal document to reference and update the activities associated with your submittals with early/actual start and finish dates from the schedule activities.

*In Edit mode, expand the Schedule section to associate Project Management module activities and their early and actual dates with submittal activities.*

*Indicates that dates were read from a schedule.*

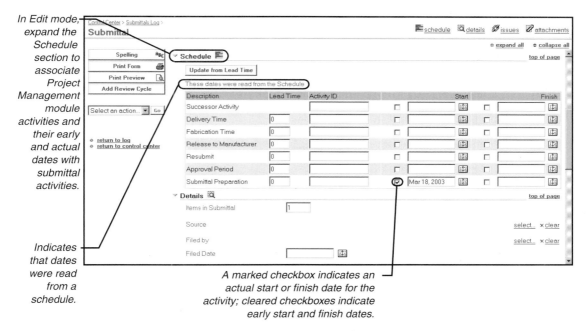

*A marked checkbox indicates an actual start or finish date for the activity; cleared checkboxes indicate early start and finish dates.*

For details on linking to a Project Management module schedule, see the *Exchanging Contract Manager Module Data with a Project Management Module Schedule* chapter.

**Update scheduling information** Click Update from Schedule in the Schedule section in the Submittal document window. You can also customize the Workspace to update submittals by clicking Customize this Page to add an Update Submittals object to the Workspace.

*If the top-level folder is highlighted in the Project View, and you click Update from Schedule/Update from Lead Time in the Update Submittals object in the Workspace, all schedules linked to Contract Manager module projects will be updated. If one project is highlighted in the Project View, only the schedule linked to that project is updated.*

For detailed information on customizing your Workspace, see *Customize Workspace dialog box* in Help.

**Record scheduling information** Expand the Schedule section in the Submittal document window and click Select in the Activity ID column to select activities from the linked Project Management module schedule.

Whenever the Project Management module schedule has been updated, click Update from Schedule to ensure that you are using the most current dates.

 *The module assumes you are using activities with conventional, finish to start relationships, and it calculates dates based on a seven-day workweek calendar.*

In the following example, the early start date of the selected schedule activity was used to update dates for the Submittal Preparation activity and the required start date. The early finish date for the Approval Period activity was used to update the submittal required finish date, as well as the dates for this activity.

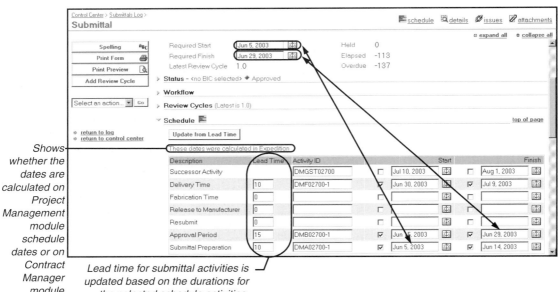

*Shows whether the dates are calculated on Project Management module schedule dates or on Contract Manager module dates.*

*Lead time for submittal activities is updated based on the durations for the selected schedule activities.*

**Specify the activity that succeeds the current one** Select the applicable activity from the Successor Activity field. The dates for all other start and finish times are based, in succession, on the date of the selected successor activity. For example, the finish date of the Delivery Time activity is one day before the start date of the Successor activity; if the start date of the Successor activity is 12/30/00, the finish date of the Delivery Time activity is 12/29/00. This ensures that materials needed to perform the Successor activity are delivered in time for construction to begin.

**Specify the submittal activity duration** To calculate the start date for the activity, enter the number of days to deduct from the finish date of the activity specified. For example, if you enter 30 days for the lead time for an activity with a finish date of 12/29/02, the start date for that activity becomes 11/30/02. If you change the number in this field or change an activity after dates have been calculated, you are prompted to overwrite the dates with new start and finish dates.

If you use Project Management module activities to update submittal activity dates, the lead time calculation is based on the number of days of duration for each schedule activity.

If you do not use schedule activities to update submittal activity dates, you can manually enter the days of lead time necessary for each submittal activity to complete. You must first specify the Successor activity and its corresponding dates, then enter the lead time for the remaining submittal activities. To update the dates for activities based on the Successor activity dates and the lead times entered, click Update from Lead Time in the Schedule section of the Submittal document. The original dates will be overwritten with dates calculated from the lead times.

**Record scheduling information** Click Select in the Activity ID column to select the Successor activity in the Schedule section of the Submittal document window. Update the schedule dates for the submittal manually or use the date popup.

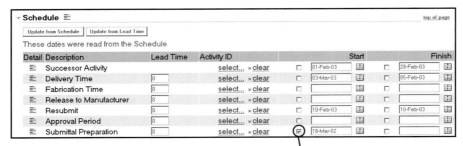

A marked checkbox indicates an actual start or finish for an activity.

## Viewing the Status and Details of a Submittal

In the Submittal and Status sections of the Submittal document window, you can quickly check who is currently responsible for a submittal item, how long the individual has had it, and how many days it is overdue.

In the Details section in the Submittal document window, enter the number of items attached to the submittal, the company and initials of the contact who produced the submittal items (Source), a drawing number, and the company or name of the contact who filed the drawing, and filed date, if applicable.

*Primary submittal coordinator from the Project Settings dialog box.*

*Returned contact.*

You can optionally select a date for the first Approved By person (the primary submittal contact for the project) when he or she approves the submittal; the module does not supply a value for this field. The module completes the second Approved By Date field when the submittal has a status of Approved; you can change this date.

## Submittals Bar Chart

For more information on this feature, see *Submittals Bar Chart window* in Help.

You can view the Submittals log in a bar chart. The Submittals Bar Chart window provides a graphical representation of the Submittals log window in a schedule format, similar to the Schedule Data window. The bar chart shows submittals that have a Required Start date or at least one latest date (Received, Sent, Returned, or Forwarded).

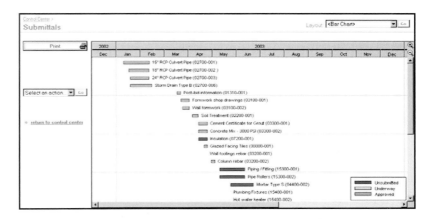

To access this feature, choose Bar Chart from the Submittals log window Layout menu.

# Compiling a Submittal Distribution List

The Distributions section within the Review Cycles section of the Submittal document window enables you to record the names of contacts who should receive a copy of the submittal. You can specify distribution to an individual contact, company and/or to a distribution list that lists the individual contacts for each submittal revision row.

*Click Companies in the Project Information folder in the Project View, then click Define Distribution Lists to create a distribution list containing multiple contacts.*

**Compile a distribution list**  Open the submittal in Edit mode. In the Review Cycles section, expand the Distributions section and click Add to select contacts from the Distribute Submittal dialog box. Click Select to open the Select Contacts dialog box and choose the contacts to put on the submittal distribution list. Click Save. Mark the Transmit checkbox if you want a transmittal created for each contact listed. Each transmittal issued per individual on the list also contains the same remarks and number of copies you specify in the Distribute Submittal dialog box; you can change them individually as appropriate. Click Save when finished.

After you select the contacts, you can enter other information required in the Distributions section by clicking the contact's icon to open the Submittal Distribution dialog box.

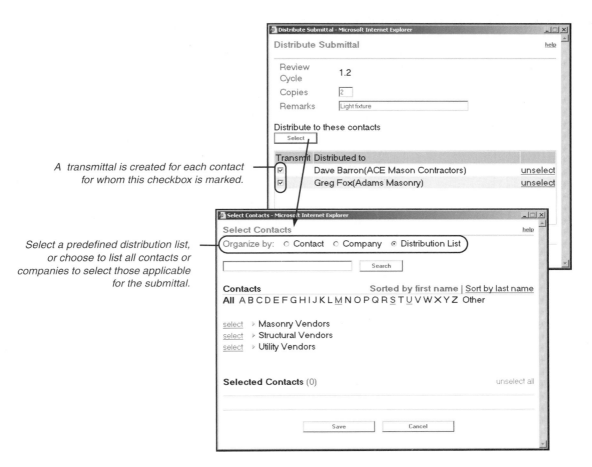

A transmittal is created for each contact for whom this checkbox is marked.

Select a predefined distribution list, or choose to list all contacts or companies to select those applicable for the submittal.

For more information about creating transmittals, see the *Preparing Transmittals* chapter.

Use the Transmittal Queue to generate transmittals based on the revision updates and distribution contacts.

 *In the Communication section in the Project Settings dialog box, you can specify whether transmittals are generated automatically from revised submittals. The default setting is to generate transmittals automatically.*

Transmittal entries are automatically entered in the Transmittal Queue when you specify a contact in the Distributions section of the Review Cycles section of the Submittal document window and mark the Transmit (create transmittal) checkbox for that distribution. Transmittals are also created when you enter sent or forwarded dates in the Review Cycles section in the Submittal document window, or in the Submittal Package document window.

# Producing Transmittals from Submittals

You can create a transmittal for each contact listed in the Distributions section in the Review Cycles section of the Submittal document window and for each updated submittal.

From the Transmittal Queue, you can create any transmittals shown and add them to the Transmittals log. You can then print them for multiple recipients on your distribution list.

For more information about defining Project Settings, see the *Setting Up Dictionaries and Preferences* chapter.

**Create a transmittal from a submittal**   Click Transmittal Queue located at the top of the Submittal screen to open the Transmittal Queue. The queue automatically contains an entry for each item in the Distributions section. It also contains a list of the submittals for which you entered (or edited) a date in either the Sent or Forwarded field in the Review Cycles section.

 *If you do not want transmittals created automatically, go to the Communication section of the Project Settings dialog box and clear the Create Transmittals from Submittal Revisions and the Create Transmittals from Distribution List checkboxes. Distribution lists will not be sent to the Transmittal Queue.*

Select the entry for which you want to create a transmittal and click Create, or click Create All to create transmittals for all items in the list. In either case, the transmittals are added to the Transmittals log and includes any attachments from the originating documents to the transmittals generated.

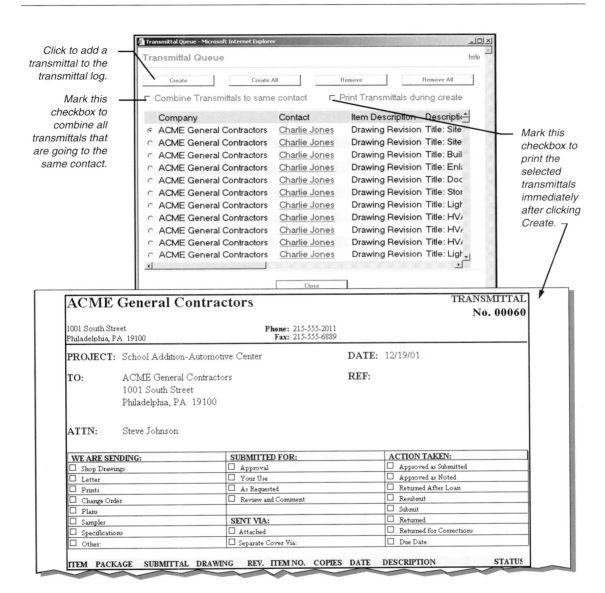

Click to add a transmittal to the transmittal log.

Mark this checkbox to combine all transmittals that are going to the same contact.

Mark this checkbox to print the selected transmittals immediately after clicking Create.

# Submittal Reports and Forms

Standard reports and forms are provided for you to use to print submittal information, as well as a dunning letter to inform responsible participants of overdue items.

From the Submittal or Submittal Package document window, click Select an Action, then Advanced Print. Click Go. Select a report, form, or dunning letter, then click Print.

| ACME General Contractors | | | | | | | | | School Addition-Automotive Cente | | |
|---|---|---|---|---|---|---|---|---|---|---|---|
| **Submittals** | | | | | | | | | | | |
| Job No: JBAA450 | | | | by Ball In Court | | | | | Date: | 12/24/0 | |
| Project No: PRJAA450 | | | | | | | | | Page: | 1 of | |
| | | | Latest | | | Required | | | Latest Dates | | |
| BIC | Package | Submittal | Revision | Title | Status | Start | Finish | Received | Sent | Returned | Forwarded |
| | | | Sue Johnson | | | | | | | | |
| | 08000 | 08000-001 | 1.0 | Custom Frames | NEW | | | | | | |
| | 08000 | 08000-002 | 1.0 | Custom Doors | NEW | | | | | | |
| | | | Dave Barron | | | | | | | | |
| | 04400 | 04400-002 | 1.0 | Mortar Type S | NEW | 5/25/00 | 6/23/00 | | | | |
| | | | Steve Johnson | | | | | | | | |
| | | 03100-001 | 1.0 | Formwork shop drawings | APP | 3/23/00 | 4/3/00 | 3/23/00 | 3/27/00 | 4/7/00 | |
| | | 03100-002 | 1.0 | Wall formwork | APP | 3/23/00 | 4/3/00 | 3/25/00 | 3/27/00 | 4/7/00 | |
| | | 09900-001 | | Paint Submittal | | | | | | | |
| | | 11000-001 | | Lockers | | | | | | | |
| | | 15600-001 | | Fan Coil Units | | | | | | | |
| | | | Chris Atkinson | | | | | | | | |
| | 03200 | 03200-004 | 1.0 | Foundation wall rebar | NEW | 4/25/00 | 5/22/00 | 5/5/00 | 5/5/00 | | |
| | 04400 | 04400-001 | 1.0 | Mortar Type N | NEW | 5/25/00 | 6/23/00 | 6/4/00 | 6/4/00 | | |
| | 05300 | 05300-001 | 1.0 | Roof Panels | NEW | 6/9/00 | 6/23/00 | 6/9/00 | 6/12/00 | | |
| | | | Eric Thompson | | | | | | | | |

# Tracking Materials Deliveries

Use the Materials Delivery log to track materials delivered to your site. By recording each materials delivery in the Contract Manager module, you will always know what has been delivered, how much of it was delivered, the dollar value of the delivery, and what remains to be delivered.

This chapter describes two ways you can use the Contract Manager module to record materials deliveries. If daily reports are part of your routine, you can record materials deliveries in the daily report and let the Contract Manager module update your materials delivery records. Conversely, you can update the Materials Delivery log and have the module record materials deliveries in your daily reports.

If you use requisitions for payment, you can include materials deliveries effective during the pay period.

# Adding Materials Delivery Records

Add materials delivery records when you need to closely track materials delivered to your company, the amounts to be delivered, and the amount of money spent on materials to date.

Tracking materials deliveries is a two-step process. First, create a materials delivery record for each material you plan to track, and then update the record each time you receive a delivery of that material.

For more information about contracts and purchase orders, see the *Managing Contracts and Purchase Orders* chapter.

You can add materials delivery records directly in the Materials Delivery log, or you can allow them to be automatically generated from a lump sum or unit price purchase order (PO) or contract. If you set up contracts or POs, and you plan to track materials deliveries, generating your materials delivery records from contracts and POs generally saves time. If you generate a requisition from a PO or contract, you can also automatically add materials delivery records to the requisition schedule of values.

The module will automatically link the Line Item number in the Requisition section of the Materials Delivery document window with the correct line item from the requisition's Schedule of Values section if you generate both the material and the requisition from the same contract/PO. The order of generation is not important.

### Generate materials delivery documents from a contract or PO

Add a contract or PO or edit an existing unapproved one. Click the Line Items icon to go to the Line Items section and click Add Lump Sum or Add Unit Price. Type a unique material name for each line item in the Material Name field (do not select an existing one). Enter costing information in the Costing section. Click Save and Close when you are finished. In the Contract or PO document window, choose Select an Action, Generate Materials, then click Go and respond to the questions in the Generate Materials dialog box.

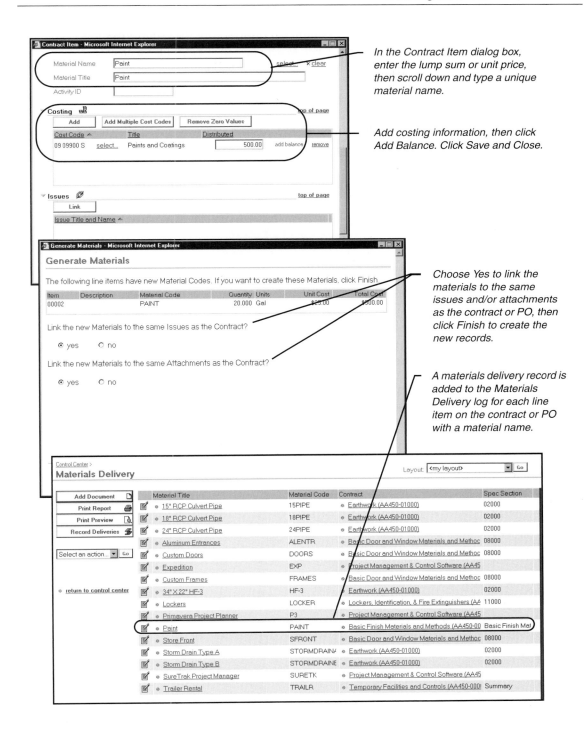

In the Contract Item dialog box, enter the lump sum or unit price, then scroll down and type a unique material name.

Add costing information, then click Add Balance. Click Save and Close.

Choose Yes to link the materials to the same issues and/or attachments as the contract or PO, then click Finish to create the new records.

A materials delivery record is added to the Materials Delivery log for each line item on the contract or PO with a material name.

### Add materials delivery documents directly to the Materials Delivery log

Click Materials in the Logs folder, then choose Add Document. Enter the information about the material you plan to track. As you create each document, add the corresponding deliveries in the Delivery Ticket section. The quantity received is copied to the Delivered field (in the Cost section), and the total value of the delivery (Total field) and the remaining balance in the Balance field are calculated.

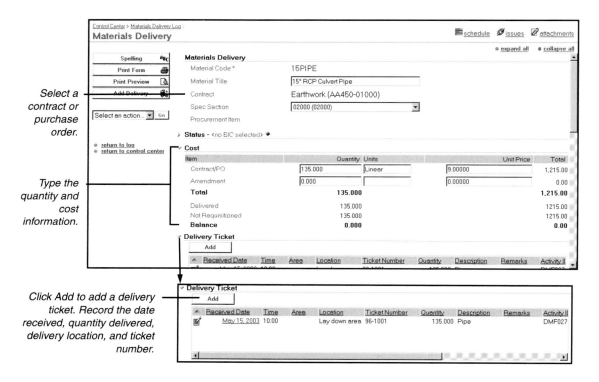

*Select a contract or purchase order.*

*Type the quantity and cost information.*

*Click Add to add a delivery ticket. Record the date received, quantity delivered, delivery location, and ticket number.*

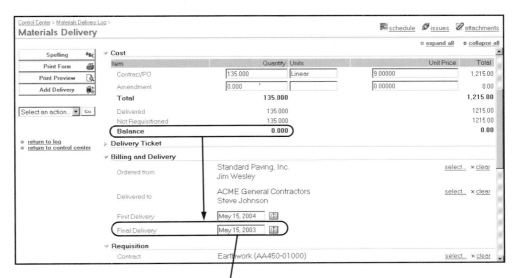

When the balance equals zero, The module copies
the date of the last delivery to the Final Delivery field.

**Record a delivery** Click Materials in the Logs folder in the Project
View, then open the materials delivery document. Choose Select an
Action, Add Delivery, then click Go. Enter the information about the
material delivered and save it. A new line is then added to the Delivery
Ticket section of the document,

## Using Project Management Module Schedule Dates

For details about linking to a Contract Manager module schedule, see the *Exchanging Contract Manager Module Data with a Project Management Module Schedule* chapter.

Once you link the Contract Manager module to a Project Management module schedule, you can view early and actual start and finish dates, original and remaining durations, percent complete, and total float for individual activities you associate with Contract Manager module documents. Click the Schedule icon at the top of the page or scroll down to the Schedule section while in a Contract Manager module document (in which you have entered an activity from the linked Project Management module project). You can use schedule activities as a reference or use their early/actual schedule dates to update dates in Contract Manager module documents. For materials delivery, you can choose to update the start date and the completion date in the Schedule section in the Materials Delivery document window with the start date and completion date of the activity ID you select.

# Adding a Materials Delivery Ticket and Posting to Multiple Materials at Once

When a delivery is made, you usually receive types of materials you have received before, which already exist in your materials log. You can log multiple items that have been delivered on a ticket all at once through the Materials Delivery log.

**Add a materials delivery ticket**  You can add a materials delivery ticket from the Materials Delivery log for one material or multiple materials. Click Record Deliveries, then click Add to list all available materials. You can quickly log multiple materials as having been delivered against that ticket. Select the materials that have been delivered from the list. After you click Save, you can enter the quantity, location, and so on for each item in the ticket.

*Enter a number for the ticket.*

*Click to view all available materials in the Materials Delivery log.*

*After you select materials and click Save, you can enter the quantity, location, and other information.*

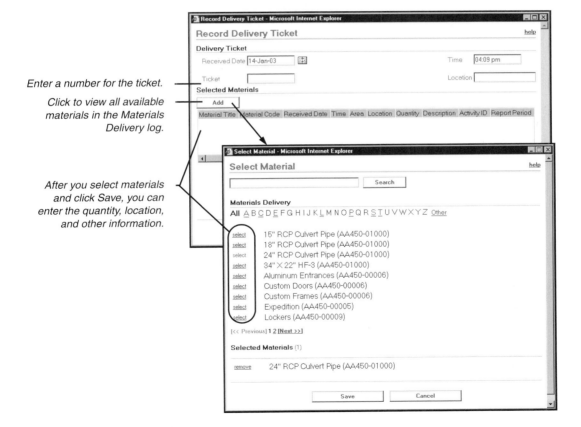

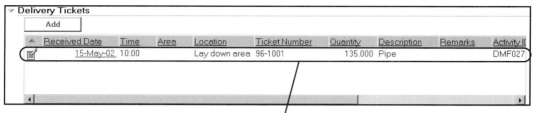

The delivery is then posted to the Delivery Ticket
section of the Materials Delivery document window.

 You can also add materials from the Materials section of a
daily report. For more information about this feature, see the
Using Daily Reports chapter.

# Including Materials Deliveries on Requisitions

Contracts usually require partial payments at regular intervals based on the amount of work accomplished and materials installed. The contract price is divided into a list of component prices or work items, so that progress can be measured more precisely. This list, called a schedule of values, accompanies each payment requisition. At the end of each period, a requisition for payment is submitted that shows the value of work performed and materials installed since the last payment.

For details on setting requisition preferences, see the *Setting Up Dictionaries and Preferences* and *Preparing Requisitions for Payment* chapters.

Materials delivered and approved change orders applicable to each period can be collected and added to the corresponding requisition. When you generate a new requisition, you are prompted to "get" approved changes, materials delivery, and/or schedule dates. For example, if you have a contract that requires pipe, and you must purchase the pipe, the units of pipe are recorded in the Line Items section of the Contract document window. You can generate a materials delivery document from the contract, and once the pipe arrives, enter the arrival date in the Delivery Ticket section of the Materials Delivery document window.

Next, generate a requisition from the contract to get paid for the pipe. In the Requisition document window's Schedule of Values section, choose More Commands, Get Materials Delivery to collect costs on the materials you purchased for the period. The Contract Manager module prompts you to "get" approved change orders, materials deliveries, and/or schedule dates. The materials information is then inserted in the Schedule of Values section in the Requisition document window. You can then send the requisition to the recipient's Inbox, or print a form.

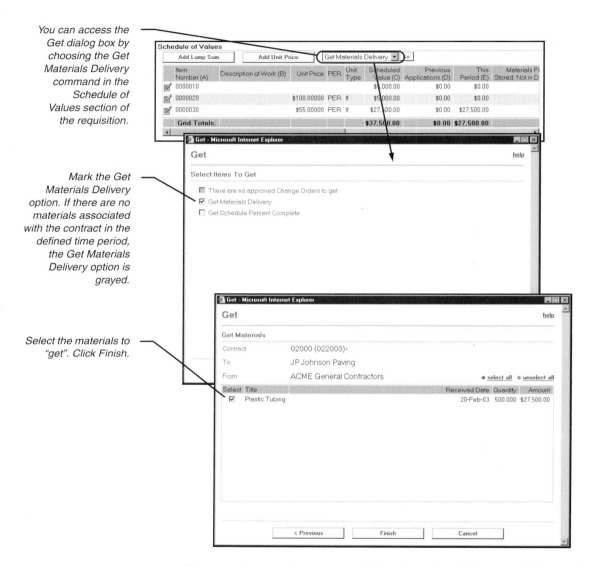

You can access the Get dialog box by choosing the Get Materials Delivery command in the Schedule of Values section of the requisition.

Mark the Get Materials Delivery option. If there are no materials associated with the contract in the defined time period, the Get Materials Delivery option is grayed.

Select the materials to "get". Click Finish.

You can also generate a new requisition from the existing requisition, and get materials. From the Requisition document window, choose Select an Action, Generate Requisition, then click Go.

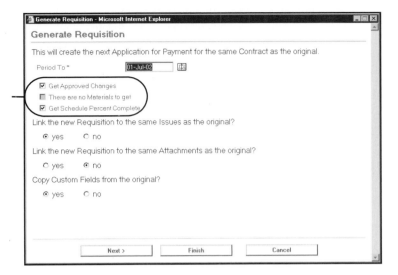

*When you generate a new requisition from an existing requisition, you are also prompted to "get" approved changes, materials delivery, and schedule dates.*

You can set requisition options for how costs for materials are handled when generating a new requisition. To access the Requisition Options dialog box, choose Select an Action, Requisition Options from a Contract or Purchase Order document window. Preferences set here apply to this contract/PO and override the preferences set in the Requisitions section of the Project Settings dialog box.

*Choose this option to retain costs for materials stored in column F (Materials Presently Stored, Not in D or E) in the Schedule of Values section.*

The Delivery Ticket section in the Materials Delivery document window contains a Requisitioned Date column that indicates when a delivery has been included in a requisition for payment.

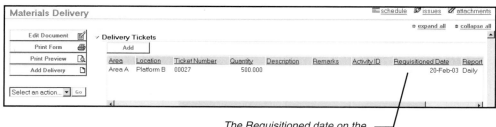

The Requisitioned date on the
Delivery Ticket is blank until you
perform a "get" in the requisition.

# Materials Delivery Reports, Forms and Dunning Letters

Standard reports and forms are provided for you to use to print contract and materials delivery records. You can also generate a dunning letter containing materials deliveries past due.

From the Materials Delivery document window, click Select an Action, then Advanced Print. Click Go. Select the report, form, or dunning letter, then click Print.

| ACME General Contractors | | | | | | | | | School Addition-Automotive Center |
|---|---|---|---|---|---|---|---|---|---|
| **Materials Delivery** | | | | | | | | | |
| Job No:   JBAA450 | | | | | | | | Date: | 12/24/01 |
| Project No: PRJAA450 | | | | | | | | Page: | 1 of 1 |
| Material | Ordered From | Delivered To | Units | Unit Price | Contract Amnt / Qnty | Deliverec Amnt / Qnty | Not Requisitioned Amnt / Qnty | Balance Amnt / Qnty | First / Final Delivery |
| 15PIPE | STDPAV | ACMEGC | Linear | $9.00 | $1,215.00 | $1,215.00 | $1,215.00 | $0.00 | 5/15/00 |
| 15" RCP Culvert Pipe | | | Spec Section: 02000 | | 135.00 | 135.00 | 135.00 | 0.00 | 5/15/00 |
| 18PIPE | STDPAV | ACMEGC | Linear | $11.00 | $1,650.00 | $1,100.00 | $1,100.00 | $550.00 | 5/15/00 |
| 18" RCP Culvert Pipe | | | Spec Section: 02000 | | 150.00 | 100.00 | 100.00 | 50.00 | |
| 24PIPE | STDPAV | ACMEGC | Linear | $14.50 | $3,132.00 | $1,450.00 | $1,450.00 | $1,682.00 | 5/22/00 |
| 24" RCP Culvert Pipe | | | Spec Section: 02000 | | 216.00 | 100.00 | 100.00 | 116.00 | |
| ALENTR | SUPPLY | ACMEGC | Lump Sum | $18,600.00 | $18,600.00 | $0.00 | $0.00 | $18,600.00 | |
| Aluminum Entrances | | | Spec Section: 08000 | | 1.00 | 0.00 | 0.00 | 1.00 | |
| DOORS | SUPPLY | ACMEGC | Each | $2,950.00 | $88,500.00 | $0.00 | $0.00 | $88,500.00 | |
| Custom Doors | | | Spec Section: 08000 | | 30.00 | 0.00 | 0.00 | 30.00 | |
| EXP | PRIMAV | ACMEGC | License | $2,500.00 | $2,500.00 | $2,500.00 | $2,500.00 | $0.00 | 3/30/00 |
| Expedition | | | | | 1.00 | 1.00 | 1.00 | 0.00 | 3/30/00 |
| FRAMES | SUPPLY | ACMEGC | Each | $2,330.00 | $69,900.00 | $0.00 | $0.00 | $69,900.00 | |
| Custom Frames | | | Spec Section: 08000 | | 30.00 | 0.00 | 0.00 | 30.00 | |
| HF-3 | STDPAV | ACMEGC | Linear | $39.40 | $3,546.00 | $0.00 | $0.00 | $3,546.00 | |
| 34" X 22" HF-3 | | | Spec Section: 02000 | | 90.00 | 0.00 | 0.00 | 90.00 | |
| LOCKER | SCHOOL | ACMEGC | Each | $110.00 | $55,000.00 | $0.00 | $0.00 | $55,000.00 | |

# Using Daily Reports

Daily reports provide a history of project events, including a description of physical conditions, a summary of the work accomplished at the job site, lists of materials used and delivered, a record of visitors to the site, and a report of any problems encountered that day. You can also include schedule activities if the Contract Manager module is linked to a Project Management module project, add attachments to the report to clarify its contents, and optionally filter those activities by responsibility.

This chapter describes how to create and use daily reports.

# Preparing a Daily Report

Use daily reports to enter information about important daily events. You can use these detailed records when you need to explain delays or justify costs.

**Prepare a daily report**  Click Daily Reports in the Logs folder in the Project View to open the Daily Reports log window, then click Add Document. the module enters the current date and day and the report period, which you can edit. Select the company and contact associated with the report in the Contractor field. In the Status section, assign priority and approval information for the report. In the Work Activity section, record descriptions of progress, delays, new conditions, problems, and anything else that may affect the project schedule or cost.

*Select a report period.*

*Expand and add any descriptive information you want to include in the daily report.*

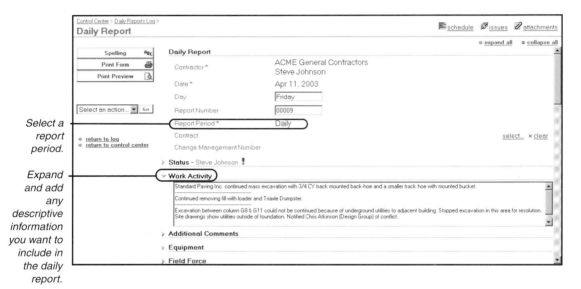

# Reporting Resource Use

Use the Equipment and Field Force sections in the Daily Report document window to list the equipment and labor resources used during the day.

**Record resource use**  Click Daily Reports in the Logs folder in the Project View, then click the document icon for the daily report. Expand the Equipment section and click Add. Enter information describing the equipment in the Daily Equipment Record dialog box, including remarks about any problems with the equipment and what it was used for.

To record field personnel, expand the Field Force section, then click Add. Enter information about labor use in the appropriate fields in the Daily Labor Record dialog box.

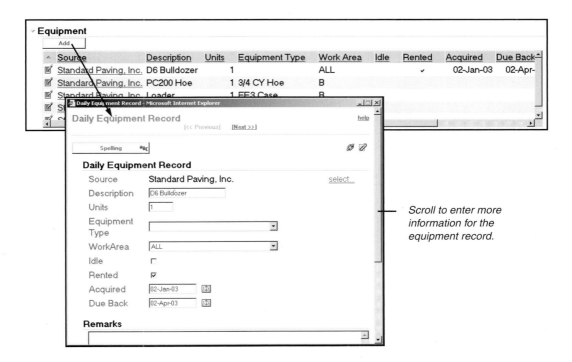

*Scroll to enter more information for the equipment record.*

# Listing Visitors

Use the Visitors section in the Daily Report document window to record the names of site visitors and the companies they represent.

**List visitors**   Click Daily Reports in the Logs folder in the Project View, then click the document icon for the daily report. Expand the Visitors section and click Add. Enter information about the visitor, including the arrival time, in the Daily Visitor Log dialog box.

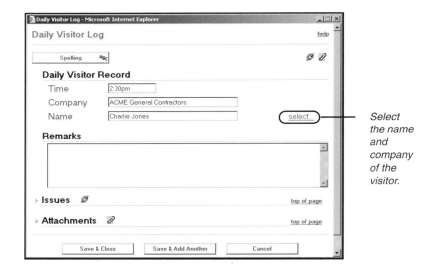

*Select the name and company of the visitor.*

# Recording Materials Deliveries

**Record materials deliveries**  Click Daily Reports in the Logs folder in the Project View, then click the document icon for the daily report. Expand the Materials section and click Add. Enter information about the delivery. When you select the Material Name that describes what was delivered, the contract number to which it refers will appear in the Contract field in the Delivery Ticket dialog box. When different contracts are issued for the same material, record each delivery separately in the Materials section. To change the contract in the Delivery Ticket window, a different material must be selected.

*Enter the material information.*

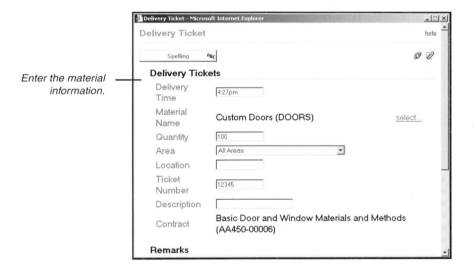

For more information about materials deliveries, see the *Tracking Materials Deliveries* chapter.

# Linking Daily Reports and Materials

When you record deliveries in the Materials section, each material available for selection is linked to its contract or purchase order in the Materials section. The matching delivery record is then copied from the Materials section in the Daily Reports document window to the Delivery Ticket section in the Materials Delivery document window.

**Assign multiple materials to a daily report at once**  From the Materials section, you can create a material ticket, then quickly assign material deliveries to the daily report.

For example, to record materials deliveries on a daily report, click Record Delivery Ticket in the Materials section and enter a ticket number and location in the Record Delivery Ticket dialog box. Click Add to add materials to the delivery ticket. All available materials from the Materials Delivery log appear in the Select Material dialog box. Select the materials to add to the daily report from the list.

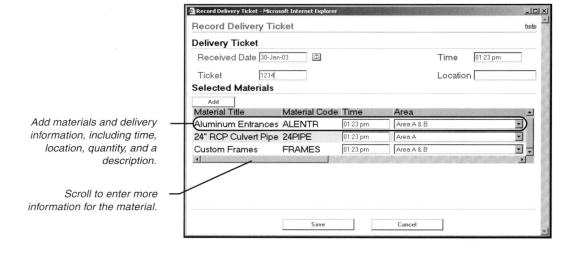

Add materials and delivery information, including time, location, quantity, and a description.

Scroll to enter more information for the material.

# Including Schedule Activities

You can include activities from the linked Project Management module project when you create a daily report. The daily report shows all activities that should be underway (with no actual finish) based on their date range (start to early finish) falling within or on the date of the daily report in the Contract Manager module. By including underway schedule activities, you can compare actual progress to the schedule and convey that information to the participants to whom you send the report.

You can also limit the activities included in the daily report by using a specific activity code from the Project Management Module Activity Codes Dictionary. By default, this code is Responsibility. To copy activities from the Project Management module schedule into the Daily Report document window Schedule section for only the contractor appearing in the daily report, define the Responsibility code in the Activity Code Definitions dialog box for the project database to which your Contract Manager module project links. Assign activities to this contractor using the Responsibility code in the Project Management module project. You must also mark the Use Responsibility to Filter Activity Retrieval in Daily Reports checkbox in the Schedule section in the Project Settings dialog box to specify that you want to run this activity code selection to filter activities for the daily report.

*Define the Responsibility code in your project and assign values to activities for it.*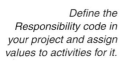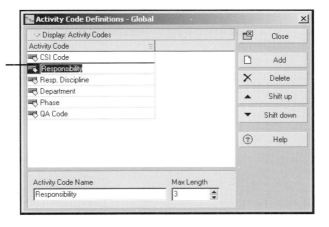

*You can use the Schedule section without Project Management module activities; just type the information.*

In the Daily Report document window, expand the Schedule section to see a list of activity IDs; titles; start (ES) and finish (EF) dates; percent complete (PCT); original and remaining durations (RD); total float (TF); and free float (FF) of each underway activity from the Project Management module project. Worked On is checked if work has been performed for an activity.

*Click to add schedule activities and to include underway schedule activities and/or meetings on the report.*

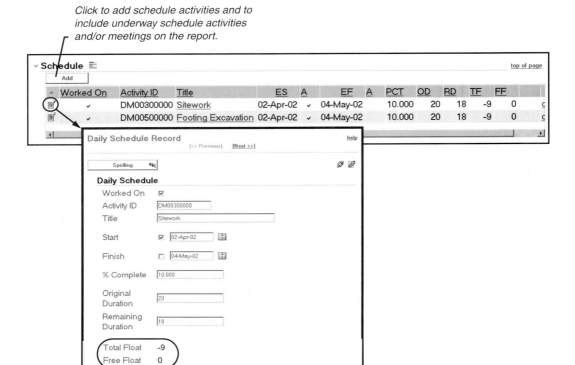

*You can add, delete, or change any of the activity data shown in this list, except total float (TF) and free float (FF).*

 *If the Use Responsibility to Filter Activity Retrieval in Daily Reports checkbox is marked in the Project Settings dialog box Schedule section, only the linked Project Management module activities that have an RESP value assigned to them will appear in the Contractor field of the Daily Report document window. If the checkbox is cleared, all linked Project Management module activities in the same date period will appear.*

# Recording Weather Conditions

You can track weather conditions for the day in the daily report for up to three periods or shifts.

Click Daily Reports in the Logs folder of the Project View, then click the document icon for the daily report. Expand the Weather section and enter information about the weather for each period. Select an amount of time for the Length of Suitable Conditions field.

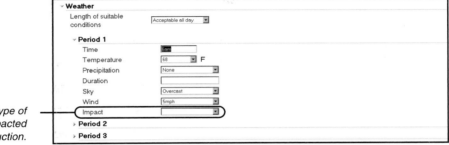

*Select the type of weather that impacted production.*

# Adding Attachments

You may want to include a photograph taken at the job site, a drawing submitted for bid by a subcontractor, or other files with your daily report to clarify a point or substantiate a decision. You can do so by attaching the file to the report. This is especially useful if you took a digital photo at the job site; you can simply attach the file to that day's daily report.

For more information about attaching files to Contract Manager module documents, see the *Working with Log and Document Windows* chapter.

**Attach a file to a daily report**  Click Daily Reports in the Logs folder in the Project View, then click the document icon for the daily report. In the Attachments section, click Attach File to select the file you want to attach to the daily report. Click Attach URL to attach a Web address to the daily report.

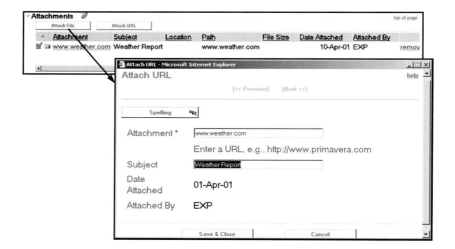

You can also attach files to individual components of the daily report. For example, you can attach files to items in the Field Force section or Materials section. In this case, any files you attach apply only to the specific item to which you attach them, not to the entire daily report.

 *Attachments added to a row in the Materials section also appear in the corresponding delivery record in the Materials Delivery log.*

# Generating Daily Reports

To save time entering data, you can create a daily report from an existing one. Simply generate a copy of the existing report, then modify the copy.

**Generate a daily report** Click Daily Reports in the Logs folder in the Project View. Open the daily report you want to copy. Choose Select an Action, Generate Document, then click Go to open the Generate Daily Report wizard. Edit the fields to reflect any changed information, then click Next. Choose which information to copy, then click Finish. Only the work activity, equipment, and field force information are copied to the new report; the module does not copy visitors and materials.

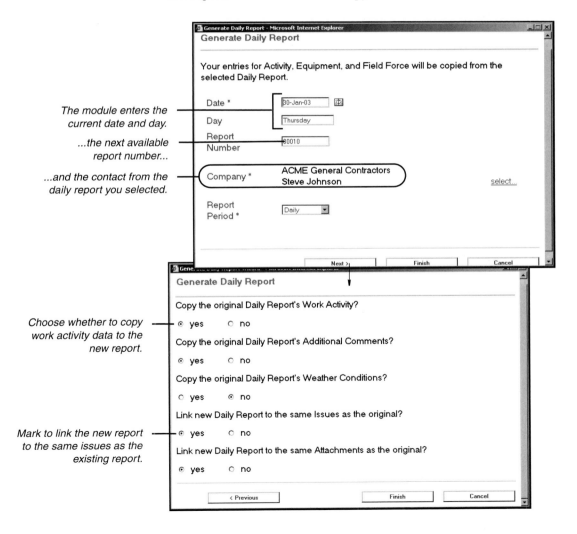

The module enters the current date and day.

...the next available report number...

...and the contact from the daily report you selected.

Choose whether to copy work activity data to the new report.

Mark to link the new report to the same issues as the existing report.

# Reports and Forms for Daily Reports

Standard reports and forms are provided for you to use to print daily reports.

From the Daily Report document window, click Select an Action, Advanced Print. Click Go. Select the report or form, then click Print.

| **ACME General Contractors** | | | | | | | **School Addition-Automotive Center** |
|---|---|---|---|---|---|---|---|
| **Daily Reports** | | | | | | | |
| Job No:    JBAA450 | | | | | | | Date:    11/25/03 |
| Project No: PRJAA450 | | | | | | | Page:    1 of 7 |

| Date | Company | Number | Temperature | Sky | Wind | Precipitation | Activity |
|---|---|---|---|---|---|---|---|
| 3/30/03 | Sunday | | | | | | |
| | Standard Paving, Inc. | S0001 | 62 | Clear | Light | None | Building demolition completed. |
| | | | | | | | Acme setting up paint mixing room. |
| 3/31/03 | Monday | | | | | | |
| | ACME General Contractors | 00001 | 72 | Clear | Light | None | Began mobilizing on site.  Gelco installing the construction fence and trailers. |
| | | | | | | | Standard Paving Inc. completed building demolition. |
| | | | | | | | Acme setting up paint mixing room. |
| 4/3/03 | Thursday | | | | | | |
| | ACME General Contractors | 00002 | 68 | Overcast | 5mph | None | Continued to mobilize on site.  Gelco continued installing the construction fence and trailers. No power, heat, etc. on-site as of yet. |
| | | | | | | | Sitework contractor Standard Paving watered down construction road. |
| | | | | | | | Acme setting up paint mixing room. |

# Tracking Insurance Certificates

**In this chapter**

**Adding an Insurance Certificate**

The Insurance log provides a convenient place to record information about the insurance policies for all project participants. This chapter describes how you can use this log to keep track of the policies you carry for your company and the companies that work for you.

# Adding an Insurance Certificate

Every contractor carries several types of insurance for his or her company and employees, and some contracts require proof of insurance for all project participants, including subcontractors. With the Insurance log, you can conveniently store information about relevant insurance policies for all project participants, including worker's compensation and bonding.

**Add an insurance certificate**  Click Insurance in the Logs folder in the Project View, then click Add Document. This opens a new Insurance document window and automatically sets the status to New and the priority to Normal. Enter the information about the policy in the fields provided. In the Insurance section, add information about the contract between your organization and the insured organization.

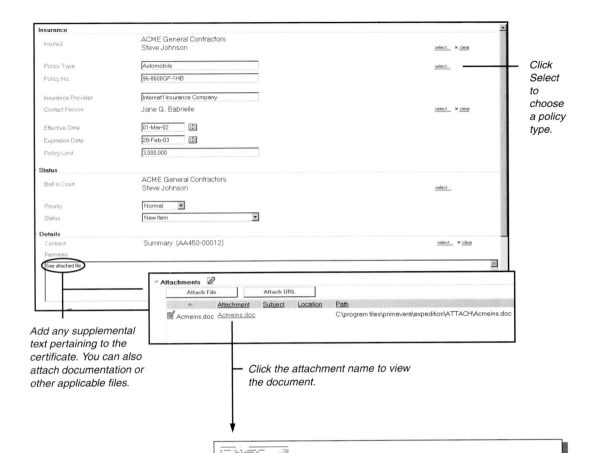

*Click Select to choose a policy type.*

*Add any supplemental text pertaining to the certificate. You can also attach documentation or other applicable files.*

*Click the attachment name to view the document.*

*When this policy expires, you can replace it with an updated attachment or modify the attached file from the originating application, such as Microsoft Word.*

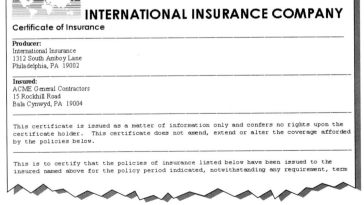

# Insurance Reports and Forms

Standard reports and forms are provided for you to use to print a list of insurance certificates, details about a certificate, or a notification that an updated certificate is needed. From the Insurance document window, click Select an Action, then Advanced Print. Click Go. Select the report or form, then click Print.

| ACME General Contractors | | | | | | | | | School Addition-Automotive Center | | |

**Insurance Log**

| Job No: | JBAA450 | | | | | | | | Date: | 12/26/01 | |
| Project No: PRJAA450 | | | | | | | | | Page: | 1 of 1 | |

| | | | | | | | | | Contract | |
| Insured | Policy Type | Policy Number | Effective | Expires | Insurance Company | Type | To | From | Number |
| --- | --- | --- | --- | --- | --- | --- | --- | --- | --- |
| ACMEGC | Automobile | 96-8608GF-1HB | 3/1/00 | 2/28/01 | Internat'l Insurance Company | CON | ACMEGC | PHILASCH | AA450-00012 |
| ACMEGC | General Liability | 96-3122GF-1FD | 3/1/00 | 2/28/01 | Internat'l Insurance Company | CON | ACMEGC | PHILASCH | AA450-00012 |
| ACMEGC | Umbrella | 96-8467GF-3DS | 3/1/00 | 2/28/01 | Internat'l Insurance Company | CON | ACMEGC | PHILASCH | AA450-00012 |
| ACMEGC | Workers Compensation | 96-73S4GF-S23 | 3/1/00 | 2/28/01 | Internat'l Insurance Company | CON | ACMEGC | PHILASCH | AA450-00012 |
| BRINK | Automobile | 96224-GF633-9 | 2/1/00 | 1/30/01 | National Insurance Co., Inc. | CON | BRINK | ACMEGC | AA450-00300 |
| BRINK | General Liability | 96450-AA900-7 | 2/1/00 | 1/30/01 | National Insurance Co., Inc. | CON | BRINK | ACMEGC | AA450-00300 |
| BRINK | Workers Compensation | 96-WRKS-900Y0 | 2/1/00 | 1/30/01 | National Insurance Co., Inc. | CON | BRINK | ACMEGC | AA450-00300 |
| MASON | Automobile | 96-09789-CC-G5 | 3/1/00 | 2/28/01 | Mutual Insurance Company | CON | MASON | ACMEGC | AA450-00602 |
| MASON | General Liability | 96885-XC226-9 | 3/1/99 | 2/29/00 | Mutual Insurance Company | CON | MASON | ACMEGC | AA450-00602 |
| MASON | Workers Compensation | 96-99897CC-13 | 3/1/00 | 2/28/01 | Mutual Insurance Company | CON | MASON | ACMEGC | AA450-00602 |
| STDPAV | Automobile | 1089-96-009GF | 2/1/00 | 1/30/01 | Internat'l Insurance Company | CON | STDPAV | ACMEGC | AA450-01000 |
| STDPAV | General Liability | 96500-AB789-X | 2/1/00 | 1/30/01 | Internat'l Insurance | CON | STDPAV | ACMEGC | AA450-01000 |

# Producing Punch Lists

The Punch List log provides a convenient place to create lists of items that must be completed before the project can be finished. For example, before you can close out a contract, any damages incurred during construction must be repaired, and missing equipment must be noted. Punch lists make it easy to record and track the status and cost of outstanding items.

This chapter describes how to create punch lists, add items to punch lists, and print punch list items.

# Creating Punch Lists

Use punch lists to record items that must be completed before the end of your project.

**Create a punch list**   Click Punch Lists in the Logs folder in the Project View, then click Add Document. Type a name and title for the punch list, and indicate the participants between whom the punch list exists. In the Details section, you can add a description.

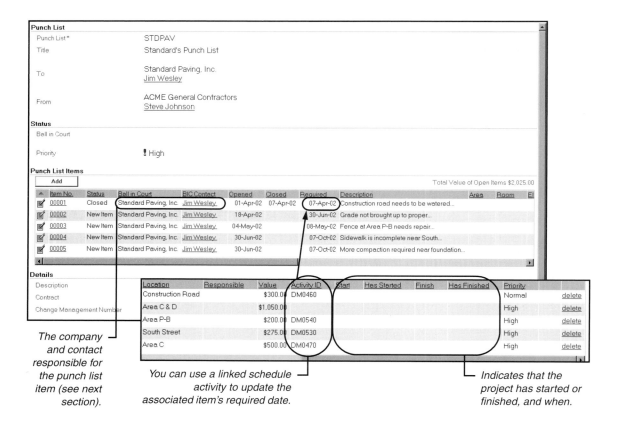

*The company and contact responsible for the punch list item (see next section).*

*You can use a linked schedule activity to update the associated item's required date.*

*Indicates that the project has started or finished, and when.*

# Adding Items to a Punch List

Once you establish a punch list for a particular contractor, you can add items to the list as they occur.

**Add a punch list item** Click Punch Lists in the Logs folder in the Project View, then click the document icon for the punch list. In the Punch List Items section, click Add. The module numbers the new item sequentially, enters the current date in the Opened field, gives it a status of New, a priority of Normal, and a required date seven days from the opened date; you can edit these fields.

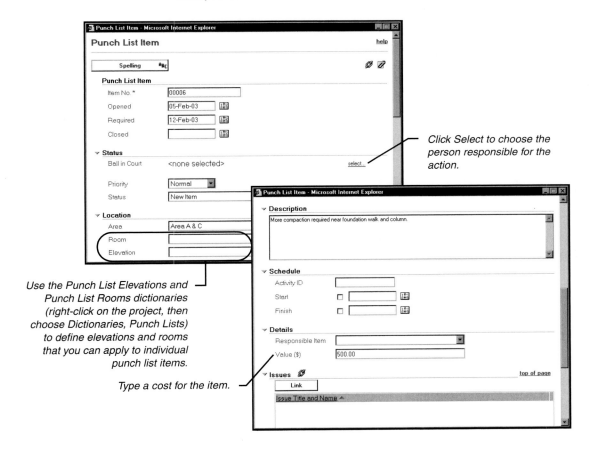

Click Select to choose the person responsible for the action.

Use the Punch List Elevations and Punch List Rooms dictionaries (right-click on the project, then choose Dictionaries, Punch Lists) to define elevations and rooms that you can apply to individual punch list items.

Type a cost for the item.

For details on exporting data from the Contract Manager module and importing them to a Project Management module schedule, see the *Exchanging Contract Manager Module Data with a Project Management Module Schedule* chapter.

When the item is complete, enter a date in the Closed field. To select a date, click the calendar icon. If you export punch list data to your Project Management module schedule, the closed date is used to update the actual finish of the corresponding activity in the project.

# Punch List Reports and Forms

Standard reports and forms are provided for you to use to print punch list information. From the Punch List document window, click Select

an Action, then Advanced Print. Click Go. Select the report or form, then click Print.

| ACME General Contractors | | | | | | | School Addition-Automotive Center | | |
|---|---|---|---|---|---|---|---|---|---|
| **Punch Lists** | | | | | | | | | |
| Job No:   JBAA450 | | | | | | | Date: | 10/7/03 | |
| Project No: PRJAA450 | | | | | | | Page: | 1 of 1 | |

| Punch List Item No. | Status | Ball In Court | | Opened | Closed | Required | Location | Description | Value |
|---|---|---|---|---|---|---|---|---|---|
| STDPAV | Standard's Punch List | | | | | | | | |
| 00001 | CLO | STDPAV | JW | 4/1/03 | 4/7/03 | 4/7/03 | Construction Road | Construction road needs to be watered down to remove dust. | $300.00 |
| 00002 | NEW | STDPAV | JW | 4/18/03 | | 6/30/03 | Area C & D | Grade not brought up to proper level gratings | $1,050.00 |
| 00003 | NEW | STDPAV | JW | 5/4/03 | | 5/8/03 | Area P-B | Fence at Area P-B needs repair due to damage caused while parking | $200.00 |
| 00004 | NEW | STDPAV | JW | 6/30/03 | | 10/7/03 | South Street | Sidewalk is incomplete near South St. entrance | $275.00 |
| 00005 | NEW | STDPAV | JW | 6/30/03 | | 10/7/03 | Area C | More compaction required near foundation walk & column F & G | $500.00 |

# Part 6

# Exchanging Contract Manager Module Data

**In this part**

**Exchanging Contract Manager Module Data with a Project Management Module Schedule**

**Exchanging Contract Manager Module Data with Other Applications**

*T*his part shows you how, with a few simple steps, you can link to and exchange Contract Manager module data with a Project Management module project.

*Exchanging Contract Manager Module Data with a Project Management Module Schedule* describes how you can base Contract Manager module dates on required schedule dates, stay current with schedule changes, and update Project Management module dates with data from the Contract Manager module.

*Exchanging Primavera Data with Other Applications* shows you how to export Primavera data to other applications, such as spreadsheets or databases, and import data to Primavera from other applications for submittals, the company directory, cost worksheet cost codes and titles, and specification sections using comma-separated value (.CSV) files.

# Exchanging Contract Manager Module Data with a Project Management Module Schedule

This chapter describes how you can review dates from a Project Management module schedule from within the Contract Manager module to see how schedule delays or other factors affect a project. Once you specify the Project Management module project schedule to link to the Contract Manager module project, you can use early and actual activity dates from the schedule to update start and finish dates in the Contract Manager module.

In addition, you can create or update activities in the Project Management module based on Contract Manager module activity data.

# Setting Up Project Management Module Schedules for Use with the Contract Manager module

If you use the Contract Manager module and the Project Management module, you can exchange project data between the products in the way that works best for your organization. This section suggests steps for setting up projects to benefit from the interchange.

**Management checklist**  Setting up a smooth export/import process between the Contract Manager module and the Project Management module requires some initial planning. The owner, construction manager, or other person responsible for managing contracts should work with the Project Management module project controls coordinator to build the schedule and standardize the procedures used to create and update projects.

*You can import Contract Manager module data into Project Management module 3.5x, 4.0, 4.1, and 5.0.*

The Project Management module project controls coordinator should perform the following steps before importing Contract Manager module data:

1  If you plan to export requisition data to update costs in the Project Management module project, specify two decimal places for calculations in the Project Management module project for compatibility with the Contract Manager module schedule of values cost.

2  When assigning cost codes to activities in the Project Management module project, do not assign resources to activities for which you plan to update costs. The costs are exchanged as expenses rather than resources. Also, make sure the cost codes are the same as those being used in the Contract Manager module database from which you are exporting data.

Cost codes exchanged between the Project Management module project and the Contract Manager module should be no longer than 30 characters.

The Contract Manager module exports one cost account code and corresponding distribution amount per document but will not recognize the cost code for activities with an assigned resource associated with their cost code.

3   If you plan to create new activities in the Project Management module project from the Contract Manager module, define the Responsibility activity code in the Project Management module Activity Codes dialog box. The company abbreviation in the Contract Manager Module Company Directory will be assigned as Responsibility code values for the new activities during the export.

4   Notify the person responsible for the Contract Manager module contract control that these steps have been completed.

5   The Contract Manager module administrator links the Project Management module project to the Contract Manager module project and incorporates the schedule activities in the documents. The data can then be imported into the Project Management module.

**Contract Manager module documents linked to activities**   You can import data from the Contract Manager module to create and update activities in a Project Management module project for the following types of documents:

| | | |
|---|---|---|
| ■ Change Orders | ■ Drawing Sets | ■ Purchase Orders |
| ■ Budgeted Contracts and Committed Contracts | ■ Materials | ■ Requisitions (Schedule of Values) |
| ■ Daily Reports | ■ Punch Lists | ■ Submittals |

You can also create cost accounts and RESP codes in a Project Management module schedule by exporting data from the Contract Manager module.

You can associate and update dates for the following Contract Manager module documents with Project Management module activities:

| | | |
|---|---|---|
| ■ Change Management | ■ Materials | ■ Punch List Items |
| ■ Change Order Line Items | ■ Noncompliance Notices | ■ Purchase Orders and Purchase Order Line Items |
| ■ Budgeted Contract Line Items/Committed Contract Line Items | ■ Notices | ■ Requests for Information |
| ■ Daily Reports | ■ Procurement Items | ■ Submittals and Submittal Packages |
| ■ Drawing Sets | ■ Proposals | ■ Trend Line Items |

# Linking to a Project Management Module Schedule

You can link projects scheduled in the Project Management module to Contract Manager module projects. Once this link is established, you can use activities in these projects to build and update Contract Manager module project data. You can create a connection from the Contract Manager module to any Project Management module project. You can then specify the project name in the Contract Manager module using the Schedule section in the Project Settings dialog box.

 *Before you can access schedule data, you need to set up the Project Management module connection using the Contract Manager Module Server Configuration utility. See the Contract Manager Module Installation Guide for more information.*

Note the following before linking the Contract Manager module to a Project Management module project:

■    You can link one Project Management module project group or project per Contract Manager module project.

■    The Contract Manager module assumes a continuous, seven-day work calendar for the linked Project Management module project regardless of its calendar assignment in the Project Management module schedule.

■    You must update the data for the Project Management module project each time you change values in the Activity Codes dialog box. In the Project Management module, choose File, Commit Changes, then File, Refresh Data to refresh the data and save changes.

### To connect a Contract Manager module project to a Project Management module project

1   From your PC, open the Contract Manager module.

2   Right-click on the project name in the Project View and choose Project Settings.

3   In the Schedule section, select Primavera from the Schedule drop-down list.

4   Select the database from the drop-down list, then select the project to which you want to connect.

5   Click Save. Project Management module activities will appear in Activity ID selection lists within Contract Manager module documents for the linked project.

*Even if you do not have access to the Project Management module from your PC, you can view schedule data from within a Contract Manager module project.*

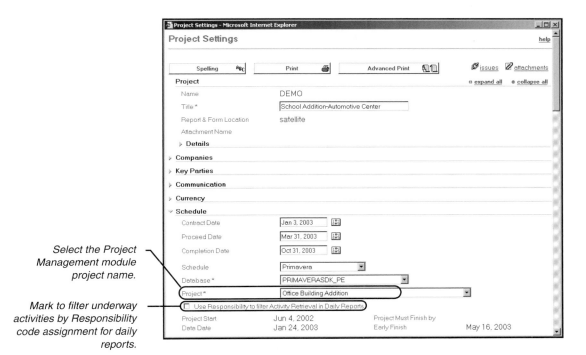

*Select the Project Management module project name.*

*Mark to filter underway activities by Responsibility code assignment for daily reports.*

You must manually change activity IDs associated with existing Contract Manager module documents if the Contract Manager module project is later linked to a different Project Management module project.

**Display a chart of all activities in the linked Project Management module project**  Click Schedule in the Project Information folder.

*The activities are listed by early start date.*

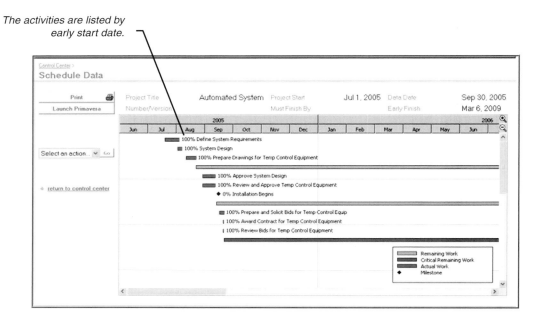

# Importing Contract Manager Module Data into Project Management Module Projects to Create or Status Activities

When you create new activities in the Project Management module project from the Contract Manager module, the activity ID and description, early start, early finish, cost code and title, and company abbreviation (for the RESP activity code in the Project Management module project) are added.

**Import Contract Manager module data into the Project Management module project**  To import Contract Manager module data, open the Project Management module project into which you want to import. Choose File, Import from Contract Manager.

*Choose the options you want to import from the Contract Manager module.*

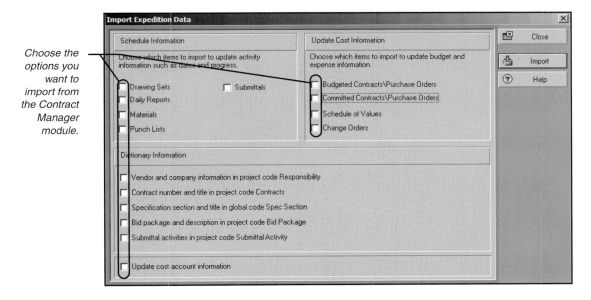

After marking the checkboxes for the options you want to import into the Project Management module, click Import. Before the import begins, the Contract Manager Import Report dialog box appears, which shows all fields that will be updated. Click Commit Changes to execute the import.

Once complete, you can view the updated information in the Project Management module. You can also open the original documents in the Contract Manager module from the link in the Project Management module. Customize the activity detail to show the Contract Manager module Docs tab. Highlight the Contract Manager module document and click View.

# Assigning Activity IDs to Contract Manager Module Documents

After you create all the necessary activities in the Project Management module schedule and link the Contract Manager module project to it, you can assign activity IDs to Contract Manager module documents and view early and actual start and finish dates, original and remaining durations, percent complete, and total float for individual activities.

**Assign activity data** Open the Contract Manager module document in Edit mode and click Select in the Schedule section to select an activity ID to assign to the document. To view activity data, click the Schedule icon. You can use this function in contracts, submittals, requisitions, daily reports, and other documents in which you assigned activity IDs.

If you are working with submittals, the seven different activities associated with the submittal are displayed. Other documents display one activity.

You can create activities and update actual dates and costs for Project Management module activities based on the associated Contract Manager module document for which you have recorded start or completed dates. Use Project Management module activities to update submittal activity dates. If you choose to update submittals from the schedule, the dates are updated from the linked application. When you select an activity in the Submittal Preparation field, the start date will update the required start date. Updating the Approval Period finish date will update the required finish date. If you choose to update submittals from the lead time, the dates are calculated based on the duration of each schedule activity.

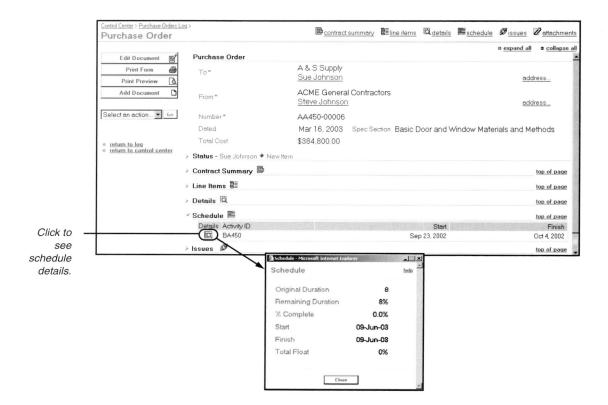

Click to
see
schedule
details.

# Importing Field Mappings from the Contract Manager Module into the Project Management Module

The release CDs contain lists of the field mappings when an import of the Contract Manager module data is performed from within the Project Management module. These are:

- **ExpMappings85.pdf** – This file lists the field mappings for the Transfer from Expedition 8.5 to the Project Management module (using the Import from Contract Management utility in the Project Management module).

- **ExpMappings9xandlater.pdf** – This file lists the field mappings for the Transfer from Expedition 9.x and later to the Project Management module (using the Import from Contract Management utility in the Project Management module).

Access these files from the release CD.

*Project Management Module Notes:*
*Project Management module task table information can be found on the Status Tab in the Project Management module.*

*Project Management module taskactv table information can be found on the Codes Tab in the Project Management module.*

*Project Management module projcost table information can be found on the Expenses Tab in the Project Management module.*

*Project Management module actvcode and actvtype table information can be found in Activity Code dictionaries. Select Enterprise, Activity Codes.*

*Project Management module account table information can be found in the Cost Account dictionary. Select Enterprise, Cost Accounts*

*Contract Manager Module Notes:*
*The following Contract Manager module documents are found in the Logs folder: Drawing Sets, Daily Reports, Materials, Punch Lists, Submittals.*

*The following Contract Manager module documents are found in the Contract Information folder: Budgeted Contracts, Committed Contracts, Purchase Orders, Schedule of Values, Change Orders*

# Retrieving Field Mappings from the Project Management Module into the Contract Manager Module

This section lists the field mappings when retrieving Project Management module data into the Contract Manager module.

 *In the following list of field mappings, the word Expedition should be replaced with the words Contract Manager.*

**Change Orders**

| Expedition Display | Expedition table | Expedition field name | PM table | PM field name | PM display |
|---|---|---|---|---|---|
| Completed Date | CHMT_Table | completion_date | task | act_end_date, reend_date or target_end_date[1] | Finish |
| Has Completed | CHMT_Table | has_completed | task | Calculated[2] | Finished |
| Has Started | CHMT_Table | has_started | task | Calculated[3] | Started |
| Start Date | CHMT_Table | start_date | task | act_start_date or target_start_date[4] | Start |
| Activity ID | CHMT_Table | ref_activity_id | task | task_code | Activity ID |

**Change Order Line Item**

| Expedition Display | Expedition table | Expedition field name | PM table | PM field name | PM display |
|---|---|---|---|---|---|
| Activity ID | CHDT_Table | ref_activity_id | task | task_code | Activity ID |

**Change Management**

| Expedition Display | Expedition table | Expedition field name | PM table | PM field name | PM display |
|---|---|---|---|---|---|
| Activity ID | CEMT_table | activity_id | task | task_code | Activity ID |

**Proposals**

| Expedition Display | Expedition table | Expedition field name | PM table | PM field name | PM display |
|---|---|---|---|---|---|
| Activity ID | CPMT_table | ref_activity_id | task | task_code | Activity ID |
| Completion Date | CPMT_table | completion_date | task | act_end_date, reend_date or target_end_date[1] | Finish |
| Has Completed | CPMT_table | has_completed | task | Calculated[2] | Finished |
| Has Started | CPMT_table | has_started | task | Calculated[3] | Started |
| Start Date | CPMT_table | start_date | task | act_start_date or target_start_date[4] | Start |

**Proposal Line Item**

| Expedition Display | Expedition table | Expedition field name | PM table | PM field name | PM display |
|---|---|---|---|---|---|
| Activity ID | CPDT_table | ref_activity_id | task | task_code | Activity ID |

1: When act_end_date is set, then value equal to act_end_date; when act_end_date not set and reend_date is set and later than target_end_date, then value equal to reend_date; in all other cases value is set to target_end_date

2: When act_end_date is used as the completion_date, has_completed is checked; in all other cases it is unchecked

3: When act_start_date is used as the start_date, has_started is checked, in all other cases it is unchecked

4: When act_start_date is set, then start_date is act_start_date; in all other cases start_date is target_start_date

## Daily Report

| Expedition Display | Expedition table | Expedition field name | PM table | PM field name | PM display |
|---|---|---|---|---|---|
| Activity ID | DSCH | activity_id | task | task_code | Activity ID |
| Activity ID Title | DSCH | activity_title | task | task_name | Activity Name |
| Early Finish | DSCH | early_finish | task | act_end_date, reend_date or target_end_date[1] | Finish |
| Early Start | DSCH | early_start | task | act_start_date or target_start_date[4] | Start |
| Free Float | DSCH | free_float | task | free_float_hr_cnt | Free Float |
| Has Finished | DSCH | has_finished | task | Calculated[2] | Finished |
| Has Started | DSCH | has_started | task | Calculated[3] | Started |
| Original Duration | DSCH | original_duration | task | target_drtn_hr_cnt | Original Duration |
| Remaining Duration | DSCH | remaining_duration | task | remain_drtn_hr_cnt | Remaining Duration |
| Percent Complete | DSCH | percent_complete | task | Calculated[5] | Physical %, Duration % or Units % |
| Total Float | DSCH | total_float | task | total_float_hr_cnt | Total Float |
| Activity ID | DSCH | activity_id | task | task_code | Activity ID |
| Activity ID Title | DSCH | activity_title | task | task_name | Activity Name |
| Early Finish | DSCH | early_finish | task | act_end_date, reend_date or target_end_date[1] | Finish |
| Early Start | DSCH | early_start | task | act_start_date or target_start_date[4] | Start |
| Free Float | DSCH | free_float | task | free_float_hr_cnt | Free Float |
| Has Finished | DSCH | has_finished | task | Calculated[2] | Finished |
| Has Started | DSCH | has_started | task | Calculated[3] | Started |
| Original Duration | DSCH | original_duration | task | target_drtn_hr_cnt | Original Duration |
| Remaining Duration | DSCH | remaining_duration | task | remain_drtn_hr_cnt | Remaining Duration |
| Percent Complete | DSCH | percent_complete | task | Calculated[5] | Physical %, Duration % or Units % |
| Total Float | DSCH | total_float | task | total_float_hr_cnt | Total Float |

1: When act_end_date is set, then early_finish equal to act_end_date; when act_end_date not set and reend_date is set and later than target_end_date, then early_finish equal to reend_date; in all other cases early_finish is set to target_end_date
2: When act_end_date is used as the completion_date, has_finished is checked; in all other cases it is unchecked
3: When act_start_date is used as the start_date, has_started is checked, in all other cases it is unchecked
4: When act_start_date is set, then early_start is act_start_date; in all other cases early_start is target_start_date
5: When task.complete_pct_type equals 'CP_Phys' percent_complete equals task.phys_complete_pct
5: When task.complete_pct_type equals 'CP_Drtn' percent_complete equals 0.0 if target_drtn_hr_cnt is null or 0 or if remain_drtn_hr_cnt is null; otherwise percent_complete equals (target_drtn_hr_cnt - remain_drtn_hr_cnt)*100
5: When task.complete_pct_type equals 'CP_Units' percent_complete equals 0 if actual_completion_units is null or 0; otherwise percent_complete equals (actual_units/actual_completion_units)*100

## Punch List Items

| Expedition Display | Expedition table | Expedition field name | PM table | PM field name | PM display |
|---|---|---|---|---|---|
| Activity ID | PNDT | ref_activity_id | task | task_code | Activity ID |
| Finish Date | PNDT | finish_date | task | act_end_date, reend_date or target_end_date[1] | Finish |
| Has Finished | PNDT | has_finished | task | Calculated[2] | Finished |
| Has Started | PNDT | has_started | task | Calculated[3] | Started |
| Start Date | PNDT | start_date | task | act_start_date or target_start_date[4] | Start |

1: When act_end_date is set, then finish_date equal to act_end_date; when act_end_date not set and reend_date is set and later than target_end_date, then finish_date equal to reend_date; in all other cases finish_date is set to target_end_date
2: When act_end_date is used as the completion_date, has_finished is checked; in all other cases it is unchecked
3: When act_start_date is used as the start_date, has_started is checked, in all other cases it is unchecked
4: When act_start_date is set, then start_date is act_start_date; in all other cases start_date is target_start_date

## Materials Delivery

| Expedition Display | Expedition table | Expedition field name | PM table | PM field name | PM display |
|---|---|---|---|---|---|
| Completion Date | MDMT_table | completion_date | task | act_end_date, reend_date or target_end_date[1] | Finish |
| Start Date | MDMT_table | start_date | task | act_start_date or target_start_date[4] | Start |
| Activity ID | MDMT_table | ref_activity_id | task | task_code | Activity ID |

## Materials Delivery Ticket

| Expedition Display | Expedition table | Expedition field name | PM table | PM field name | PM display |
|---|---|---|---|---|---|
| Activity ID | MDDT | ref_activity_id | task | task_code | Activity ID |

1: When act_end_date is set, then value equal to act_end_date; when act_end_date not set and reend_date is set and later than target_end_date, then value equal to reend_date; in all other cases value is set to target_end_date
2: When act_end_date is used as the completion_date, has_completed is checked; in all other cases it is unchecked
3: When act_start_date is used as the start_date, has_started is checked, in all other cases it is unchecked
4: When act_start_date is set, then start_date is act_start_date; in all other cases start_date is target_start_date

**Submittal Package**

| Expedition Display | Expedition table | Expedition field name | PM table | PM field name | PM display |
|---|---|---|---|---|---|
| Activity ID | SBPK | ref_activity_id | task | task_code | Activity ID |

**Submittal**

| Expedition Display | Expedition table | Expedition field name | PM table | PM field name | PM display |
|---|---|---|---|---|---|
| Activity ID | SBMT_table | construction_id | task | task_code | Activity ID |
| Construction Finish | SBMT_table | construction_finish | task | act_end_date, reend_date or target_end_date[1] | Finish |
| Construction Has Started | SBMT_table | construction_has_started | task | Calculated[3] | Started |
| Construction Has Finished | SBMT_table | construction_has_finished | task | Calculated[2] | Finished |
| Construction Start | SBMT_table | construction_start | task | act_start_date or target_start_date[4] | Start |
| Delivery Finish | SBMT_table | delivery_finish | task | act_end_date, reend_date or target_end_date[1] | Finish |
| Activity ID | SBMT_table | delivery_actv | task | task_code | Activity ID |
| Delivery Has Finished | SBMT_table | delivery_has_finished | task | Calculated[2] | Started |
| Delivery Has Started | SBMT_table | delivery_has_started | task | Calculated[3] | Finished |
| Delivery Lead Time | SBMT_table | delivery_lead_time | task | target_drtn_hr_cnt/8 | n/a |
| Delivery Start | SBMT_table | delivery_start | task | act_start_date or target_start_date[4] | Start |
| Fabricate Finish | SBMT_table | fabricate_finish | task | act_end_date, reend_date or target_end_date[1] | Finish |
| Activity ID | SBMT_table | fabricate_actv | task | task_code | Activity ID |
| Fabricate Lead Time | SBMT_table | fabricate_lead_time | task | target_drtn_hr_cnt/8 | n/a |
| Fabricate Start | SBMT_table | fabricate_start | task | act_start_date or target_start_date[4] | Start |
| Fabstart Has Finished | SBMT_table | fabricate_has_finished | task | Calculated[2] | Started |
| Fabstart Has Started | SBMT_table | fabricate_has_started | task | Calculated[3] | Finished |
| Fab Release Fin | SBMT_table | fab_release_fin | task | act_end_date, reend_date or target_end_date[1] | Finish |
| Activity ID | SBMT_table | fab_rel_activity | task | task_code | Activity ID |
| Fab Release Lead Time | SBMT_table | fab_release_lead_time | task | target_drtn_hr_cnt/8 | n/a |
| Fab Release St | SBMT_table | fab_release_st | task | act_start_date or target_start_date[4] | Start |
| Release Has Finished | SBMT_table | release_has_finished | task | Calculated[2] | Started |
| Release Has Started | SBMT_table | release_has_started | task | Calculated[3] | Finished |
| Resubmit Finish | SBMT_table | resubmit_finish | task | act_end_date, reend_date or target_end_date[1] | Finish |
| Activity ID | SBMT_table | resubmit_activity | task | task_code | Activity ID |
| Resubmit Has Finished | SBMT_table | resubmit_has_finished | task | Calculated[2] | Started |
| Resubmit Has Started | SBMT_table | resubmit_has_started | task | Calculated[3] | Finished |
| Resubmit Lead Time | SBMT_table | resubmit_lead_time | task | target_drtn_hr_cnt/8 | n/a |
| Resubmit Start | SBMT_table | resubmit_start | task | act_start_date or target_start_date[4] | Start |
| Approval Finish | SBMT_table | approval_finish | task | act_end_date, reend_date or target_end_date[1] | Finish |
| Activity ID | SBMT_table | appr_activity | task | task_code | Activity ID |
| Approval Lead Time | SBMT_table | approval_lead_time | task | target_drtn_hr_cnt/8 | n/a |
| Approval Start | SBMT_table | approval_start | task | act_start_date or target_start_date[4] | Start |
| Approve Has Finished | SBMT_table | approve_has_finished | task | Calculated[2] | Started |
| Approve Has Started | SBMT_table | approve_has_started | task | Calculated[3] | Finished |
| Required Finish | SBMT_table | required_finish | task | act_end_date, reend_date or target_end_date[1] | Finish |
| Required Start | SBMT_table | required_start | task | act_start_date or target_start_date[4] | Start |
| Activity ID | SBMT_table | submit_activity | task | task_code | Activity ID |
| Submit Finish | SBMT_table | submit_finish | task | act_end_date, reend_date or target_end_date[1] | Finish |
| Submit Has Finished | SBMT_table | submit_has_finished | task | Calculated[2] | Started |
| Submit Has Started | SBMT_table | submit_has_started | task | Calculated[3] | Finished |
| Submit Lead Time | SBMT_table | submit_lead_time | task | target_drtn_hr_cnt/8 | n/a |
| Submit Start | SBMT_table | submit_start | task | act_start_date or target_start_date[4] | Start |

1: When act_end_date is set, then value equal to act_end_date; when act_end_date not set and reend_date is set and later than target_end_date, then value equal to reend_date; in all other cases value is set to target_end_date
2: When act_end_date is used as the completion_date, has_completed is checked; in all other cases it is unchecked
3: When act_start_date is used as the start_date, has_started is checked, in all other cases it is unchecked
4: When act_start_date is set, then value is act_start_date; in all other cases value is target_start_date

**Drawing Sets**

| Expedition Display | Expedition table | Expedition field name | PM table | PM field name | PM display |
|---|---|---|---|---|---|
| Activity ID | DSMT_table | ref_activity_id | task | task_code | Activity ID |
| Completion Date | DSMT_table | required_finish | task | act_end_date, reend_date or target_end_date[1] | Finish |
| Has Completed | DSMT_table | has_completed | task | Calculated[2] | Finished |
| Has Started | DSMT_table | has_started | task | Calculated[3] | Started |
| Start Date | DSMT_table | required_start | task | act_start_date or target_start_date[4] | Start |

1: When act_end_date is set, then required_finish equal to act_end_date; when act_end_date not set and reend_date is set and later than target_end_date, then required_finish equal to reend_date; in all other cases required_finish is set to target_end_date
2: When act_end_date is used as the completion_date, has_finished is checked; in all other cases it is unchecked
3: When act_start_date is used as the start_date, has_started is checked, in all other cases it is unchecked
4: When act_start_date is set, then required_start is act_start_date; in all other cases required_start is target_start_date

**Requisition Detail**

| Expedition Display | Expedition table | Expedition field name | PM table | PM field name | PM display |
|---|---|---|---|---|---|
| Activity ID | RQDT_table | ref_activity_id | task | task_code | Activity ID |
| Description | RQDT_table | description | task | task_name | Activity Name |
| %G/C | RQDT_table | percent_complete | task | Calculated[5] | Physical %, Duration % or Units % |

**Invoice**

| Expedition Display | Expedition table | Expedition field name | PM table | PM field name | PM display |
|---|---|---|---|---|---|
| Activity ID | INVC | ref_activity_id | task | task_code | Activity ID |

5: When task.complete_pct_type equals 'CP_Phys' percent_complete equals task.phys_complete_pct
5: When task.complete_pct_type equals 'CP_Drtn' percent_complete equals 0.0 if target_drtn_hr_cnt is null or 0 or if remain_drtn_hr_cnt is null; otherwise percent_complete equals (target_drtn_hr_cnt - remain_drtn_hr_cnt)*100
5: When task.complete_pct_type equals 'CP_Units' percent_complete equals 0 if actual_completion_units is null or 0; otherwise percent_complete equals (actual_units/actual_completion_units)*100

**Contract**

| Expedition Display | Expedition table | Expedition field name | PM table | PM field name | PM display |
|---|---|---|---|---|---|
| Activity ID | CNMT_table | ref_activity_id | task | task_code | Activity ID |
| Completion Date | CNMT_table | completion_date | task | act_end_date, reend_date or target_end_date[1] | Finish |
| Has Completed | CNMT_table | has_completed | task | Calculated[2] | Finished |
| Has Started | CNMT_table | has_started | task | Calculated[3] | Started |
| Start Date | CNMT_table | start_date | task | act_start_date or target_start_date[4] | Start |

**Contract Line Item**

| Expedition Display | Expedition table | Expedition field name | PM table | PM field name | PM display |
|---|---|---|---|---|---|
| Activity ID | CNDT_table | ref_activity_id | task | task_code | Activity ID |

**Purchase Order**

| Expedition Display | Expedition table | Expedition field name | PM table | PM field name | PM display |
|---|---|---|---|---|---|
| Activity ID | CNMT_table | ref_activity_id | task | task_code | Activity ID |
| Completion Date | CNMT_table | completion_date | task | act_end_date, reend_date or target_end_date[1] | Finish |
| Has Completed | CNMT_table | has_completed | task | Calculated[2] | Finished |
| Has Started | CNMT_table | has_started | task | Calculated[3] | Started |
| Start Date | CNMT_table | start_date | task | act_start_date or target_start_date[4] | Start |

**Purchase Order Line Item**

| Expedition Display | Expedition table | Expedition field name | PM table | PM field name | PM display |
|---|---|---|---|---|---|
| Activity ID | CNDT_table | ref_activity_id | task | task_code | Activity ID |

1: When act_end_date is set, then completion_date equal to act_end_date; when act_end_date not set and reend_date is set and later than target_end_date, then completion_date equal to reend_date; in all other cases completion_date is set to target_end_date
2: When act_end_date is used as the completion_date, has_completed is checked; in all other cases it is unchecked
3: When act_start_date is used as the start_date, has_started is checked, in all other cases it is unchecked
4: When act_start_date is set, then start_date is act_start_date; in all other cases start_date is target_start_date

**Procurement**

| Expedition Display | Expedition table | Expedition field name | PM table | PM field name | PM display |
|---|---|---|---|---|---|
| Required Award Date | procure_item | required_award_date | task | target_start_date | Early Start |

**RFI**

| Expedition Display | Expedition table | Expedition field name | PM table | PM field name | PM display |
|---|---|---|---|---|---|
| Activity ID | CRQT | ref_activity_id | task | task_code | Activity ID |
| Completion Date | CRQT | completion_date | task | act_end_date, reend_date or target_end_date[1] | Finish |
| Has Completed | CRQT | has_completed | task | Calculated[2] | Finished |
| Has Started | CRQT | has_started | task | Calculated[3] | Started |
| Start Date | CRQT | start_date | task | act_start_date or target_start_date[4] | Start |

**Notices (CIC)**

| Expedition Display | Expedition table | Expedition field name | PM table | PM field name | PM display |
|---|---|---|---|---|---|
| Activity ID | CNTE | ref_activity_id | task | task_code | Activity ID |
| Completion Date | CNTE | completion_date | task | act_end_date, reend_date or target_end_date[1] | Finish |
| Has Completed | CNTE | has_completed | task | Calculated[2] | Finished |
| Has Started | CNTE | has_started | task | Calculated[3] | Started |
| Start Date | CNTE | start_date | task | act_start_date or target_start_date[4] | Start |

**Noncompliance**

| Expedition Display | Expedition table | Expedition field name | PM table | PM field name | PM display |
|---|---|---|---|---|---|
| Activity ID | NON_COMPLIANCE | ref_activity_id | task | task_code | Activity ID |
| Completion Date | NON_COMPLIANCE | completion_date | task | act_end_date, reend_date or target_end_date[1] | Finish |
| Has Completed | NON_COMPLIANCE | has_completed | task | Calculated[2] | Finished |
| Has Started | NON_COMPLIANCE | has_started | task | Calculated[3] | Started |
| Start Date | NON_COMPLIANCE | start_date | task | act_start_date or target_start_date[4] | Start |

1: When act_end_date is set, then completion_date equal to act_end_date; when act_end_date not set and reend_date is set and later than target_end_date, then completion_date equal to reend_date; in all other cases completion_date is set to target_end_date
2: When act_end_date is used as the completion_date, has_completed is checked; in all other cases it is unchecked
3: When act_start_date is used as the start_date, has_started is checked, in all other cases it is unchecked
4: When act_start_date is set, then start_date is act_start_date; in all other cases start_date is target_start_date

# Exchanging Contract Manager Module Data with Other Applications

This chapter describes how to export Contract Manager module data to other applications, such as spreadsheets or databases.

You can import data for contacts, cost codes and titles, drawings, notepads, punch lists, requests for information, specification sections, contracts, purchase orders, procurement items, daily reports, notices, and submittals into the Contract Manager module from other applications using comma-separated value files.

# Exporting Contract Manager Module Data to Other Applications

You can export Contract Manager module data into .CSV, .CSV with Headers, or Excel with Headers file formats. Select any export report from the export report environment, then create the export file using the Save As function from the Export window.

 *You must have access rights to export data.*

See the *Planning and Adding a Contract Manager Module Project* chapter, or type *access* or *security* in Help for more information.

**Export data from a Contract Manager module project**  Right-click on a project in the Project View and click Export. In the Export window select the document type from which you want to export, then click Show.

*Click to preview the report.*

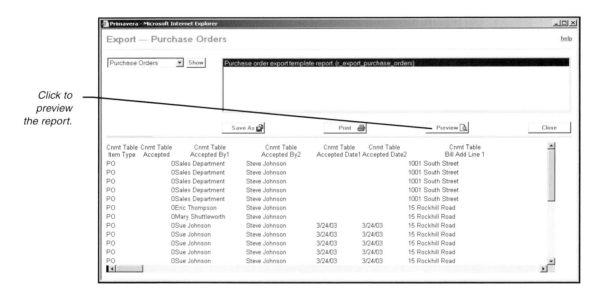

Select the report that corresponds to the type of data you want to export. Reports are available for contacts, contracts, purchase orders, cost codes, daily reports, drawings, notepads, notices, punch lists, requests for information, specification sections, and submittals. For example, to export cost codes and titles, select r_export_cost_codes from the list. Click Preview after you select a report.

*The Export window automatically defaults to the library that corresponds to the log you are in.*

Click Save As, and select an export format in the Files of Type field in the Save window. To retain the column headings in the exported file, choose the *with headers* export format, such as *Excel With Headers*.

In the Save In field, select the folder in which you want to store the export report; in the File Name field, type a name to identify the report without an extension, which the Contract Manager module supplies automatically when you specify a file type. Click Save.

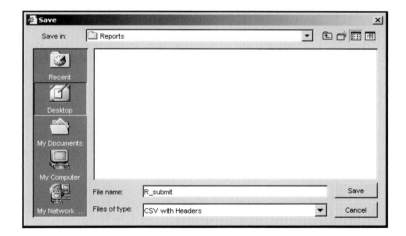

The following example shows cost codes and titles report data exported to a Microsoft Excel file called COSTACCT.

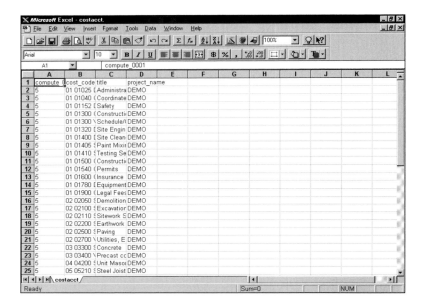

### Using the Save As Option with Reports that Contain Multi-Byte Characters

When you click the Save As button, and the report or form you selected contains multi-byte characters, do the following:

1 In the Save dialog box, click the arrow on the right side of the Save in field, and navigate to the location where you want to save the document.

2 In the File name field enter a name for the document.

3 Click the arrow on the right side of the Files of type field, choose one of the following, and click the Save button:

- **CSV with Headers** - Use this option to save the document so you can view it in Notepad.

- **Excel with Headers** - Use this option to save the document so you can view it in Microsoft Excel.

*Multi-byte documents saved in CSV with Headers format will not display properly in Microsoft Excel. Use Notepad to display these documents.*

# Importing Data from Other Applications

You can import data from comma-separated value (.CSV with Headers or Excel with Headers) files to insert and update data for the modules listed below. The import file must contain specific table and column names on the first line of the CSV file being imported. The best way to set up an import file is to first export data from the Contract Manager module to the CSV with Headers or Excel with Headers format, since the Contract Manager module supplies the correct field name placement when you run the export.

Follow these guidelines for preparing import files:

■  Use an export CSV with Headers or Excel with Headers file as a template for the import file.
Use the Excel with Headers format to import data containing carriage returns, quotes, and other punctuation.

■  You cannot import fields that cannot be edited onscreen.

■  The first row must be a "header."

■  Each row in the import file can contain both master and detail column information; master and detail columns can be interspersed.

■  Import files must include all key fields for the type of data imported; for example, import files for the Company Directory must include the contact initials. Key fields are identified in the following table; the table name (shown in all uppercase letters) precedes each field name

| Imported Data | Key Field Names |
| --- | --- |
| Company Data* | VNMT.vendor_abbrev |
| | VNDT.initials (to import addresses) |
| Cost Worksheet | CSMT_TABLE.cost_code |
| Submittals† | SBPK.package_number |
| | SBMT_TABLE.submittal_no |
| Specification Sections | SPEC.section_value |
| Punch Lists | PNMT.punch_list_name |
| | PNDT.item_number |
| Notepads | NPMT.note_pad |
| | NPDT.item_number |
| Requests for Information | CRQT.to_vendor |
| | CRQT.from_vendor |
| | CRQT.change_number |
| | CRQT.item_type |

Drawings                          DWMT_TABLE.drawing_number
Contracts/POs            CNMT_TABLE.item_type
                                      CNMT.document_number
                                        CNMT_TABLE.to_vendor
Daily Reports             CNMT_TABLE.from_vendor
                                        DRMT.vendor_abbrev
                                        DRMT.report_date
                                        DRMT.report_period
Notices                        DRMT.vendor_abbrev_ini
                                        CNTE.item_type
                                        CNTE.to_vendor
                                        CNTE.from_vendor
Procurement           PROCURE_ITEM.spec_section
                                        PROCURE_ITEM.purchase_type
                                        PROCURE_ITEM.csi_division
                                        PROCURE_ITEM.title

\* If you are importing contact initials, the VNMT.vendor_abbrev must be included in each VNDT.initials record.

† You can only import submittals that are in packages. If importing only SBMT rows, you still must include the SBPK.package_number in the import file.

 *If you get a message that your CSV with Headers file cannot be imported because it may not be formatted correctly, save the file in Excel with Headers format, and re-import the file.*

**Import data to a Contract Manager module project**  Right-click on the project you want to import data and click Import to open the Import window.

*Type the name of the file you are importing data from (or click Browse).*

*Select the document type you are populating with new data.*

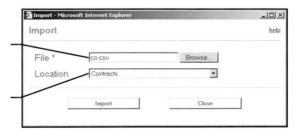

Click Import to import the data; this process adds new records to the specified document or updates records if they exist. If duplicate records are encountered during the import, they are ignored. When the import process is complete, click Close.

Import automatically displays a status window containing row numbers of duplicate rows, columns that were ignored, and any other errors. Click Print to get a printed record of all the errors.

# Import Specifications

This section lists the fields that can be imported into the Contract Manager module for each module and table.

| Module | Contract Manager Module Table Name | Column Name |
|---|---|---|
| Company | VNMT | company_name |
| Company | VNMT | contract_number |
| Company | VNMT | dbe |
| Company | VNMT | default_initials |
| Company | VNMT | default_location |
| Company | VNMT | mbe |
| Company | VNMT | remarks |
| Company | VNMT | spec_section |
| Company | VNMT | tax_id_number |
| Company | VNMT | vendor_abbrev |
| Company | VNMT | vendor_role |
| Company | VNMT | wbe |
| Contact | VNDT | address_line_1 |
| Contact | VNDT | address_line_2 |
| Contact | VNDT | address_line_3 |
| Contact | VNDT | beeper_phone |
| Contact | VNDT | city |
| Contact | VNDT | copies |
| Contact | VNDT | country |
| Contact | VNDT | country_code |
| Contact | VNDT | extension |
| Contact | VNDT | fax |
| Contact | VNDT | initials |
| Contact | VNDT | location |

| Module | Contract Manager Module Table Name | Column Name |
|---|---|---|
| Contact | VNDT | mail_address |
| Contact | VNDT | mail_method |
| Contact | VNDT | mobile_phone |
| Contact | VNDT | name |
| Contact | VNDT | office_phone |
| Contact | VNDT | paper_size |
| Contact | VNDT | postal_code |
| Contact | VNDT | state |
| Contact | VNDT | tax_id_number |
| Contact | VNDT | title |
| Contracts | CNMT_TABLE | Accepted_By |
| Contracts | CNMT_TABLE | Accepted_by_1 |
| Contracts | CNMT_TABLE | Accepted_by_2 |
| Contracts | CNMT_TABLE | Accepted_Date_1 |
| Contracts | CNMT_TABLE | Accepted_Date_2 |
| Contracts | CNMT_TABLE | Bill_Add_Line_1 |
| Contracts | CNMT_TABLE | Bill_Add_Line_2 |
| Contracts | CNMT_TABLE | Bill_Add_Line_3 |
| Contracts | CNMT_TABLE | Bill_City |
| Contracts | CNMT_TABLE | Bill_Company |
| Contracts | CNMT_TABLE | Bill_Country |
| Contracts | CNMT_TABLE | Bill_Postal_Code |
| Contracts | CNMT_TABLE | Bill_Country_Code |
| Contracts | CNMT_TABLE | Bill_State |
| Contracts | CNMT_TABLE | Bill_Vendor_Abbrev |
| Contracts | CNMT_TABLE | Bill_Vendor_Abbrev_ini |
| Contracts | CNMT_TABLE | Completion_Date |

| Module | Contract Manager Module Table Name | Column Name |
|---|---|---|
| Contracts | CNMT_TABLE | DBE |
| Contracts | CNMT_TABLE | Description |
| Contracts | CNMT_TABLE | Document_Date |
| Contracts | CNMT_TABLE | Document_Number |
| Contracts | CNMT_TABLE | Fob_Via |
| Contracts | CNMT_TABLE | Freight |
| Contracts | CNMT_TABLE | From_Add_Line_1 |
| Contracts | CNMT_TABLE | From_Add_Line_2 |
| Contracts | CNMT_TABLE | From_Add_Line_3 |
| Contracts | CNMT_TABLE | From_City |
| Contracts | CNMT_TABLE | From_company |
| Contracts | CNMT_TABLE | From_Country |
| Contracts | CNMT_TABLE | From_Country_Code |
| Contracts | CNMT_TABLE | From_Postal_Code |
| Contracts | CNMT_TABLE | From_State |
| Contracts | CNMT_TABLE | From_Vendor |
| Contracts | CNMT_TABLE | From_Vendor_ini |
| Contracts | CNMT_TABLE | Item_type |
| Contracts | CNMT_TABLE | Lump_Cost |
| Contracts | CNMT_TABLE | Lump_Tax |
| Contracts | CNMT_TABLE | Lump_Tax_Rate |
| Contracts | CNMT_TABLE | Managers_Name |
| Contracts | CNMT_TABLE | MBE |
| Contracts | CNMT_TABLE | Reference_Number |
| Contracts | CNMT_TABLE | Ref_Activity_ID |
| Contracts | CNMT_TABLE | Ref_Cost_Account |
| Contracts | CNMT_TABLE | Ref_Cost_Category |

| Module | Contract Manager Module Table Name | Column Name |
|---|---|---|
| Contracts | CNMT_TABLE | Remarks |
| Contracts | CNMT_TABLE | Ship_Add_Line_1 |
| Contracts | CNMT_TABLE | Ship_Add_Line_2 |
| Contracts | CNMT_TABLE | Ship_Add_Line_3 |
| Contracts | CNMT_TABLE | Ship_City |
| Contracts | CNMT_TABLE | Ship_Company |
| Contracts | CNMT_TABLE | Ship_Country |
| Contracts | CNMT_TABLE | Ship_Country_Code |
| Contracts | CNMT_TABLE | Ship_Postal_Code |
| Contracts | CNMT_TABLE | Ship_State |
| Contracts | CNMT_TABLE | Ship_Vendor_Abbrev_ini |
| Contracts | CNMT_TABLE | Ship_Vendor_Abbrev |
| Contracts | CNMT_TABLE | Spec_Section |
| Contracts | CNMT_TABLE | Start_Date |
| Contracts | CNMT_TABLE | Status |
| Contracts | CNMT_TABLE | Terms |
| Contracts | CNMT_TABLE | To_Add_Line_1 |
| Contracts | CNMT_TABLE | To_Add_Line_2 |
| Contracts | CNMT_TABLE | To_Add_Line_3 |
| Contracts | CNMT_TABLE | To_City |
| Contracts | CNMT_TABLE | To_Company |
| Contracts | CNMT_TABLE | To_Country |
| Contracts | CNMT_TABLE | To_Country_Code |
| Contracts | CNMT_TABLE | To_Postal_Code |
| Contracts | CNMT_TABLE | To_State |
| Contracts | CNMT_TABLE | To_Vendor_ini |
| Contracts | CNMT_TABLE | Unit_Cost |

| Module | Contract Manager Module Table Name | Column Name |
|---|---|---|
| Contracts | CNMT_TABLE | Unit_Tax |
| Contracts | CNMT_TABLE | WBE |
| Contracts | CNMT_TABLE | Has_Started |
| Contracts | CNMT_TABLE | Has_Completed |
| Contracts | CNDT_TABLE | Ball_in_court |
| Contracts | CNDT_TABLE | Ball_in_court_ini |
| Contracts | CNDT_TABLE | Completion_Date |
| Contracts | CNDT_TABLE | Item_Number |
| Contracts | CNDT_TABLE | Material_Code |
| Contracts | CNDT_TABLE | Package_Number |
| Contracts | CNDT_TABLE | Quantity |
| Contracts | CNDT_TABLE | Ref_Activity_Id |
| Contracts | CNDT_TABLE | Ref_Resource |
| Contracts | CNDT_TABLE | Sales_Tax |
| Contracts | CNDT_TABLE | Sales_Tax |
| Contracts | CNDT_TABLE | Status |
| Contracts | CNDT_TABLE | Stock_Descriptn |
| Contracts | CNDT_TABLE | Submittal |
| Contracts | CNDT_TABLE | Units |
| Contracts | CNDT_TABLE | Unit_Price |
| Cost Codes | CSMT_TABLE | cost_code |
| Cost Codes | CSMT_TABLE | title |
| Cost Codes | CSMT_TABLE | projected_to_commit |
| Daily Reports | DRMT | Additional_Comments |
| Daily Reports | DRMT | Daily_Report |
| Daily Reports | DRMT | Day_of_week |
| Daily Reports | DRMT | Precipitation |

| Module | Contract Manager Module Table Name | Column Name |
|---|---|---|
| Daily Reports | DRMT | Report_Date |
| Daily Reports | DRMT | Report_Number |
| Daily Reports | DRMT | Report_Period |
| Daily Reports | DRMT | Sky |
| Daily Reports | DRMT | Temperature |
| Daily Reports | DRMT | Vendor_Abbrev |
| Daily Reports | DRMT | Vendor_Abbrev_ini |
| Daily Reports | DRMT | Wind |
| Daily Reports | DREQ | Description |
| Daily Reports | DREQ | Equipment_Source |
| Daily Reports | DREQ | Equipment_Type |
| Daily Reports | DREQ | Remark |
| Daily Reports | DRLB | Apprentices |
| Daily Reports | DRLB | Category |
| Daily Reports | DRLB | Change_Number |
| Daily Reports | DRLB | Field_Source |
| Daily Reports | DRLB | Foremen |
| Daily Reports | DRLB | Journeymen |
| Daily Reports | DRLB | Remark |
| Daily Reports | DRLB | Supervisors |
| Daily Reports | DRLB | Work_Area |
| Daily Reports | DRVS | Company_Repsnted |
| Daily Reports | DRVS | Remark |
| Daily Reports | DRVS | Time_of_Visit |
| Daily Reports | DRVS | Vendor_Abbrev |
| Daily Reports | DRVS | Vendor_Abbrev_ini |
| Daily Reports | DRVS | Visitor_Name |

| Module | Contract Manager Module Table Name | Column Name |
|---|---|---|
| Drawings | DWMT_TABLE | area |
| Drawings | DWMT_TABLE | bid_package |
| Drawings | DWMT_TABLE | designer |
| Drawings | DWMT_TABLE | designer_ini |
| Drawings | DWMT_TABLE | discipline |
| Drawings | DWMT_TABLE | drawing_number |
| Drawings | DWMT_TABLE | drawing_phase |
| Drawings | DWMT_TABLE | file_number |
| Drawings | DWMT_TABLE | spec_section |
| Drawings | DWMT_TABLE | title |
| Notepads | NPMT | contract_number |
| Notepads | NPMT | description |
| Notepads | NPMT | note_pad |
| Notepad Items | NPDT | ball_in_court |
| Notepad Items | NPDT | ball_in_court_ini |
| Notepad Items | NPDT | date_closed |
| Notepad Items | NPDT | date_opened |
| Notepad Items | NPDT | date_required |
| Notepad Items | NPDT | item_number |
| Notepad Items | NPDT | notes |
| Notepad Items | NPDT | status |
| Notices | CNTE | Approved_Date |
| Notices | CNTE | Ball_in_court |
| Notices | CNTE | Ball_in_court_ini |
| Notices | CNTE | Change_Date |
| Notices | CNTE | Change_Issue |
| Notices | CNTE | Change_Number |

| Module | Contract Manager Module Table Name | Column Name |
|---|---|---|
| Notices | CNTE | Cntr_From_Vendor |
| Notices | CNTE | Cntr_From_Vendor_ini |
| Notices | CNTE | Cntr_Sys_Type |
| Notices | CNTE | Cntr_To_Vendor |
| Notices | CNTE | Cntr_To_Vendor_ini |
| Notices | CNTE | Completion_Date |
| Notices | CNTE | Contract_Number |
| Notices | CNTE | Cost |
| Notices | CNTE | From_Vendor |
| Notices | CNTE | From_Vendor_ini |
| Notices | CNTE | From_Manager |
| Notices | CNTE | Has_Completed |
| Notices | CNTE | Has_Started |
| Notices | CNTE | tem_Type |
| Notices | CNTE | Ref_Activity_Id |
| Notices | CNTE | Ref_Cost_Account |
| Notices | CNTE | Ref_Cost_Category |
| Notices | CNTE | Ref_From_Abbrev |
| Notices | CNTE | Ref_From_Abbrev_ini |
| Notices | CNTE | Ref_To_Abbrev |
| Notices | CNTE | Ref_To_Abbrev_ini |
| Notices | CNTE | Ref_Type |
| Notices | CNTE | Remarks |
| Notices | CNTE | Required_Date |
| Notices | CNTE | Responded_Date |
| Notices | CNTE | Spec_Section |
| Notices | CNTE | Start_Date |

| Module | Contract Manager Module Table Name | Column Name |
|--------|-----------------------------------|-------------|
| Notices | CNTE | Status |
| Notices | CNTE | Time_Change |
| Notices | CNTE | To_Manager |
| Notices | CNTE | To_Vendor |
| Notices | CNTE | To_Vendor_ini |
| Proposals | CPMT_TABLE | Approved_Date |
| Proposals | CPMT_TABLE | Approved_Date_2 |
| Proposals | CPMT_TABLE | Ball_in_court |
| Proposals | CPMT_TABLE | Ball_in_court_ini |
| Proposals | CPMT_TABLE | Change_Date |
| Proposals | CPMT_TABLE | Change_Issue |
| Proposals | CPMT_TABLE | Change_Number |
| Proposals | CPMT_TABLE | Cntr_From_Vendor |
| Proposals | CPMT_TABLE | Cntr_From_Vendor_ini |
| Proposals | CPMT_TABLE | Cntr_Sys_Type |
| Proposals | CPMT_TABLE | Cntr_To_Vendor |
| Proposals | CPMT_TABLE | Cntr_To_Vendor_ini |
| Proposals | CPMT_TABLE | Completion_Date |
| Proposals | CPMT_TABLE | Contract_Number |
| Proposals | CPMT_TABLE | Contract_Type |
| Proposals | CPMT_TABLE | From_manager |
| Proposals | CPMT_TABLE | From_Vendor_ini |
| Proposals | CPMT_TABLE | Has_Started |
| Proposals | CPMT_TABLE | Has_Completed |
| Proposals | CPMT_TABLE | tem_type |
| Proposals | CPMT_TABLE | Lump_Cost |
| Proposals | CPMT_TABLE | Lump_Tax |

| Module | Contract Manager Module Table Name | Column Name |
|---|---|---|
| Proposals | CPMT_TABLE | Lump_Tax |
| Proposals | CPMT_TABLE | Ref_Activity_Id |
| Proposals | CPMT_TABLE | Ref_Cost_Account |
| Proposals | CPMT_TABLE | Ref_Cost_Category |
| Proposals | CPMT_TABLE | Ref_From_Abbrev |
| Proposals | CPMT_TABLE | Ref_From_Abbrev_ini |
| Proposals | CPMT_TABLE | Ref_Number |
| Proposals | CPMT_TABLE | Ref_To_Abbrev |
| Proposals | CPMT_TABLE | Ref_To_Abbrev_ini |
| Proposals | CPMT_TABLE | Ref_Type |
| Proposals | CPMT_TABLE | Remarks |
| Proposals | CPMT_TABLE | Required_Date |
| Proposals | CPMT_TABLE | Responded_Date |
| Proposals | CPMT_TABLE | Signed_by_1 |
| Proposals | CPMT_TABLE | Signed_by_2 |
| Proposals | CPMT_TABLE | Spec_Section |
| Proposals | CPMT_TABLE | Start_Date |
| Proposals | CPMT_TABLE | Status |
| Proposals | CPMT_TABLE | Time_Change |
| Proposals | CPMT_TABLE | Title |
| Proposals | CPMT_TABLE | To_Manager |
| Proposals | CPMT_TABLE | To_Vendor |
| Proposals | CPMT_TABLE | To_Vendor_ini |
| Proposals | CPMT_TABLE | Unit_Cost |
| Proposals | CPMT_TABLE | Unit_Tax |
| Proposals | CPMT_TABLE | Vendor_Role |
| Proposals | CPDT_TABLE | Ball_in_court |

| Module | Contract Manager Module Table Name | Column Name |
|---|---|---|
| Proposals | CPDT_TABLE | Ball_in_court_ini |
| Proposals | CPDT_TABLE | Completion_Date |
| Proposals | CPDT_TABLE | Description |
| Proposals | CPDT_TABLE | tem_Number |
| Proposals | CPDT_TABLE | Material_Code |
| Proposals | CPDT_TABLE | Quantity |
| Proposals | CPDT_TABLE | Ref_Activity_Id |
| Proposals | CPDT_TABLE | Ref_Item_Num |
| Proposals | CPDT_TABLE | Ref_Resource |
| Proposals | CPDT_TABLE | Sales_Tax |
| Proposals | CPDT_TABLE | Sales_Tax |
| Proposals | CPDT_TABLE | Start_Date |
| Proposals | CPDT_TABLE | Status |
| Proposals | CPDT_TABLE | Stock_Number |
| Proposals | CPDT_TABLE | Units |
| Proposals | CPDT_TABLE | Unit_Price |
| Punch Lists | PNMT | contract_number |
| Punch Lists | PNMT | from_vendor |
| Punch Lists | PNMT | from_vendor_ini |
| Punch Lists | PNMT | long_descrpt |
| Punch Lists | PNMT | punch_list_name |
| Punch Lists | PNMT | short_descrpt |
| Punch Lists | PNMT | to_vendor |
| Punch Lists | PNMT | to_vendor_ini |
| Punch List Items | PNDT | ball_in_court |
| Punch List Items | PNDT | ball_in_court_ini |
| Punch List Items | PNDT | date_closed |

| Module | Contract Manager Module Table Name | Column Name |
|---|---|---|
| Punch List Items | PNDT | date_opened |
| Punch List Items | PNDT | date_required |
| Punch List Items | PNDT | description |
| Punch List Items | PNDT | duplicated_by |
| Punch List Items | PNDT | elevation |
| Punch List Items | PNDT | item_number |
| Punch List Items | PNDT | location |
| Punch List Items | PNDT | ref_activity_id |
| Punch List Items | PNDT | responsible_item |
| Punch List Items | PNDT | room |
| Punch List Items | PNDT | status |
| Punch List Items | PNDT | value |
| Request for Information | CRQT | answer |
| Request for Information | CRQT | approved_date |
| Request for Information | CRQT | approved_date2 |
| Request for Information | CRQT | ball_in_court |
| Request for Information | CRQT | ball_in_court_ini |
| Request for Information | CRQT | change_date |
| Request for Information | CRQT | change_issue |
| Request for Information | CRQT | change_number |
| Request for Information | CRQT | cntr_from_vndr |
| Request for Information | CRQT | cntr_from_vndr_ini |
| Request for Information | CRQT | cntr_to_vndr |
| Request for Information | CRQT | cntr_to_vndr_ini |
| Request for Information | CRQT | completion_date |
| Request for Information | CRQT | contract_number |
| Request for Information | CRQT | contract_type |

| Module | Contract Manager Module Table Name | Column Name |
| --- | --- | --- |
| Request for Information | CRQT | cost |
| Request for Information | CRQT | from_manager |
| Request for Information | CRQT | from_vendor |
| Request for Information | CRQT | from_vendor_ini |
| Request for Information | CRQT | has_completed |
| Request for Information | CRQT | has_started |
| Request for Information | CRQT | item_type |
| Request for Information | CRQT | ref_activity_id |
| Request for Information | CRQT | ref_from_abbrev |
| Request for Information | CRQT | ref_from_abbrev_ini |
| Request for Information | CRQT | ref_number |
| Request for Information | CRQT | ref_to_abbrev |
| Request for Information | CRQT | ref_to_abbrev_ini |
| Request for Information | CRQT | ref_type |
| Request for Information | CRQT | remarks |
| Request for Information | CRQT | required_date |
| Request for Information | CRQT | responded_date |
| Request for Information | CRQT | signed_by1 |
| Request for Information | CRQT | signed_by2 |
| Request for Information | CRQT | spec_section |
| Request for Information | CRQT | start_date |
| Request for Information | CRQT | status |
| Request for Information | CRQT | time_change |
| Request for Information | CRQT | title |
| Request for Information | CRQT | to_manager |
| Request for Information | CRQT | to_vendor |
| Request for Information | CRQT | to_vendor_ini |

| Module | Contract Manager Module Table Name | Column Name |
|---|---|---|
| Specification Section | SPEC | description |
| Specification Section | SPEC | section_value |
| Submittal Packages | SBPK | contract_number |
| Submittal Packages | SBPK | forwarded_to |
| Submittal Packages | SBPK | forwarded_to_ini |
| Submittal Packages | SBPK | package_number |
| Submittal Packages | SBPK | received_from |
| Submittal Packages | SBPK | received_from_ini |
| Submittal Packages | SBPK | required_finish |
| Submittal Packages | SBPK | required_start |
| Submittal Packages | SBPK | returned_by |
| Submittal Packages | SBPK | returned_by_ini |
| Submittal Packages | SBPK | sent_to |
| Submittal Packages | SBPK | sent_to_ini |
| Submittal Packages | SBPK | status |
| Submittal Packages | SBPK | submittal_no |
| Submittal Packages | SBPK | title |
| Submittals | SBMT_TABLE | appr_activity |
| Submittals | SBMT_TABLE | approval_finish |
| Submittals | SBMT_TABLE | approval_lead_time |
| Submittals | SBMT_TABLE | approval_start |
| Submittals | SBMT_TABLE | approve_has_finished |
| Submittals | SBMT_TABLE | approve_has_started |
| Submittals | SBMT_TABLE | code |
| Submittals | SBMT_TABLE | construction_activity |
| Submittals | SBMT_TABLE | construction_finish |
| Submittals | SBMT_TABLE | construction_has_finished |

| Module | Contract Manager Module Table Name | Column Name |
|---|---|---|
| Submittals | SBMT_TABLE | construction_has_started |
| Submittals | SBMT_TABLE | construction_start |
| Submittals | SBMT_TABLE | contract_number |
| Submittals | SBMT_TABLE | delivery_actv |
| Submittals | SBMT_TABLE | delivery_finish |
| Submittals | SBMT_TABLE | delivery_has_finished |
| Submittals | SBMT_TABLE | delivery_has_started |
| Submittals | SBMT_TABLE | delivery_lead_time |
| Submittals | SBMT_TABLE | delivery_start |
| Submittals | SBMT_TABLE | drawing |
| Submittals | SBMT_TABLE | fab_rel_activity |
| Submittals | SBMT_TABLE | fab_release_fin |
| Submittals | SBMT_TABLE | fab_release_lead_time |
| Submittals | SBMT_TABLE | fab_release_st |
| Submittals | SBMT_TABLE | fab_time |
| Submittals | SBMT_TABLE | fabricate_actv |
| Submittals | SBMT_TABLE | fabricate_finish |
| Submittals | SBMT_TABLE | fabricate_lead_time |
| Submittals | SBMT_TABLE | fabricate_start |
| Submittals | SBMT_TABLE | fabstart_has_finished |
| Submittals | SBMT_TABLE | fabstart_has_started |
| Submittals | SBMT_TABLE | filed_app_date |
| Submittals | SBMT_TABLE | filed_vendor |
| Submittals | SBMT_TABLE | filed_vendor_ini |
| Submittals | SBMT_TABLE | forwarded_to |
| Submittals | SBMT_TABLE | forwarded_to_ini |
| Submittals | SBMT_TABLE | item_number |

| Module | Contract Manager Module Table Name | Column Name |
|---|---|---|
| Submittals | SBMT_TABLE | items_in_submttl |
| Submittals | SBMT_TABLE | package_number |
| Submittals | SBMT_TABLE | received_from |
| Submittals | SBMT_TABLE | received_from_ini |
| Submittals | SBMT_TABLE | release_has_finished |
| Submittals | SBMT_TABLE | release_has_started |
| Submittals | SBMT_TABLE | required_finish |
| Submittals | SBMT_TABLE | required_start |
| Submittals | SBMT_TABLE | resubmit_activity |
| Submittals | SBMT_TABLE | resubmit_finish |
| Submittals | SBMT_TABLE | resubmit_has_finished |
| Submittals | SBMT_TABLE | resubmit_has_started |
| Submittals | SBMT_TABLE | resubmit_lead_time |
| Submittals | SBMT_TABLE | resubmit_start |
| Submittals | SBMT_TABLE | returned_by |
| Submittals | SBMT_TABLE | returned_by_ini |
| Submittals | SBMT_TABLE | second_app_code |
| Submittals | SBMT_TABLE | second_app_code_ini |
| Submittals | SBMT_TABLE | second_app_date |
| Submittals | SBMT_TABLE | sent_to |
| Submittals | SBMT_TABLE | sent_to_ini |
| Submittals | SBMT_TABLE | source_vendor |
| Submittals | SBMT_TABLE | source_vendor_ini |
| Submittals | SBMT_TABLE | submit_act_date |
| Submittals | SBMT_TABLE | submit_activity |
| Submittals | SBMT_TABLE | submit_finish |
| Submittals | SBMT_TABLE | submit_has_finished |

| Module | Contract Manager Module Table Name | Column Name |
|---|---|---|
| Submittals | SBMT_TABLE | submit_has_started |
| Submittals | SBMT_TABLE | submit_lead_time |
| Submittals | SBMT_TABLE | submit_start |
| Submittals | SBMT_TABLE | submittal_no |
| Submittals | SBMT_TABLE | title |
| Submittals | SBMT_TABLE | user_appr_date |
| Submittals | SBMT_TABLE | user_code |
| Submittals | SBMT_TABLE | user_code_ini |

# Index